Plate I

HOLBŒLL'S GREBE
Colymbus holboelli (Reinhardt)
WINTER   SUMMER

PIED-BILLED GREBE SUMMER
Podilymbus podiceps (Linnaeus)

HORNED GREBE
Colymbus auritus Linnaeus
WINTER   SUMMER

All ⅔ nat. size

Birds of America

EDITOR-IN-CHIEF
T. Gilbert Pearson
National Association of Audubon Societies

CONSULTING EDITOR
John Burroughs

CONTRIBUTING EDITORS

Edward H. Forbush
State Ornithologist, Massachusetts

Herbert K. Job
Ornithologist, Audubon Societies

William L. Finley
State Biologist, Oregon

L. Nelson Nichols
Member Linnæan Society

MANAGING EDITOR
George Gladden

ASSOCIATE EDITOR
J. Ellis Burdick

ARTISTS
R. I. Brasher   R. Bruce Horsfall   Henry Thurston

Nature Lovers Library

VOLUME ONE

THE UNIVERSITY SOCIETY INC.
New York

11021

Copyright, 1917, by
The University Society Inc.

ADVISORY BOARD

CONTENTS

	PAGE
PREFACE	vii
INTRODUCTION	xi
ORDER OF DIVING BIRDS	1
GREBES	1
LOONS	10
AUKS, MURRES, AND PUFFINS	16
ORDER OF LONG-WINGED SWIMMERS	32
SKUAS AND JAEGERS	32
GULLS	38
TERNS	54
SKIMMERS	71
ORDER OF TUBE-NOSED SWIMMERS	75
ALBATROSSES	75
FULMARS, SHEARWATERS, AND PETRELS	80
ORDER OF TOTIPALMATED SWIMMERS	88
TROPIC-BIRDS	88
GANNETS	90
DARTERS	93
CORMORANTS	95
PELICANS	101
MAN-O'-WAR-BIRDS	106
ORDER OF LAMELLIROSTRAL SWIMMERS	109
MERGANSERS	109
DUCKS	113
GEESE	154
SWANS	164
ORDER OF LAMELLIROSTRAL GRALLATORES (FLAMINGOES)	169
ORDER OF HERONS, STORKS, IBISES, ETC	173
SPOONBILLS, IBISES, AND STORKS	173
HERON FAMILY	180

  PAGE

ORDER OF MARSH-DWELLERS 197

    CRANES AND COURLANS 197

    RAILS, GALLINULES, AND COOTS 202

ORDER OF SHORE BIRDS 216

    PHALAROPES 216

    AVOCETS AND STILTS 221

    SNIPES, SANDPIPERS, ETC. 225

    PLOVERS 255

    SURF-BIRDS AND TURNSTONES 267

    OYSTER-CATCHERS 270

PREFACE

HE actual and urgent need for this book is apparent to the large and steadily increasing number of persons who are intelligently interested in American ornithology. This need is due to the fact that in all the literature of that subject there is no single work which presents a complete review of what is known to-day about American birds.

The task of preparing a comprehensive account of the bird life of a continent is far too great to be accomplished in a natural lifetime by any individual working alone; and until recently there has been no systematic coöperation between students of our native birds. It is inevitable, therefore, that continued study of the subject, aided by such coöperation, should have revealed many errors of commission and omission in the labors of Wilson, Audubon, Bonaparte, and the other earlier students of this difficult and complex science. Nevertheless, it is clear that the work of these men laid the foundation of American ornithology; for their labors not only furnished much material of scientific value, but encouraged interest in and sympathy for birds, and thereby inspired further study of these beautiful and useful forms of animate life.

The ornithological pioneers mentioned recorded not only technical descriptions of birds, but were at much pains to present observations calculated to give the reader ideas about bird personality. Later writers have confined themselves generally to one or the other of these aspects of bird life — or to regional ornithology. Doubtless the development of these two schools has been due to the realization of the enormousness of the task of presenting both technical descriptions, and accurate as well as readable characterizations of the hundreds of species which occur on this continent. In the case of the technical student, however, it discloses also the fact that one who is intent upon gathering purely " scientific " data about birds — that is, statistics and details concerning their size, color, distribution, nidification, and so on — is likely to overlook, or at least to pay little heed to habits or characteristics which have no classificatory value.

Yet it is these very characteristics, rather than the purely scientific data, which make the strongest appeal to the imagination and the sympathies of the great majority of persons who are interested in birds. Indeed, it may be doubted whether any account of a bird, however accurate and detailed it is in its presentation of merely physical facts, is actually complete if it omits or curtails reference to traits which reveal the human and æsthetic significance of that bird's natural life. Surely, the cleverness and the fine courage which a mother bird displays in concealing and protecting her eggs, are as significant as are their mere number and color.

It is the purpose of this work to present accurately and sympathetically both of these phases of bird life, that is, the physical and the moral. The utmost pains have been taken to present a precise description of the external physical appearance of each bird selected for separate treatment. The size of the bird may be considered the basic fact in its identification, and this is restricted (except in a few instances) to the average length, because that is the dimension most clearly discernible in the living bird.

The color of the bird is even more important than its size, as a means of identification, and especial care has been taken in this particular. The most accurate and detailed descriptions of the coloration of American birds are those which are included in Robert Ridgway's monumental work, *The Birds of North and Middle America*, of which seven parts have been issued by the United States National Museum. These descriptions, however, are expressed in terminology much of which is comprehensible only to the trained and essentially scientific ornithologist. Therefore, in order to employ this material in the present work, it became necessary to substitute common words for the technical terms; but in doing this great care was taken to reproduce the exact meaning of the original text. By this expedient there has been presented in plain language a vast amount of scientifically accurate descriptive material which, in its original form, would be comprehensible for the lay reader only by the constant use of an unabridged dictionary. Similar changes have been made, when they were necessary, in using Ridgway's text for the paragraphs on the distribution of species, and in the sections which characterize the generic groups. The descriptions of birds not included in Parts I to VII of *The Birds of North and Middle America*, have been written by R. I. Brasher. Special identification or "field" marks have been italicised.

Although this precise and fairly complete physical description is essential for the purposes of scientific ornithology, and often is needed by the layman to supplement or corroborate his own observation, what Mr. Burroughs calls "the human significance of our feathered neighbors" is undoubtedly that which chiefly interests the very large and increasing army of bird lovers. This human significance is reflected in natural or acquired traits which, singly or combined, often give a bird a very definite personality. To the observer who learns to detect and understand these traits, the study of birds becomes far more than a mere science devoted to the collection and classification of physical facts. For once he has adopted this point of view, he begins to see something very like distinct character and personality in the bird world; and observing the manifestations of such traces of individuality becomes to him infinitely more interesting and significant than the mere noting of the size, contour, and plumage peculiarities of a bird, or its occurrence here, there, or elsewhere at this or that time of the year.

The characterizations, or life histories, of the species which receive separate treatment in the following pages, were prepared with especial regard for portraying their interesting and distinctive traits. In most instances this treatment reveals characteristics which serve to differentiate the species with much definiteness. It is, of course, true that individual differences may occur even within the species. For example, an individual bird may display what clearly seems to be unusual confidence in man, or uncommon cleverness in concealing its nest or protecting its young. And it is frequently remarked that a certain bird may be a much more accomplished singer than are the others of his species in the same vicinity. Nevertheless there is a general similarity between the habits and temperament of birds of the same species, and therefore a description of these habits will be found to apply to the average individual bird of the species concerned.

To the technical descriptive matter of especial interest to the systematic ornithologist, and the popular characterizations intended particularly for the non-scientific student of birds, has been added — wherever it is called for — much very important and interesting matter concerning the actual usefulness of birds. This subject of economic ornithology has been carefully investigated by the United States Bureau of Biological Survey, whose experts have gathered and compiled a great mass of statistics and other data concerning the food habits of birds, the object being to convey precise information as to which are the useful and which are the harmful species. It would be difficult to overstate the value of this work if its results were generally understood, for these researches demonstrate beyond peradventure the enormous usefulness of the birds in destroying insect pests which, but for this check of their natural rate of increase, would ruin every year many millions of dollars worth of crops, and threaten with defoliation and death many kinds of trees.

The Bureau of Biological Survey endeavors to disseminate this information as widely as possible, and in order to assist in this good work the data gathered by its experts have been freely used in the following pages. This has been done not only because of the obvious

Eggs of American Birds

PLATE No. 1

1. Laughing Gull
2. Least Tern
3. Water-Turkey
4. Black Skimmer
5. Common Tern
6. Great Auk
7. Loon
8. Black Tern
9. Murre

EGGS OF AMERICAN BIRDS
(Plate Number One)

value and interest of the information thus conveyed, but because the reports and bulletins in which it is contained are likely within a few years to become unavailable through the exhaustion of the comparatively small supply printed. This, indeed, has already happened in the case of many of the most valuable bulletins, which are now unobtainable except in the larger public libraries and other repositories for such documents, and therefore have only very restricted circulation. Possessors of *Birds of America* will therefore have permanent access to the best of this very valuable material.

Finally, some explanation of the general form in which this work is presented may not come amiss in this connection. In their arrangement most ornithologies follow the evolutionary plan of proceeding from the lowest to the highest forms which, in the case of the birds, means from the Diving Birds which are considered by the scientists the lowest forms, to the Thrushes which are ranked as the highest. This is the order in which the birds are arranged in the Check-List of the American Ornithologists' Union, and the one which has been followed in these pages.

The Check-List of the American Ornithologists' Union includes the names of about twelve hundred birds to which systematic ornithologists accord full specific or "sub-specific" rank. This sub-specific distinction is often based upon very inconsiderable plumage differences of little or no interest or significance to the lay student of birds, while the character of the bird remains unchanged. In other words, a Robin is a Robin, whether he has white tips to the outer tail-feathers, as in the common Robin, or whether he lacks these spots, as in the Western Robin. *Birds of America* discusses about one thousand birds. It practically covers every species and subspecies with which a student of birds is likely to come in contact in North America.

The publishers wish to thank Mr. T. Gilbert Pearson, who, in addition to his services as Editor-in-chief, has given freely of the photographs and material assembled by the National Association of Audubon Societies; Mr. Herbert K. Job, for his photographs and helpful suggestions; Mr. Edward H. Forbush, for his advice, and, through him, the Massachusetts Board of Agriculture for ornithological literature printed by them; Mr. William L. Finley and Mr. H. T. Bohlman for pictures supplied; Dr. Jonathan Dwight, Jr., for valuable suggestions and criticisms, and permission to quote from *The Auk*; Dr. R. W. Shufeldt for critical suggestions; Mr. C. Walter Short for his interest and practical advice on manufacturing details; Mr. H. J. Vredenburgh for his careful supervision of the photo-engraving; Dr. Frank M. Chapman for permission to quote from his books; Mrs. Florence Merriam Bailey for permission to quote from her book, *Handbook of Western Birds of the United States*; Mrs. Mabel Osgood Wright, for permission to quote from her book *Birdcraft*; Mr. John Burroughs for permission to quote from his *Works*; Mr. C. William Beebe for photographs; Elizabeth Torrey and John W. Seabury for permission to quote from the *Works* of Bradford Torrey; Mr. Winthrop Parkhurst for permission to quote from the *Works* of H. E. Parkhurst; Mr. William Leon Dawson for permission to quote from *Birds of Ohio*, *Birds of Washington*, and *Birds of California*; Mrs. Olive Thorne Miller for permission to quote from *The Children's Book of Birds* and *A Bird Lover in the West*; Mr. F. Schuyler Mathews for quotations from his *Field Book of Wild Birds and their Music*; Mr. Ralph Hoffman for quotations from his *Guide to the Birds of New England and Eastern New York*; Mr. Walter H. Rich for permission to quote from his *Feathered Game of the Northeast*; Mr. H. T. Middleton, Mr. Silas A. Lottridge, Mr. A. A. Allen, and all others who have so generously contributed of their best in photographic studies; the United Fruit Company for the use of paintings for reproduction on the title pages; and the Hercules Powder Co., for quotations from *Game Farming for Profit and Pleasure*.

The following publishers have courteously granted these permissions: D. Appleton & Co. for quotations from the *Works* of Frank M. Chapman; Houghton Mifflin Co. for " To an Oriole " by Edgar A. Fawcett, quotations from *The Children's Book of Birds* and *A Bird Lover in the West* by Olive Thorne Miller, quotations from *Handbook of Birds of the Western*

United States by Florence Merriam Bailey, quotations from the *Works* of John Burroughs, quotations from the *Works* of Bradford Torrey, and quotations from *Guide to the Birds of New England and Eastern New York* by Ralph Hoffman; The John Lane Co. for quotations from *Birds by Sea and Land* by John Maclair Boarston; the Macmillan Co. for quotations from the *Works* of Mabel Osgood Wright; Elizabeth C. T. Miller for quotations from *Birds of Ohio* by William Leon Dawson; G. P. Putnam's Sons for quotations from *Field Book of Wild Birds and their Music* by F. Schuyler Mathews; T. Y. Crowell Co., for quotation from *Feathered Game of the Northeast* by Walter H. Rich; and Charles Scribner's Sons for quotations from the *Works* of H. E. Parkhurst.

To the United States Department of Agriculture and the members of the Biological Survey, to the New York State Museum and its director Dr. John M. Clarke, and to the American Museum of Natural History and its director Dr. Frederic A. Lucas and the members of its scientific staff are due special thanks for the material and pictures supplied by them.

The careful workmanship of The J. B. Lyon Company of Albany, the Phœnix Engraving Company, of New York City, and the Zeese-Wilkinson Company, of New York City, have made possible the mechanical perfection of these volumes.

Courtesy of H. T. Middleton

WILD-LIFE PHOTOGRAPHER SNAPPING A PIED-BILLED GREBE IN A POND

INTRODUCTION

By T. Gilbert Pearson, B. S.

HERE is to-day in the United States a very wide interest in the conservation of wild birds. This is manifested in the great interest which the public shows in proposed legislative enactments for bird-protection, in the propagation of various game-birds on private and public properties, in the building and erection of innumerable boxes for the convenience of nesting birds, and in the constantly increasing financial support given to the National Association of Audubon Societies, and its many affiliated state and local bird protection clubs throughout the country.

A lively curiosity has spread among all classes of thinking people as to the names of the birds they see, what they feed on, and something of their coming and going, with the result that the demand for bird books has become very great. No publisher of general literature would to-day deem his list of books adequate without one or more standard works on some phase of ornithology. Literary magazines constantly are publishing articles on the habits of birds, the migration of birds, the economic value of birds, the æsthetic interest in bird life.

There have been recorded in North America eight hundred distinct species of wild birds, and four hundred additional subspecies, or climatic varieties. This refers to the territory lying north of the Rio Grande — and not to Middle America, which includes Mexico and Central America. Naturally the individuals of some of these species are far more numerous than are others. For example, during historic times there probably never were more than a few thousand specimens of the California Vulture, while such common species as the Robin and the Mourning Dove run into the millions.

Some birds are extremely rare, for example only one specimen of the Scaled Petrel has ever been taken in North America, and that was in Livingston county, New York, although the natural habitat of all Petrels is on the open seas.

No one state contains all these various forms of bird-life. From the latest available information the following list shows the number of birds that have been recorded in the various states of the Union:

Alabama, 275; Arizona, 371; Arkansas, 255; California, 541; Colorado, 403; Connecticut, 334; Delaware, 229; District of Columbia, 293; Florida, 362; Idaho, 210; Illinois, 390; Indiana, 321; Iowa, 356; Kansas, 379; Kentucky, 228; Louisiana, 323; Maine, 327; Maryland, 290; Massachusetts, 369; Michigan, 326; Minnesota, 304; Missouri, 383; Nebraska, 418; Nevada, 250; New Hampshire, 283; New Jersey, 358; New Mexico, 314; New York, 412; North Carolina, 331; North Dakota, 338; Ohio, 330; Oregon, 328; Pennsylvania, 300; Rhode Island, 293; South Carolina, 337; Tennessee, 223; Texas, 546; Utah, 214; Vermont, 255; Virginia, 302; Washington, 372; West Virginia, 246; Wisconsin, 357; Wyoming, 288. For the remaining five states no list of birds has been published.

Among the twelve hundred species and subspecies there are a considerable number that are exotic and are never seen in this country save on rare occasions when blown far by storms they wander to our shores. Among this class may be mentioned such species as the Scarlet Ibis from South America, the Mew Gull from northern Europe, the Giant Fulmar of the southern oceans, and the Lapwing, Rook, and Wheatear from the old world.

Birds vary greatly in the extent of their natural range and here again comparison may be made between the California Vulture and the Robin; the one ranging in suitable localities from southern Florida to Alaska, the other being restricted to the California mountains. The bird of greatest range in the world is the Arctic Tern, which in the northern summer haunts the North American coastline from Maine to the Arctic seas, and during our winter feeds along the shores of the Antarctic continent. Most birds have a much more restricted range and but few are found in every state. Some species occur only along the Pacific coast, others only in the northeastern States and Canada, and still others are confined to the south Atlantic and Gulf States.

The earlier legislative enactments for bird-protection in the United States dealt almost entirely with game-birds. So persistently was this class of birds shot, trapped, and netted after the coming of the Europeans, that it soon became apparent that restrictive measures must be taken if some of the more popular game-birds were to be preserved for posterity. These laws at first were quite amateurish, but as a result of experience they later were established along certain definite lines, viz., first, those setting aside certain seasons of the year when the birds could be killed, the idea of this being to afford them protection during the period of incubation and caring for the young; second, forbidding certain methods of capture as for example " fire lighting " at night, netting, and shooting into flocks with large swivel guns; and, third, limiting the number that might be taken in a day or season.

It was found that the ordinary civil officers could not, or would not, enforce the game laws satisfactorily, hence there soon developed a plan of employing special state officers known as game wardens whose specific duty it was to see that the laws protecting birds and game were observed. In order to raise funds for the employing of these officers and also to increase the restrictions on gunners the custom arose of requiring hunters' license fees of all who desired to kill these State assets. These fees run from one dollar to three dollars for a resident of the State and from five to seventy-five dollars for a non-resident of the State. This hunting license fund in some of the larger States at times amounts to $200,000 or more annually.

It was not until about the middle eighties that public attention was drawn strongly to the desirability of preserving that group of birds usually referred to as " non-game birds." By a campaign of education the Audubon Society, first formed at that time, began to educate the public sentiment on the subject with the result that the law usually known as the Audubon Law and which has for its purpose the protection of this large group of birds, has been enacted in the Legislatures of all the States with the exception of six. By the enactment of the Federal Migratory Bird Law on March 4, 1913, a provision protecting these birds was created which covers the United States. On December 10, 1916, a treaty between this country and Great Britain was ratified, which extends protection to non-game birds in the Dominion of Canada.

The best place to study wild birds is on a Bird Reservation for here the birds have greatly lost their fear of man, and primitive conditions, so far as the birds are concerned, have thus largely been restored. In one of the protected sea-bird colonies of North Carolina I have photographed Royal Terns standing unafraid on the sands not twelve feet distant. They had become so accustomed to the warden in charge that they had regained their confidence in man. At Lake Worth I saw a man feed Scaup Ducks that swam to within two yards of his boat. In thousands of door-yards throughout the country wild birds, won by kind treatment, now take their food or drink within a few feet of their human protectors. This is because the door-yards have been made little bird reservations. I have a number of friends who regularly feed Chickadees in winter as the birds perch on their outstretched hands. It is astonishing how quickly wild creatures respond to a little reasonable treatment, as may readily be learned by any householder who will try the experiment. With a little patience any teacher may instruct her pupils in the simple art of making the birds feel at home in the vicinity of the school-house.

Eggs of American Birds

PLATE No. 2

1. Whip-poor-will
2. Nighthawk
3. Yellow-billed Cuckoo
4. Belted Kingfisher
5. Least Bittern
6. Sora
7. Bob-white
8. Red Phalarope
9. Wilson's Phalarope
10. Spotted Sandpiper
11. Wilson's Plover
12. California Quail
13. Semipalmated Sandpiper
14. Killdeer
15. Florida Gallinule
16. Sparrow Hawk
17. Ruffed Grouse
18. Wilson's Snipe
19. Woodcock
20. Sharp-shinned Hawk
21. White Ibis
22. Little Blue Heron
23. Clapper Rail
24. White-faced Glossy Ibis

From a Drawing by Henry Thurston

EGGS OF AMERICAN BIRDS
(Plate Number Two)

There are some kinds of birds that, as far as we know their history, have always built their nests in the holes of trees. Woodpeckers have strong chisel-shaped bills and are able to excavate nesting cavities, but there are others that do not possess such powers. These must depend on finding the abandoned hole of some Woodpecker, or the natural hollow of some tree. It not infrequently happens that such birds are obliged to search far and wide for a hole in which they can make their abode. It is the custom of those who take care of lawns and city parks to chop away and remove all dead limbs or trees that may die. As there are very few Woodpeckers that ever attempt to dig a nesting hole in living trees, such work of the axeman means that when the season comes for the rearing of young, all mated Wood-peckers must move on to where more natural conditions await them. This results in an abnormal reduction of the number of holes for the use of the weaker billed hole-nesting species which must now seek for the few available hollows and knot-holes. But even these places are often taken away from them for along comes the tree doctor, who on the pretext of aiding to preserve the trees, fills up the natural openings with cement and the birds are literally left out in the cold. It is plain to see, therefore, that one reason why many birds do not remain in our towns through the spring months, is due to the absence of places where they may lay their eggs and rear their young.

Photo by A. A. Allen

HOUSE WREN

Building its nest in a nesting box on a porch

To overcome this difficulty the Audubon Society several years ago began to advocate the building and erection of suitable nesting boxes, and to-day the practice is gaining wide usage. More people every year are putting such boxes upon poles or nailing them to trees about their homes, and city authorities in some instances now include bird-boxes among the annual expenditures in the care of their parks. Some of the boxes that may be purchased are very ornate and make beautiful additions even to the most carefully kept estates. One may buy these boxes at prices varying from thirty-five cents to thirty-five dollars each. It is not necessary, however, to buy the boxes to be put up for birds. Equally useful ones may readily be made in the Manual Training Department of the school, or in the basement or wood-shed at home. If one does not know how to begin one may buy a bird-box, or write to the Audubon Society for a free circular of directions, and construct similar ones for himself. People sometimes make the mistake of thinking it is absolutely necessary that such boxes should conform strictly to certain set dimensions. Remember, however, that the cavities in trees and stumps which the birds naturally use, show a wide variety of size, shape and location. A large, commodious, many-roomed, and well painted Martin house, makes a pleasing appearance on the landscape, but it may not be attractive to the Martins. As a boy I built up a colony of more than fifteen pairs of these birds by the simple device of rudely partitioning a couple of soap boxes. The openings of the different rooms were neither uniform in size or shape, but were such as an untrained boy would cut out with a hatchet. A dozen gourds each with a large hole in the side completed the tenements for this well contented Martin community.

There are a few simple rules on the making and placing of bird-boxes that should be observed.

1. In the case of all nest-boxes, except those designed for Martins, the opening should be several inches above the floor, thus conforming to the general plan of the Woodpecker's hole, or the natural cavity in a tree.

2. As a rule nest-boxes should be erected on poles from ten to thirty feet from the ground, or fastened to the sides of trees where limbs do not interfere with the outlook. The main exception to this rule is in the case of Wrens, where the boxes or gourds intended for their use may be nailed or wired in fruit trees or about out-buildings.

3. Martin houses should be erected on poles at least twenty feet high and placed well out in the open, not less than one hundred feet from buildings or large trees.

4. All boxes should be taken down after the nesting season and the old nesting material removed.

Much may be done to bring the birds about the home by placing food where they may readily get it. The majority of land-birds that pass the winter in Canada or the colder parts of the United States, feed mainly on seeds. Cracked corn, wheat, rice, sunflower seed, and bird-seed which may be purchased readily in any town, are therefore exceedingly attractive articles of diet. Bread crumbs are enjoyed by many species. Food should not be thrown out on the snow unless there is a crust or the snow has been well trampled down. Usually it should be placed on boards. Various feeding devices have been made of such character as to prevent the food being covered or washed away by snow or rain. Suet tied to the limbs of trees on the lawn will give comfort and nourishment to many a Chickadee, Nuthatch, and Downy Woodpecker. To make a bird sanctuary, therefore, nesting sites and food are among the first requirements. There appears to be no reason why town and city parks everywhere should not be made into places of great attraction for the wild birds.

At Meriden, New Hampshire, there is a tract of land containing thirty-two acres of field and woods, which is dedicated to the comfort and happiness of wild birds. It is owned by the Meriden Bird Club. The entire community takes an interest in its maintenance, and here birds are fed and nesting places provided. It is in the widest sense a " community sanctuary." There are now a number of these coöperative bird-havens established and cared for in much the same manner. One is in Cincinnati, another in Ithaca, New York, and still another at Greenwich, Connecticut.

The best equipped of this class of community bird-refuges, as distinguished from private estates, or Audubon Society, State, or Federal bird-reservations, is Birdcraft Sanctuary, located in Fairfield, Connecticut. This tract of ten acres was presented to the Connecticut Audubon Society in June, 1914. A cat-proof fence surrounds the entire place. That it may not look aggressive, it is set well inside the picturesque old wall. Stone gate-posts and a rustic gate greet the visitor at the entrance on the highway. There is a bungalow for the caretaker and a tool and workshop of corresponding style. Several rustic shelters and many seats are about. The various springs on the place were assembled into a pond. Trails were cut through the brush and the turf grass, and a charming bit of old orchard on the hill-top, was restored for the benefit of worm-pulling Robins. Stone basins were constructed for bird-baths, houses are put up for all sorts of birds, from Wren boxes, von Berlepsch model, Flicker boxes and Owl boxes, to a Martin hotel; and lastly, the natural growth has been supplemented by planting pines, spruce, and hemlocks for windbreakers, and mountain ash, mulberries, sweet cherries, flowering shrubs, and vines for berries. Not only were all these things done, but there has been built and equipped a small museum of Natural History, which for good taste and usefulness one would need to travel far to find its equal.

The interest in this subject is growing every day, in fact, America is to-day planning new homes for her birds — homes where they may live with unrestricted freedom, where

food and lodging in abundance, and of the best, will be supplied, where bathing-pools will
be at their service, where blossoming trees will welcome them in the spring, and fields of grain
in the fall, quiet places where these privileges will bring to the birds much joy and contentment.   Throughout this country there should be a concerted effort to convert the ceme-
teries, city parks, and estates into sanctuaries for the bird-life of this land.

With a little trouble, seasoned with good judgment, one may soon have birds feeding
on a tray within a few yards of the window or even on the window sill.   Abundant opportunity is thus given for photographing birds under the best possible conditions for successful
results.   With every possible convenience at hand one may get better pictures of birds on a
feeding tray than one could ever hope to do in a state of wild Nature.

Photographing birds then is an excellent occupation, for the merest novice may hope
for success.   It is a good thing to do this too from the standpoint of the bird's well being.
I have never known a bird photographer who was not a bird lover; for to know the birds is
to protect them.

Photograph by W. L. Finley

**H. T. BOHLMAN PHOTOGRAPHING A COLONY OF WHITE PELICANS AND CORMORANTS IN TULE LAKE,
NORTHERN CALIFORNIA**

Present operations in the United States, in the line of bird-reservations, grew out of the
distinct need of preserving certain classes of birds from becoming extinct.   The birds that we
may distinctly call farm-land birds, such as the native Sparrows, the Warblers, Wrens,
Orioles, and many other common insectivorous birds, have increased in America since the
advent of white man.

It is chiefly the birds that could be commercialized, either for their flesh, or their feathers
that have suffered great diminution in numbers in North America as a result of man's activities.   An important effort to preserve this class of birds is now being carried on in the United
States by the establishment of bird-reservations.   Reservation work began in 1902, under
the National Association of Audubon Societies.   This is the best organized and most liberally
financed bird protective organization in the world, and has been in active operation for
many years.

One of the States that early adopted the Audubon Law was Florida.   On the Atlantic
coast of that state, in Indian River, there is an island of about four acres, where two thousand

Brown Pelicans have been coming, from the time whereof the memory of man runneth not to the contrary, to lay their eggs and rear their young. About the time this law was enacted long quills became very popular in the millinery trade. Some of us found that the millinery stores in large cities were selling feathers taken from the Bush Turkey, the Albatross, the Brown Pelican, and also from the old Turkey Buzzard of the South. Certain people tried to secure the repeal of the Florida law, so that the Pelicans might be killed for their feathers.

This caused the question to rise: Would it be possible to get the government of the United States to take hold of that island in some way? A man who kills a bird would rather be haled before a local magistrate where the jury probably would be composed of friends and neighbors, who themselves had killed birds. In such a case it was a simple matter

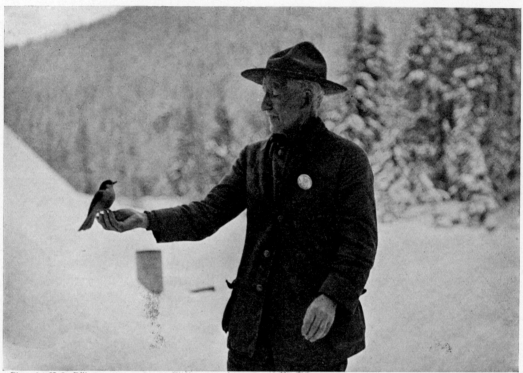

Photo by H. L. Dillaway   Courtesy of Nat. Asso. Aud. Soc.
PARK RANGER AND CAMP ROBBER (GRAY JAY)
Mount Ranier in background

to leave the plough for a day and stand trial. But in a Federal court it is a different proposition. Here a man may have to travel half way across the state to attend court, and must appear before a jury composed of strangers — a situation to be dreaded.

There did not seem to be any way whereby this Federal control could be secured until the matter was finally taken up with President Roosevelt, who said, " If the land office will recommend that this land is not good for agricultural purposes we will make it a bird-reserve under the care of the Department of Agriculture, provided the Audubon Society will agree to hire a man to act as guardian on the island." In a very short time the matter was arranged, and the President declared the island a bird-sanctuary in perpetuity — a breeding place for wild birds for all time. He took a short cut in doing this for there was no specific law giving the executive such authority. Along the coast of Florida were found nine other small islands suitable for this purpose, and Mr. Roosevelt made them all Federal bird-reservations.

Later inquiry was made about places suitable for sanctuaries for other birds, for, bear in mind, many large birds over extended areas were threatened with extirpation to supply the demand for the market. Sea Gulls along the coast, Terns, Grebes, Ducks, Geese, and others in the West were in imminent danger from this cause. So the National Association of Audubon Societies began to look for breeding places of Ducks and other birds in the West. Examination was made in various parts of the country and many more bird reservations were the result. When President Roosevelt went out of office, we had thirty-eight bird reserves. President Taft took an interest in the subject and also segregated quite a number. One of the largest of these bird-sanctuaries is the delta of the Yukon, which is as large as the State of Connecticut.

One bird reserve was created in the western group of the Hawaiian Islands, including the Laysan Island. This, by the way, was raided in the summer of 1915 by Japanese feather hunters. The Pribilof Islands were also made a reserve, as well as the Aleutian Chain. There are to-day seventy United States bird-reserves in all. At first the Government made no appropriation to protect and guard these birds. Therefore, it became the duty of the Audubon Society to ask for aid from its members and friends who were willing to give money for an idea — people willing to provide funds to protect Egrets in Florida or Cormorants and Gulls on the Three-Arch Rocks in Oregon, whether or not they could ever hope to see personally the sanctuaries. After the lapse of six years, the Government made a small grant for the purpose, although, to-day, the Audubon Society owns and operates the patrol launches on the Government reserves, and still helps to pay the salaries of some of the wardens. The Government is appropriating more money each year to this work, and the gentlemen of the Biological Survey who have the work in charge are exercising every means at their command to successfully protect the birds.

President Wilson made the Panama Canal Zone a bird-reserve in 1913. There are many bird-reserves which the Audubon Society is protecting that are not on Government territory. These are cared for by the Society's paid agents. The islands

T. GILBERT PEARSON PHOTOGRAPHING YOUNG HERONS

In the marshes of Klamath Lake, Oregon

along the coast of Maine are great breeding places for sea-fowl of various kinds. There are forty-two islands where they nest, and there are sixteen Audubon wardens in service there in summer. The Society also has wardens guarding islands along the coasts of Connecticut, New York, New Jersey, and North Carolina. There are still others in Florida and Louisiana. About sixty important colonies of water-birds are protected by the Audubon Society in the southern states. It has been able to buy some and to lease others. In some cases merely the consent of the owners is obtained. The result is that certain water-birds on the Atlantic coast, such as Herring Gulls and several species of Terns, have come back in great numbers.

The Audubon Society is trying to guard the Egrets in the South and we know of about twenty thousand of these birds left in the United States. Two of the Society's agents, while on guard, have been shot and killed by plume-hunters, and the colonies have been raided and the plumes sent to New York.

In North America the great nursery for wild Ducks and Geese is the region between the Great Lakes and Hudson Bay on the east and the Rocky Mountains on the west. There are three great flights of Ducks and Geese in autumn from that section of the country. Those heading for the Atlantic Seaboard chiefly cross the States diagonally, reaching the Atlantic Coast about Maryland. In a reactionary migratory movement, many of them go back along the coast at least to Long Island and swing back and forth, according to weather conditions. The other end of this movement goes down the coast. There is also a great flight down the Mississippi Valley. Under the migratory bird laws, the Mississippi, between Memphis and St. Paul, is a reservation. In the sunken ground of Arkansas there are two large bird-reserves, and on one of these many Ducks find a refuge. This was a famous place for market hunters in days gone by. More than 300,000 Ducks were taken there in one year. Another larger series of bird-reservations is situated in the State of Louisiana. These include 234,000 acres of marsh-land, where numbers of Ducks and Geese now find a safe refuge. These reservations were made by the private purchase of Charles Willis Ward, E. A. McIlhenny, Mrs. Russell Sage, and the Rockefeller Foundation.

This widespread interest in birds both on the part of the Government and private individuals has had happy results. Not only are our birds protected, but unusual opportunity has been given to study them. The advance in field work, coupled with the constant improvement of photography, has obtained results little short of astounding.

When the present work on *Birds of America* was projected, some months ago, we of the editorial board began as a first move, to take stock of the situation. We felt that the time was at last ripe for a new book on the subject that should be a final repository of all this vast treasure of scattered information. Patient field ornithologists, on the one hand, and laboratory naturalists, on the other, had given us wonderfully rich material which only awaited assembling. The task even ten years ago would have proved far more difficult. What was clearly needed, was to make a thorough canvass of the field and produce a work at once popular and scientific, and at the same time comprehensive—a record of our wild birds prepared in such form as to meet the needs of both the laymen and the trained naturalist. Ornithologists all over the country heartily endorsed the project; indeed we have seldom seen a work which aroused more enthusiasm in the doing than *Birds of America*. The official check list of the American Ornithologists' Union has been followed for classification, and we have included not only our common living birds as found to-day, but also many rarer forms and some recently extinct, such as the Passenger Pigeon. We have tried, in a word, to present a complete picture and story of our feathered wild bird life.

ORDER OF DIVING BIRDS

Order *Pygopodes*

MOST aquatic of all our birds are the Diving Birds. Not only are their bodies made so that they can propel themselves on land only with difficulty, but their food consists entirely of fish and other aquatic animals. Their flesh is coarse and unpalatable. They are the lowest form of bird life and are the most closely allied to the reptiles, from which birds are supposed to have originated. Birds of this order spend nearly their entire time in the water. They nest on the ground or on rocks. The young are covered with down when hatched, and as soon as this natal down is dry they are able to take to the water.

The scientific name given to this order, *Pygopodes*, is from two Greek words meaning " rump " and "foot," and refers to the position of the legs in relation to the rest of the body — a characteristic peculiar to this order. The tibia or drumstick is buried beneath the skin and feathers, bringing the heel joint close to the tail. The birds, therefore, sit or stand in an almost perpendicular position, and walk with great difficulty and awkwardness. The toes are either webbed or broadly lobed. Both body and neck are elongated, giving a boat-shaped appearance to the bird. The bill is horny and pointed and has no pouch; it can be opened very wide. The wings are very short, scarcely reaching the base of the tail. The latter is never long, and sometimes it is so rudimentary as to make the bird appear tailless. The plumage is dense, and there is no sexual variation in color. The body is almost entirely encased in a layer of fat.

According to the development of the tail, the Diving Birds are divided into two suborders: the first is the *Colymbi*, and contains the one family of Grebes; and the second is the *Cepphi*, and contains two families, the Loons and the Auks, Murres, and Puffins.

GREBES

Order *Pygopodes;* suborder *Colymbi;* family *Colymbidæ*

THE Grebes are much less pronounced, and consequently less interesting bird characters, than are the Loons, though both families have some of the same physical characteristics, notably skill in the water and clumsiness on land. They are smaller than the Loons and are more likely to be found in inland bodies of fresh water, though their migrations take them to the sea where they are by no means entirely out of their element. Like the Loons, when pursued the Grebes try to escape by diving and swimming under water, where they propel themselves by their feet; and generally they show decided disinclination to take to their wings, though they are swift and strong flyers. Grebes undoubtedly dive with remarkable quickness, but, as in the case of the Loons (and for the same reasons), their cleverness in this operation has been much exaggerated, as at any reasonable distance they are quite unable to dodge a rifle bullet, especially if it be propelled by smokeless powder.

Grebes have feet which are lobate, that is, each toe has one or more separate membranes which are joined only at the base. The toes are flattened and the nails short and round. The shanks are so flattened as to be nearly blade-like. The bill, which is cone-shaped, is about the length of the head. The head is generally ruffed or crested, at least in the breeding season, and the neck long. The wings are short and the tail is invisible. The plumage is compact, smooth, and rather hair-like; when well dressed by the bird it is absolutely waterproof, and, therefore, Grebes, though water birds, are never wet. The extreme posterior position of the legs causes the birds to sit up like Penguins.   On land they sometimes progress on their bellies after the manner of seals.   In flight the feet are extended backward and serve as a rudder, as the tail would in another bird.

A dense, matted, raft-like structure, made of rushes and the like, and often floating, but usually anchored to some aquatic plant, forms the nest of these strange birds.   On this platform are laid from two to nine eggs of dull white or greenish-white.   The nest is always damp and the eggs sometimes are hatched when they actually are partly covered with water. " When out of the shell," says one observer, " the young has not far to walk; he looks for a few moments over the edge of his water-drenched cradle and down he goes with the expertness of an old diver."   Grebes usually are gregarious.   When incubation of the full number of eggs has actually begun, the sitting bird upon leaving the nest (unless she is frightened away) completely conceals the eggs with moss and rushes.

Few birds have suffered more from the millinery trade than have the Grebes, whose dense and beautiful breast plumage has been much used for decorating hats.   Legislation of various kinds curbs this barbaric practice in many parts of the country.

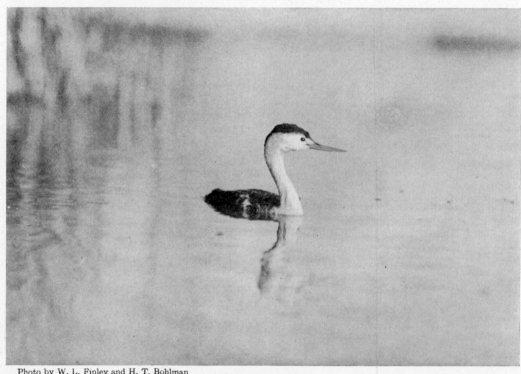

Photo by W. L. Finley and H. T. Bohlman

WESTERN GREBE

The most remarkable point about the food habits of Grebes is that the stomachs almost invariably contain a considerable mass of feathers.   Feathers are fed to the young, and there is no question that they play some essential though unknown part in the digestive economy.   As they are finely ground in the gizzards it is probable that finally they are digested and the available nutriment assimilated.   Feathers constituted practically 66 per cent. of the contents of the 57 Horned Grebe's stomachs examined.   However, it is not likely that they furnish a very large percentage of the nourishment needed by the birds.   As the nutritive value of the feathers is unknown, this part of the stomach contents is ignored.   The other items of food are assigned 100 per cent., and the percentages are given on that basis. Various beetles, chiefly aquatic, compose 23.3 per cent. of the food; other insects (including aquatic bugs, caddis and chironomid larvæ, dragon-fly nymphs, etc.), nearly 12 per cent.; fishes, 27.8 per cent.; crawfish 20.7 per cent.; and other crustacea 13.8 per cent.   A little other animal matter is taken, including snails and spiders, and a small quantity of vegetable food was found in two stomachs.

It has been claimed that Grebes live exclusively on fish and do mischief in fish hatcheries. The results obtained by stomach examination show that they do not depend wholly or even chiefly upon fish. On the contrary, they eat a large number of crawfishes, which often severely damage crops, and consume numbers of aquatic insects which devour small fishes and the food of such fishes.

WESTERN GREBE

A. O. U. Number 1

Æchmophorus occidentalis (*Lawrence*)

Other Names.— Western Dabchick; Swan Grebe.

General Description.— Length, 24 to 29 inches. Color above, brownish-black; below, satiny-white. Head with short crest on top but none on sides; bill, slender; neck nearly the length of the body.

Color.— ADULTS: Forehead, dark ash; crest and narrow line down back of neck, sooty-blackish shading on upper parts into brownish-black; the feathers of back with grayish margins; primaries, dusky-brown, white at base; secondaries, white, some dark on outer webs; sides of head, chin, throat, and entire under parts, pure satiny-white; bill, yellowish-olive; feet, dull olive, yellowish on webs; outer edge and soles of feet, blackish; iris, orange, pink, or carmine with a white ring; a narrow bare space from bill to eye, lavender.

Nest and Eggs.— NEST: A matted structure of tule stems, grass, and water-plants, with a slight depression in the center; afloat on the water; usually lightly fastened to the living reeds so that it will move up and down but not be carried away from its position. EGGS: Sometimes 3 but usually 4 or 5, pale bluish-green but stained a light brown from contact with the decomposed vegetable matter of the nest.

Distribution.— Western North America; breeds from British Columbia, southern Saskatchewan, southern Alberta, and southern Manitoba south to northern California, Utah, and northern North Dakota; winters from southern British Columbia and California southward to central Mexico; casual east to Nebraska, Kansas, Wisconsin, Minnesota, and Quebec.

For years, the lake region of southern Oregon was the most profitable field in the West for the plume hunter. The Western Grebe was the greatest sufferer. This diver of glistening-white breast and silvery-gray back was sought not without reason. The Grebe hunters call the skin of this bird fur rather than feathers, because it is so tough it can be scraped and handled like a hide, and because the thick warm plumage seems more like the fur of a mammal than the skin of a bird. These skins, when prepared and placed on the market in the form of coats and capes, brought the prices of the most expensive furs.

Formerly there were immense colonies of Western Grebes living along the north shore of Tule, or Rhett, Lake, Lower Klamath Lake, and Malheur Lake. Plume hunters, however, sought out these big colonies and shot great numbers of the birds during the nesting season, leaving the eggs to spoil and the young to starve to death. This decreased the numbers so rapidly that within a few seasons the birds were exterminated in places.

Malheur Lake is a large body of shallow water surrounded on all sides by great stretches of tules. The whole border is a veritable jungle, an almost endless area of floating tule islands between which is a network of channels. Here is the typical home of the Western Grebe. In the edge of the tules, the Grebe gathers tule stems and other vegetation, making a floating raft

Photo by F. M. Chapman   Courtesy of Nat. Asso. Aud. Soc.

TWO WESTERN GREBES JUST HATCHED

which is anchored. Around the edges of one of these islands, which was two acres in extent, we found between forty and fifty nests. The usual number of eggs was four or five.

On several occasions, we watched a Grebe chick cut his way out of the shell and liberate himself. After he gets his bill through in one place, he goes at the task like clockwork. He turns himself a little and begins hammering in a new place and keeps this up until he has made a complete revolution in his shell. The end or cap of the egg, cut clear around, drops off, and the youngster kicks himself out into the sunshine. It doesn't take his coat long to dry.

The Grebe parents have an interesting way of taking their young with them. The chicks ride on the back of the mother or father just under the wing-coverts with the head sticking out. Sometimes one may see an old Grebe carrying two or three young on his back. At the slightest alarm, the old bird raises the feathers and covers the chicks completely. One can readily tell when a Grebe has chicks on his back, even if not visible, because he appears to swim higher in the water. Normally, the body is almost submerged. An old Grebe not only swims, but dives readily, keeping the young in place on his back.

WILLIAM L. FINLEY.

HOLBŒLL'S GREBE

Colymbus holbœlli (*Reinhardt*)

A. O. U. Number 2   See Color Plate 1

Other Names.—American Red-necked Grebe; Red-necked Grebe; Holbœll's Diver.

General Description.— Length, 19 inches. IN SUMMER: Glossy greenish-black above, and silvery-white below. IN WINTER: Grayish-brown above, and grayish-white below. Neck shorter than body; bill, nearly as long as head; crest lacking or inconspicuous. Largest of the Grebes.

Color.— ADULTS IN SUMMER: *Crown, back of neck, and upper parts, glossy greenish-black,* darker on head, more brownish on back where the feathers are edged with grayish; wing-coverts and primaries, dusky-brown; *secondaries, white* with brown tips and black shafts; *a broad area including chin, throat, and sides of head, silvery-gray,* lightening along juncture with black of crown; rest of neck and upper part of breast, deep brownish-rufous; under parts, silvery-white shaded along sides with pale ash, each feather with a dark shaft line and terminal spot, producing a dappled effect;

bill, dusky, yellow below and at base; iris, carmine with a white ring. ADULTS IN WINTER, AND YOUNG: Crown, neck all around, and upper parts, grayish-brown, the feathers of back with lighter edges; sides of head and throat, whitish; under parts, grayish-white, the mottling of summer plumage obsolete; bill, obscured but showing some pale yellow below; iris, as in summer.

Nest and Eggs.— NEST: Attached to live rushes; constructed of reeds, decayed vegetable matter, grass, and mud. EGGS: 3 to 5, dull white, usually soiled with brownish.

Distribution.— North America at large, eastern Siberia, and southwest to Japan; breeds from northwestern Alaska across British America to northern Ungava, south to northern Washington, Montana, and southwestern Minnesota; common throughout the United States in winter; south to southern California, southern Colorado, the Ohio valley and North Carolina; casual in Georgia and Greenland.

Some Grebes colonize in breeding, as do the Western and Eared Grebes. In Holbœll's Grebe, however, we have the one large species of North America which is distinctly a lover of personal solitude. Its breeding grounds, or perhaps more properly waters, are the sloughs and marshes of the northwest States and Canadian provinces. Here, in the deep bogs, it places its soggy semi-floating pile of decaying vegetation amid the areas of reeds or canes growing from the water. One can seldom see the brooding bird on the nest. On being approached she hastily pulls débris

over the three or four dirty-white eggs, completely covering them, then slips into the water and dives, showing herself no more until the intruder has surely vanished.

During the breeding season these Grebes are very noisy. The male (probably it is he) swims into the open water of the lakes, if such there be, and emits the most astonishing succession of yells and wailings, which probably are the happy expression of the torrent of his tender emotions, though to our ears they may rather resemble cries of distress. Later in the season he gets bravely over such manifestations of weakness, and is silent enough for anyone. Then he is usually seen "by his lonesome," out on some body of water, frequently on the ocean, well off the beach, where he can exercise to fine advantage his really great powers of diving.

Holbœll's Grebes are hardy birds, and often winter as far to the north as they can find open water, and are frequent in winter along our North Atlantic coast. They have a fatal tendency to linger too late in the northern lakes, and thus they get caught in the ice, or, driven to fly south, cannot find open water, and fall exhausted on the land or into snow banks. This is notably the case in the month of March, when they migrate north earlier than is safe. Since they cannot rise on wing except from water, as their wings are small, many of them perish out of their element. It is a common occurrence for farmers and others to pick them up in fields or roads, helplessly waddling about on legs set too far "aft" to make them handy ashore. But in

the water there is no bird more swift and facile, better able to take care of itself, more able in the pursuit of the small fry which constitute its normal prey.   HERBERT K. JOB.

Photo by H. K. Job

NEST OF HOLBŒLL'S GREBE

HORNED GREBE

Colymbus auritus *Linnæus*

A. O. U. Number 3   See Color Plate 1

Other Names.— Hell-diver; Water-witch; Devil-diver; Pink-eyed Diver; Dipper.

General Description.— Length, 14 inches. Color above, grayish-brown or dusky-gray; below, white. In summer, adults have crests or ruffs on cheeks and sides of head.

Color.— ADULTS IN SUMMER: Crown, chin, throat, and crest, *glossy greenish-black;* a stripe from bill through eye and above it, widening behind to nape, *brownish-yellow;* upper parts, grayish-brown; feathers, paler-edged; primaries, dusky-brown; *secondaries, white;* neck all around (except for dusky stripe behind), sides, and flanks, rich brownish-rufous; rest of under parts, silky-white; bill, dusky tipped with yellow; iris, carmine with white ring; feet, dusky outside, yellow inside. ADULTS IN WINTER, AND YOUNG: Ruff, obsolete;

forehead, crown to level of eyes, a narrow strip down back of neck and upper parts, dusky-gray; feathers of back with lighter edges; wings, as in summer; chin, throat, and sides of head, pure silky-white; front of neck and lower abdomen, washed with gray; bill, dusky, yellowish or bluish-white below.

Nest and Eggs.— NEST: A buoyant platform of dead reeds, grass, and vegetation. EGGS: 3 to 7, white.

Distribution.— Northern part of northern hemisphere; breeds from the lower Yukon across British America to southern Ungava and the Magdalen Islands, south to southern British Columbia, across United States on about the parallel 45° to Maine; winters from southern British Columbia, southern Ontario, and Maine south to the Gulf coast and Florida; casual in Greenland.

Horned Grebes are commonly known as "Hell-divers" or "Water-witches," because of their facility in disappearing and the mystery as to where they go. This species often mystifies the hunter by sinking slowly backward until nearly out of sight or by diving and disappearing altogether, until the novice is ready to make oath

that the bird has committed suicide for fear of his deadly marksmanship; but the Grebe merely submerges and swims beneath the surface until among the water plants, where it remains secure with its beak just protruding unnoticed above the water, or hidden by some overhanging leaf. When wounded it sometimes dives and swims along under water to the cover of overhanging vegetation on the bank, when it creeps ashore unseen and hides amid the verdant cover.

Photo by H. K. Job　　　Courtesy of Outing Pub. Co.
HORNED GREBE (Spring Plumage)

This Grebe is one of the quickest of divers, often escaping a charge of shot by its activity in going under. When alarmed it lies very low in the water, and, if it can get its head and neck beneath the surface before the shot reaches the spot, its vital parts are likely to escape unharmed. It frequents small ponds and little streams with grassy banks, but where much persecuted by gunners seeks the larger lakes or the sea for greater safety. Ordinarily in swimming under water it does not appear to use its wings, but probably all diving birds utilize their wing power when in pursuit of elusive prey. Mr. C. W. Vibert of South Windsor, Connecticut, kept a bird of this species that was seen to raise its wings slightly when swimming beneath the surface.

When storms prevail at sea in fall and winter flocks of Grebes often are driven into the ponds of the interior. At such times they may be seen asleep on the water in the daytime with the head drawn down on the back and the bill thrust into the feathers of the shoulder or breast, keeping their place head to the wind by a sort of automatic paddling. Sometimes a sleepy bird uses only one foot and so swings about in a circle.

EDWARD HOWE FORBUSH.

EARED GREBE

Colymbus nigricollis californicus (*Heermann*)

A. O. U. Number 4

Other Names.— American Eared Grebe; Eared Diver.

General Description.— Length, 12 to 14 inches. Color above, dusky; below, white. In summer adults have *long, fan-shaped ear-tufts of fine feathers.*

Color.— ADULTS IN SUMMER: *Ear-tufts, golden-brown; crown, chin, throat, and neck all around, black;* upper parts, dusky; primaries, dusky; secondaries, white, dusky at base; sides, deep purplish-brown with a wash of the same color across breast and on under tail-coverts; under parts, silky white; abdomen, tinged with gray; bill, black; feet, olive, dusky outside and on soles; iris, red; eyelids, orange. ADULTS IN WINTER: No ear tufts; crown and narrow band on back of neck and upper parts, grayish-dusky; chin, throat, and sides of head, white; under parts, silvery-white; sides and flanks, tinged with gray.

Nest and Eggs.— NEST: A floating platform of reeds and vegetation, on shallow lagoons, ponds, or lakes. EGGS: 4 to 6, soiled white.

Distribution.— Western North America; breeds from Central British Columbia, Great Slave Lake, Saskatchewan, and Manitoba south to southern California, northern Arizona, northern Nebraska, and northern Iowa; winters from central California southward to Cape San Lucas and Guatemala; east to Kansas in migration; casual in Missouri, Indiana, and Ontario.

Out on the main part of Malheur Lake in southeastern Oregon, we came upon a colony of Eared Grebes. These birds were nesting well out in the open water. I counted one hundred and sixty-five nests scattered over an area of two or three acres. Some homes were but a few feet apart. The nest itself was a very interest-

ing structure. It was built entirely of water weeds, commonly called milfoil, which grew in the shallow water. The nest consisted of the long slender runners pulled together from a distance of several feet around. It looked to me as if these weeds when piled together, would sink. On the contrary, I found the nest quite buoyant. Long red stems, kept alive by the water, often extended to the bottom. In a few cases, I found the birds had collected pieces of dry tule stems as a sort of lining to their platform nests. From a distance, the nest colony presented a line of blood-red against a background of green tules.

When we approached the Eared Grebe colony, paid no attention to this. I watched one bird as she pulled up the stems out of the water and from the lining of the nest covering her eggs completely, so when we came near, there was not an egg in sight. I do not know whether this habit develops more from the idea of protecting the eggs from enemies, or from the idea of keeping them warm when the mother is away. The

Photo by W. L. Finley and H. T. Bohlman

EARED GREBE (Spring Plumage)

Though a water-bird, it is never wet

everything was bustle and hurry. The birds were trying to cover their eggs before leaving. It seemed to be a habit in this colony to cover the eggs, while the Western Grebe on the same lake eggs often lie partly in the water. The sun, I think, helps a good deal in hatching the eggs during the day, the bird keeping a more careful vigil at night. WILLIAM L. FINLEY.

PIED-BILLED GREBE

Podilymbus podiceps (*Linnæus*)

A. O. U. Number 6   See Color Plate 1

Other Names.— Hell-diver; Devil-diver; Water-witch; Dabchick; American Dabchick; Pied-billed Dabchick; Dipper; Diedapper; Didapper; Divedapper; Carolina Grebe; Thick-billed Grebe.

General Description.— Length, 13 inches. Color above, brownish-black; below, lighter brown and white. Bill, short and thick; no crests.

Color.— ADULTS: Crown, back of head, and neck, grayish-black streaked with lighter; upper parts, brownish-black; sides of head and neck, brownish-gray; chin and throat, black; primaries and *secondaries, chocolate-brown; below, pale brownish-ash*, thickly mottled with dusky on sides; lower abdomen, mostly dusky; *bill, whitish, dusky on ridge and tip with a black encircling* *band* a little forward of the center; feet, greenish-dusky outside, leaden-gray inside; iris, brown; eyelids, whitish. ADULTS IN WINTER: General coloration on head and upper parts more brownish than in summer; the feathers of back with paler edges; neck, breast, and sides, light brown mottled with dusky; under parts, pure silky white; lower abdomen, grayish.

Nest and Eggs.— NEST: A floating structure of dead grass, reeds, mud, and vegetable matter, unattached or fastened to living rushes. EGGS: 6 to 9, white, sometimes tinged with greenish.

Distribution.— North and South America; breeds from British Columbia, southern Mackenzie, southern Keewatin, Quebec, and New Brunswick southward to Chile and Argentina; winters from Washington, Texas, Mississippi, and the Potomac valley southward.

The Pied-billed Grebe is the most widely distributed of the American Grebes and in the United States is the only one that breeds over most of the region east of the Mississippi. It

appointed Hawk has gone his way. As a diver it has few equals in the bird world. Many times, especially in the days when muzzle-loading shotguns were still in vogue, I have seen it

Drawing by R. I. Brasher

PIED-BILLED GREBE (¼ nat. size)

A more accomplished swimmer than any Duck

is at home in the water to an astonishing degree, in fact "Water-witch" is one of the favorite local names by which it is known. It is a more accomplished swimmer than any Duck of which I have knowledge, for it possesses the wonderful faculty of lowering its body in the water to any desired stage of submersion, and this it can do either while swimming or while remaining stationary, as may suit its fancy. At times only the bill and eyes will appear above the surface, and in this attitude it can remain apparently without distress until the bewildered hunter or the dis-

dive at the flash of discharge and be safely beneath the surface before the death-seeking shot came over the water. "Hell-diver," by the way, is another name applied to Grebes as well as to Loons.

The remarkable nest made by this species is quite in keeping with its other unusual and secretive characteristics. It is made of decaying vegetation brought up from the bottom of the shallow pond where it breeds. This unattractive mass is usually piled on a platform of green stems of water plants, which, because of their fresh condition, will readily float and are of sufficient buoyancy to bear the weight of the nest, the eggs, and the brooding bird. In Florida, where I have examined perhaps fifty of their nests, I never found more than six eggs in any one of them, but observers farther north speak of finding as many as eight and nine. In color they are dull white, unspotted, but sometimes tinged with greenish, and always soiled or stained.

When leaving its nest the Grebe pulls the water-soaked material well over the eggs, so that usually they are completely hidden from view. While in this condition anyone not acquainted with the nesting habits of the bird would surely pass it by unnoticed, never dreaming that in that little mass of floating, rotting water-plants the cherished treasures of a wild bird lay concealed.

Audubon said that the food of the Pied-billed Grebe " consists of small fry, plant-seeds, aquatic insects, and snails; along with this they swallow gravel." Wayne writes: " During the breeding season, the food consists mainly of leeches." They should never be shot, for they are worse than useless for food. They certainly do no harm, and an ever-increasing class of bird-students take much pleasure in spying upon their interesting movements.

They have many enemies, among which may be mentioned minks, fish, frogs, snakes, and muskrats. Birds of prey undoubtedly take their share. One day with much labor I climbed an enormous pine tree to a nest of the Bald Eagle around which the old birds were circling. Upon reaching it after a prolonged and heart-breaking effort I found it to contain only one object — a Pied-billed Grebe, with its feathers still damp and the blood spots on its head but half dried.

T. GILBERT PEARSON.

Photograph by A. A. Allen

PIED-BILLED GREBE

Swimming up to its newly hatched young that has struggled from the nest

LOONS

Order *Pygopodes;* suborder *Cepphi;* family *Gaviidæ*

S a family the Loons of the present seem to be very much the same kind of
birds as were those of which we have fossil remains in strata representing
what the geologists call the Miocene Epoch of the Tertiary Period. They
are birds of considerable size, and are famous especially for their skill and
swiftness in swimming and diving and for their weird and unearthly cries.
Their quickness in diving to escape danger is truly astonishing, and has, naturally enough, furnished occasion for frequent exaggeration, also excuses for
much bad shooting by gunners who assert that they held true, but the Loon
"dodged the shot." They have a peculiar faculty of sinking gradually in
the water without apparent effort and with little or no rippling of the surface
of the water.

Summer   Winter

Drawing by R. I. Brasher

LOON (⅛ nat. size)

A clumsy, awkward traveler upon land, but almost unexcelled as a diver

Loons take wing with considerable difficulty, but once in the air their flight is swift
and usually in a straight line. At all times the sexes present the same general appearance.
Their prevailing colors are blackish or grayish above, with the under parts whitish; in summer
the darker parts become speckled with white. These markings do not appear in the young
nor in the winter plumage of the adults; the very young are covered with a sooty grayish
down, changing to white on the lower abdomen. The head is never crested, but both head
and neck are velvety. The plumage of the body is hard and compact. The wings are
pointed, short, and rather narrow. The eighteen or twenty tail feathers are short and stiff.
The hind toe is small and the front toes are fully webbed. The bill is stout, straight, narrow,
sharp-pointed, and sharp-edged; it is so constructed that it serves as a spear for catching
and holding the slippery fish which are the bird's chief diet.

Though related to the Auks, which show a highly developed gregarious instinct, the
Loons are essentially solitary birds, and commonly are found singly or in pairs. The formation of ice in their natural habitats, however, at times forces a considerable number of
individuals to occupy the same comparatively small stretches of open water.

The distribution of the Loons is circumpolar, and the single genus includes five species.
In the breeding period they occur generally in the cooler regions of the northern hemisphere,
and frequently some distance north of the Arctic Circle; in winter they scatter southward

Photograph of habitat group

Courtesy of American Museum of Natural History

LOONS

They are among the most aquatic of birds

into the temperate regions, especially along the seacoasts.   The nests are rude structures, composed of moss and grass sometimes plastered with a little mud, and are built on the ground usually along the shore of a lake and frequently on top of the abandoned lodge of a muskrat.   The birds seem to make no attempt to hide their nests, but the two eggs, by reason of their olive or brownish shades, which are broken by blackish or brownish spots, are decidedly inconspicuous.

The cry of the Loon has been variously described as mournful, mirthful, sinister, defiant, uncanny, demoniacal, and so on.   At any rate, it is undeniably distinctive and characteristic, and is almost certain to challenge the dullest ear and the most inert imagination, while in those who know instinctively the voices of Nature, especially when she is frankly and unrestrainedly natural, it produces a thrill and elicits a response which only the elect understand.

LOON

Gavia immer (*Brünnich*)

A. O. U. Number 7   See Color Plate 2

Other Names.— Common Loon; Big Loon; Great Northern Diver; Imber Diver; Hell-diver; Ember-Goose; Walloon; Ring-necked Loon; Black-billed Loon; Guinea Duck; Greenhead.

General Description.— Length, 28 to 36 inches. In SUMMER: Upper parts, glossy black with white spots; under parts, white. In WINTER: Upper parts, grayish-brown without spots.

Color.— ADULTS IN SUMMER: Head and neck all around, glossy purplish-black with greenish reflections; a patch of sharp white streaks on lower throat; another of the same kind on each side of neck, separated in front, but sometimes meeting behind; *entire upper parts, wing-coverts, and inner secondaries, glossy black, thickly marked with white spots* — those of shoulders, inner secondaries, and back, large, square, and regularly arranged traversely, those of other parts oval, smallest on rump and wing-coverts; upper tail-coverts, greenish-black; primaries, dusky; *lower parts from neck, white;* sides of breast, streaked with black; bill and feet, black; iris, red. ADULTS IN WINTER, AND

YOUNG: Crown, neck and upper parts, in general, grayish-brown, *the feathers of back with lighter edges;* primaries, black; tail, gray-tipped; sides of breast, mottled; chin, throat, and neck in front (narrowly), and under parts, white with some dark feathers on sides and under tail-coverts, thus no black or white spots; bill, dusky, bluish-white at base and below; feet, lighter than in summer; iris, brown.

Nest and Eggs.— NEST: Usually a hollow in the sand, without nesting material; in some localities a rough nest is constructed of sticks and reeds; occasionally the top of an old muskrat house is utilized. EGGS: 2, dark olive-gray, stained with brown and spotted with black.

Distribution.— Northern part of northern hemisphere; in North America breeds from Alaska across Arctic North America to Greenland, south to northern California, across the United States at about the parallel 42° to Nova Scotia; winters from southern British Columbia, the Great Lakes, and southern New England to Lower California, the Gulf coast, and Florida.

Of all the wild creatures which still persist in the land, despite settlement and civilization, the Loon seems best to typify the untamed savagery of the wilderness. Its wolf-like cry is the wildest sound now heard in Massachusetts, where nature has long been subdued by the rifle, ax, and plow. Sometimes at sea, when I have heard the call of the Loon from afar, and seen its white breast flash from the crest of a distant wave, I have imagined it the signal and call for help of some strong swimmer, battling with the waves.

It is generally believed that in migration at least the Loon passes the night upon the sea or the bosom of some lake or river. The Gulls,

Auks, Puffins, and Cormorants, which live upon the sea, usually alight upon the high shores of some rocky island or on some lonely sand bar at night, but the Loon is often seen at sea when night falls, and its cries are heard by the sailors during the hours of darkness. Notwithstanding the general belief that it normally sleeps on the water, I believe that it prefers to rest on shore at night, when it can safely do so. Audubon satisfied himself that on its breeding grounds it was accustomed to spend the night on shore. On an island off the coast of British Columbia, where there was no one to trouble the birds, I once saw, just at nightfall, a pair of Loons

Plate 2

RED-THROATED LOON
Gavia stellata (Pontoppidan)
SUMMER   WINTER

COMMON LOON
Gavia immer (Brünnich)
SUMMER   WINTER
All ⅕ nat. size

BLACK-THROATED LOON
Gavia arctica (Linnaeus)
SUMMER

resting flat on their breasts at the end of a long sandy point. Cripples instinctively seek the shore when sorely wounded, but on our coast a Loon must keep well off shore to insure its safety, and probably few but cripples ever land on shores frequented by man.

The Loon's nest is usually a mere hollow in the bog or shore near the water's edge on some island in a lake or pond. Sometimes the nest is lined with grasses and bits of turf; more rarely it is a mere depression on the top of a muskrat's house, and more rarely still it is placed on the shore of the lake or in some debouching stream. Where the birds are not much disturbed, and where food is plentiful, two or three pairs sometimes nest on the same island. No doubt there was a time when nearly every northern pond of more than a few acres contained its pair of Loons, in the breeding season, and this is true to-day of ponds in parts of some Canadian Provinces. The nest is usually so near the margin that the bird can spring directly into the water, but sometimes in summer the water recedes until the nest is left some distance inland.

The Loon is a clumsy, awkward traveler upon land, where, when hurried, it flounders forward, using both wings and feet. Audubon, however, says that his son, J. W. Audubon, winged a Loon which ran about one hundred yards and reached the water before it was overtaken. Its usual method of taking to the water from its nest is by plunging forward and sliding on its breast. It cannot rise from the land, hence the necessity of having the nest at the water's edge.

When the young are hatched the mother carries them about on her back a few days, after which they remain afloat much of the time until they are fully grown. If food becomes scarce in their native pond they sometimes leave it and travel overland to another. Dr. James P. Hatch of Springfield, Mass., says that early in the morning the parents and the well-grown young run races on the lake, using their broad paddles for propulsion and their half-extended wings for partial support. Starting all together they race down the lake, and then, turning, rush back to their starting point. Such exercises no doubt strengthen the young birds for the long flights to come.

The Loon finds some difficulty in rising from the water, and is obliged to run along the surface, flapping its short wings, until it gets impetus enough to rise. It is said that it cannot rise at all unless there is wind to assist it. Its great weight (from eight to nearly twelve pounds) and its short wings make flight laborious, but its rapid wing-beats carry it through the air at great speed. When it alights it often shoots spirally down from a great height, and plunges into the water like an arrow from a bow. It lands with a splash, and shoots along the surface until its impetus is arrested by the resistance of the water.

The Loon is almost unexcelled as a diver. It is supposed to be able to disappear so suddenly at the flash of a rifle as to dodge the bullet, unless the shooter is at point-blank range, but when two or three crack shots surround a small pond in which a Loon is resting it can usually be secured by good strategy. I once saw a Loon killed on the water with a shotgun, but the bird was taken at a disadvantage. It was on the Banana River, Fla., in January, 1900, and it had followed the fish (which were then very numerous) into the shallow water near the shore. Shoals extended out from the shore fully three hundred yards, so that the bird, in diving and swimming under water, could not use its wings to advantage. It was much impeded by the shoals and the vegetation on the bottom, and in swimming was so near the surface that its course could be followed readily by the ripple that it made. Two strong rowers were thus enabled to follow and overtake it. It escaped the first charge of shot, but its pursuers came so close the second time that the shot went home. In deep water, where the bird can use its wings and fly under water like a bolt from a crossbow, it can easily elude a boat. In old times the gunner used to "toll" the Loon within gunshot by concealing himself and waving a brightly colored handkerchief, while imitating the bird's call. But this will rarely succeed to-day in luring one within reach of a shotgun.

Loons are rather solitary in the autumn migration. They leave their northern homes and some begin to move southward in September, but many remain in the northern lakes until the ice comes. They move south along the larger rivers of the interior, but most of those near the Atlantic take the sea as their highway.

The Loon feeds very largely on fish. As it rests lightly on the surface it frequently thrusts its head into the water and looks about in search of its prey. When pursuing swift fish under water it often uses its wings, by means of which it can overtake the swiftest. This has been repeatedly observed. It can travel much faster under water in this manner than it can on the surface by use of the feet alone.

EDWARD HOWE FORBUSH, in *Game Birds, Wild-Fowl and Shore Birds.*

The Yellow-billed Loon, (*Gavia adamsi*) White-billed Loon, or Adams's Loon, as it is variously called, is of the same general coloration as the Common Loon. The throat and neck patches, however, are smaller and the bill, which is larger and differently shaped, is pale yellowish white. It is subject to corresponding seasonal changes.

It breeds in northern Siberia, on the islands north of Europe, and in North America from northwestern Alaska, northern Mackensie, and Boothia Peninsula south to the mouth of the Yukon and to Great Slave Lake. Its nests and eggs, as far as known, are similar to those of the more familar Loon. In migration the Yellow-billed is found a little south of its breeding range, and specimens have been reported from Colorado and Greenland.

BLACK-THROATED LOON

Gavia arctica (*Linnæus*)

A. O. U. Number 9   See Color Plate 2

Other Names.— Arctic Loon; Arctic Diver; Black-throated Diver.

General Description.— Length, 27 to 30 inches. In SUMMER: Upper parts, glossy greenish-black with white spots; lower parts white. In WINTER: Upper parts, grayish-brown without spots.

Color.— ADULTS IN SUMMER: *Chin, throat, and front of neck, purplish-black,* shading gradually into *clear soft warm gray of crown, back of head, and hindneck,* deepest on forehead and face, lightest behind, and separated from black of front of neck by white streaks; a short crescent of white streaks across upper throat; sides of breast and neck striped with pure white and glossy black, the black diminishing behind into pure white of under parts; upper parts, glossy greenish-black, each feather on shoulders and back with two white square spots near end forming traverse rows; wing-coverts thickly specked with small oval white spots; a narrow dusky band across lower belly; under tail-coverts, with dusky spots; bill, black; feet, dusky; iris, red. ADULTS IN WINTER, AND YOUNG: Upper parts of head and neck, dark grayish-brown; sides of head, grayish-white finely streaked with brown; *upper parts, brownish-black, feathers with broad gray margins, giving a scaly appearance;* rump, brownish-gray; primaries and their coverts, brownish-black; secondaries and tail-feathers, dusky margined with gray; forepart of neck, grayish-white faintly dotted with brown, its sides streaked with same; lower parts, pure white; sides of body and lower tail-coverts, dusky edged with bluish-gray; bill, light bluish-gray, dusky on ridge; feet, dusky; iris, brown.

Nest and Eggs.— NEST: A depression in the tundra or constructed roughly of decayed vegetation. EGGS: 2, deep amber to pale greenish-gray.

Distribution.— Northern part of northern hemisphere; breeds from Kotzebue Sound, Alaska, west along northern coast of Siberia, on islands north of Europe, and from Cumberland Sound south to Ungava; winters in the southern Canadian provinces; rarely south to Colorado, Nebraska, Iowa, northern Ohio, and Long Island, N. Y.

The general appearance of the Black-throated Loon is like that of its relative, the Common Loon, but it is somewhat smaller and not nearly so well known in America since it is seldom seen south of the northern States. There seems to be no reliable record of its appearance south of Long Island. Throughout the interior of Norway and Sweden and far up into Lapland, it breeds quite commonly. It is considered to be of rare occurrence in most parts of the British Isles, but on the little islands in the fresh-water lochs from central Scotland northward, and on the Orkney and Shetland islands, may be found its nests.

Its habits also are like those of the larger member of its species. Its progress under water has been estimated at not less than eight miles an hour.

The Pacific Loon or Pacific Diver (*Gavia pacifica*) is confined to the West. It breeds from Point Barrow, Banks Land, northern Mackenzie, and Melville Peninsula, south to the base of the Alaskan Peninsula, Great Slave Lake, and central Keewatin and winters along the Pacific coast from southern British Columbia to Lower California, and Guadalupe Island. In coloration it is similar to the Black-throated Loon, but the gray of the head averages lighter and the light spots of the back larger and fewer in number.

RED-THROATED LOON

Gavia stellata (*Pontoppidan*)

A. O. U. Number 11   See Color Plate 2

Other Names.— Sprat Loon, Red-throated Diver; Little Loon; Cape Race; Cape Racer; Scape-grace.

General Description.— Length, 25 inches. Color above, brownish-black with white spots; below, white.

Color.—ADULTS IN SUMMER: Crown and broad stripe down back of neck, streaked in about equal amounts with glossy greenish-black and white; *throat, sides of head, and sides of neck, clear warm gray* with a triangular *chestnut patch on lower throat;* upper parts, brownish-black with a green gloss, thickly spotted with dull whitish; primaries, dusky; tail, dusky, narrowly tipped with white; under parts, pure white, shaded along sides and on under tail-coverts with dusky brown; bill, dusky lead color; feet, black; iris, hazel. ADULTS IN WINTER, AND YOUNG: Crown and hindneck, bluish-gray; sides of neck, mottled with brownish and white; upper parts, brownish-black, *everywhere thickly marked with small oval and linear spots of whitish;* chin, throat, sides of head, white; no colored throat patch; under parts, as in summer; amount of spotting variable; in young birds spots usually lengthened into oblique lines, producing a regular diamond-shaped reticulation.

Nest and Eggs.— NEST: On banks of small ponds; a mere hollow in the ground. EGGS: 2, from deep reddish-brown to grayish-green, thinly spotted with brownish-black.

Distribution.— Northern part of northern hemisphere; breeds from Alaska across Arctic America to Greenland, south to Commander Islands, western Aleutian Islands, Glacier Bay, across British America to New Brunswick and Newfoundland; winters from southern British Columbia to southern California, and from the Great Lakes and Maine to Florida; rare in the interior; breeds also in Arctic Europe and Asia, and winters south to the Mediterranean and southern China.

The Red-throated Loon is mainly a salt-water bird while it sojourns in Massachusetts, although occasionally it is seen on some lake or river. Probably, like many other birds, it was oftener seen on fresh water in early times than now. It is still not uncommon on the Great Lakes, and David Bruce of Brockport, N. Y., stated that he had found it on Lake Ontario during every month of the year. In severe weather, when the lakes freeze, this bird, like the Common Loon, is sometimes taken on the ice, from which it is unable to rise, and is easily captured. In autumn it may be seen in small parties or flocks floating and feeding near our coasts. Like Grebes and some other water-fowl, it often lies on its side or back while afloat, exposing its white under parts while engaged in dressing or preening the plumage. This species migrates mainly along the coast in autumn, but as it is not so commonly seen there in spring, some portion of the flight may go north through the interior.

Its habits are similar to those of the Common Loon. It is perhaps equally difficult to shoot on the water. When surprised on land it seeks to escape by a series of hops or leaps, using both wings and feet.

EDWARD HOWE FORBUSH, in *Game Birds, Wild-Fowl and Shore Birds.*

Photo by H. T. Middleton

BIRD-STUDYING

AUKS, MURRES, AND PUFFINS

Order *Pygopodes;* suborder *Cepphi;* family *Alcidæ*

IT is a curious and interesting fact that at opposite ends of the earth there should be forms of bird-life which, though entirely unrelated and differing from each other even in the signal respect that one is equipped with wings and uses them, while the other is flightless, nevertheless present similar and somewhat grotesque physical peculiarities, and much similarity in their habits. These birds are the Auks of the Arctic and the Penguins of the Antarctic regions, and their external similarity lies in the fact that in both the legs are set so far back on the body that the birds assume a man-like posture, and are clumsy and uncouth in their appearance on shore. In the water both are expert swimmers and divers, though here again they differ in that the Auks use their feet in swimming, whereas the Penguins swim entirely with their wings, and use their feet only in steering their course.

The Auks, Murres, and Puffins include diving Arctic sea-birds grouped under the scientific name *Alcidæ*, and embracing about a dozen genera and some thirty species. All members of the family are essentially birds of the Arctic regions, and are especially numerous on the Alaskan and Siberian coasts. Though the Auks resemble the Penguins superficially and in their habits, anatomically their nearest relatives are the Loons and Grebes. From the Loons, however, they differ in lacking a hind toe, and from the Grebes in the possession of a well-developed tail.

Photo by W. L. Finley and H. T. Bohlman

TUFTED PUFFIN ON NEST

Burrow unearthed

The wings are short, but they are used with great efficiency when the birds swim under water. In their sitting posture on land the birds' feet extend horizontally in front, and they appear to be resting on their rumps. On the sea they are in their element, and here they get all of their food, which includes fish, taken chiefly by pursuit under water, and other animal forms. Because of this life their plumage is remarkably thick and dense, and is much used by the Eskimos in making clothing.

In distribution the Auks are very unequally divided between the two northern oceans, the Atlantic having few forms in comparison with the Pacific. The largest number of species and the most diversified forms are found on the northern coasts of the Pacific, though the aggregate of individuals of any species found there does not, according to Dr. Coues, exceed that of several Atlantic Ocean species. The same authority says that a " more or less complete migration takes place with most species, which stray southward, sometimes to a considerable distance, in the autumn and return again to breed in the spring. A few species appear nearly stationary." Many of the migrating Auks pass the winter on the open sea or on drifting ice.

At the approach of spring weather, the birds return to their northern breeding grounds where they gather in immense numbers on rocky cliffs along the coast. No nest is built, but the single egg, which is laid in niches or on ledges, is covered constantly by one or the other of the parents. The color of the egg varies greatly with the different species. The young are helpless when they are hatched, and it is not known with certainty what methods are employed by the parents to get them to the water. It seems not unlikely that the chicks are sometimes carried to the sea by the adults, though doubtless many of them reach the water by scrambling and falling down the cliffs. These Auk colonies are frequently raided by foxes, weasels, and other predacious animals and birds, not to mention the Indians and Eskimos who depend largely upon the birds and their eggs for winter food.

TUFTED PUFFIN

Lunda cirrhata (*Pallas*)

A. O. U. Number 12

Other Name.— Sea Parrot.

General Description.— Length, 15 inches. Color above, black; below, brown; *bill, high, much compressed*, ridged on sides; a fold of naked skin at corner of mouth.

Description.— ADULTS IN SUMMER: A tuft of straw-yellow feathers on each side of head about 4 inches long, completely surrounding eyes and continuous with white of face, forehead, and chin (narrowly); crown between the crests and entire *upper parts*, except a line on wing along fore-arm (which is white), *glossy blue-black;* entire under parts from chin, including most of sides of head, sooty-brownish, more grayish on abdomen; under tail-coverts, wings, and tail, black; *bill, feet, and eye-ring, vermilion;* base of bill, pale

oily-green; rosette of mouth, yellow; iris, white. ADULTS IN WINTER: No crests or white on face; bill, mostly dusky with some touches of reddish; feet, pale salmon; iris, pale blue; otherwise like summer birds.

Nest and Eggs.— The single egg is laid on the bare ground at the end of a burrow or in natural cavities among rocks, sometimes within sight, sometimes as much as five feet from the entrance; it is dead-white, showing obscure shell markings of pale lavender or brownish.

Distribution.— Coasts and islands of the Arctic Ocean, Bering Sea, and North Pacific, from Cape Lisburne, Alaska, south to Santa Barbara Islands, California, and from Bering Sea to Japan; accidental in Maine and Greenland.

The islands of the north Pacific, scattered along the shores of British Columbia, form, with their surrounding waters and the verdant coast line, a veritable summer wonderland. Here the mirage makes birds sitting upon the water appear like fleets of ships. Sound is magnified until the explosion of a gun and its echoes roar along the shores, a carnival of sound. Swift tides boil through narrow, rocky passes, while the shimmering heat of summer gives a touch of wavering unreality to all the scene. In this enchanted realm thousands of queer birds move to and fro, and none is queerer than the Tufted Puffin.

Each looks like a masked caricature of a bird as it comes on, pushing its great red beak straight ahead, its red, splay feet spread widely, its long, cream-colored side plumes flying in the wind, and its little wings "working for two." In spring both male and female acquire a white face, which gives them a masked appearance, and the great, gaudily colored beak reminds one of Mr. Punch and his big red nose. The beak, a remarkable appendage, is much larger and showier in the breeding season than at any other time. There are eighteen horny plates, ingeniously formed and arranged, sixteen of which fall off after the breeding season, much reducing the dimensions of the basal part. The underlying plates are then brown in color. At the same time the white of the face with its plumes disappears, the entire head becomes blackish, and the bird remains merely a commonplace Puffin until the next breeding season.

On the Farallons, off the California coast, where these Puffins nest on barren rocks, they deposit their eggs in holes or cavities among the rocks, but on the northern coast, where each rocky islet has a cap of some four feet of earth, they burrow into this at the top of the precipice overlooking the sea. Some of their tunnels extend but a few inches. These are believed to be made by the young birds. Others delve deeply, and in an old colony a bank will be honeycombed in every direction. If one wishes to examine into their housekeeping, under these circumstances he must fasten a rope to rock or tree, rig a "bo'sun's chair," and let himself over the cliff, excavating with his hands like a dog digging out a woodchuck, the stream of dirt passing down the cliff until it reaches the sea far below. Even then he may not easily succeed in finding the eggs or young in the interminable labyrinth of passages penetrating the earth. Where the tops of islands are hilly, the Puffins dig into the turf, where the land slopes at an angle of about 45°, and often they go in to a depth of three or four feet.

The single egg, which appears white, is in reality spotted inside the shell structure, as may be seen by holding it up to a very strong light. The young one is a real Puffin, as it is covered with down like a powder puff, but as it sits at the mouth of the burrow it looks, at a distance, like a little rat peeping out of its hole.

There has been much speculation regarding the utility of the bill of the Puffin, and it has been suggested that it is used to crush mollusks, but this does not seem to be the case, at least during the breeding season, as small fish appear to form its principal food. Apparently it does not use its bill, but rather its feet, in digging, though this may be an error, and possibly both are used; but certainly the beak is an excellent weapon of defense as all who have attempted to dig out Puffins will testify. Nature has put the most powerful weapon of the mother bird where it will have most effect. As she sits facing the entrance to her burrow she can deliver the more effective blows in defense of her nest and young because of the great size and crushing strength of her weapon, backed as it is by her hard head and sturdy neck.

Puffins breed on islands occupied also by Gulls, Guillemots, Murres, Cormorants, and other birds. After the breeding season they go to sea where they remain all winter. Their habits and roosting places at this season are practically unknown.

The natives of the coasts and islands of the north Pacific catch Puffins in nets, using their bodies for food and their skins for clothing. The skins are tough and are sewn together with the feathered side in, to make coats or "parkas," as they are called. Thus the Puffins contribute to the comfort and welfare of these simple, primitive people.   EDWARD HOWE FORBUSH.

PUFFIN

Fratercula arctica arctica (*Linnæus*)

A. O. U. Number 13   See Color Plate 3

Other Names.— Common Puffin; Puffin Auk; Labrador Auk; Sea Parrot; Pope; Bottle-nose; Tammy Norie; Coulterner; Tinker.

General Description.— Length, 13 inches. Color above, black; below, white; *bill very deep* and ridged.

Description.— ADULTS IN SUMMER: Crown, grayish-black, separated by a narrow ashy collar from dark color of upper parts; sides of head with chin and throat, ashy; nearly white between eyes and bill, with a dark dusky patch on side of throat; upper parts,

Plate 3

BLACK GUILLEMOT
Cepphus grylle (Linnaeus)
WINTER   SUMMER

BRUNNICH'S MURRE
Uria lomvia lomvia (Linnaeus)
SUMMER   WINTER
EGG

RAZOR-BILLED AUK
Alca torda Linnaeus
SUMMER

PUFFIN
Fratercula arctica arctica (Linnaeus)
SUMMER

All ¼ nat. size

DOVEKIE
Alle alle (Linnaeus)
SUMMER   WINTER

glossy blue-black continuous with a broad collar around neck in front, not reaching bill; under parts from neck, pure white; sides, dusky; *base of bill and first ridge, dull yellowish, next space, grayish-blue; rest of bill, vermilion, yellow below;* rosette of mouth, orange; feet, vermilion; iris, pale bluish-white; conical shaped projections above and behind eye, grayish-blue; eyelids, vermilion. ADULTS IN WINTER: Face, dusky; no eye-ring or appendages on eyelid; rosette of mouth,

shrunken; feet, orange; most of horny appendages on bill have been shed, leaving it small and pale.

Nest and Eggs.— NEST: A burrow in the ground 1 to 4 feet in length. EGGS: 1, white or brownish-white, plain or marked with faint spots, dots, or scratches of lavender; laid at the end of burrow on a thin lining of grass.

Distribution.— Coasts and islands of north Atlantic; breeds in North America from Ungava south to the Bay of Fundy and Maine; winters south to Massachusetts; rarely to Long Island, and Delaware Bay.

Drawing by R. I. Brasher

PUFFIN (⅓ nat. size)

The Sea Parrot of the north Atlantic

" Whether at rest or on the wing, the Puffin is a curious looking creature," says John Maclair Boraston, the English ornithologist. "At rest they stand rank above rank on the topmost rocky ledges facing the sea, their black backs, collars, and crowns, white faces and underparts, combining with their erect attitude and disposition, incline to give them something of military uniformity and regularity. But when one noted the great tri-colored beak, the apparently spectacled eyes, and remarked the mild surprise with which the birds regarded our intrusion, one could not resist the idea that there was something ludicrously artificial in the make-up of the Puffin; for surely there never was a bird less bird-like in its appearance than the Puffin at rest. They were tame enough to allow us to approach almost within striking distance, had we been disposed to

strike anything so mild-mannered as a Puffin. When the bird is on the wing, the flight is rapid, but labored, the wings beating violently, and as the bird flies, especially if returning to its burrow with fish, it utters a peculiar sound — a deep-throated, mirthless laughter, as it were, which may be imitated by laughing in the throat with the lips closed.

" It is a matter of speculation how the Puffin, which catches fish by diving, contrives to retain the first fish in its bill while it captures a second or a third. Possibly the tongue is used to hold it to the roof of the mouth, while the under mandible is lowered to make the later captures." (*Birds by Land and Sea.*)

Much of the grotesqueness of this bird's appearance is due to its uncouth beak, which is very large, flattened laterally, banded with red, blue, and yellow, and embossed with horny excrescences. These growths appear only in the mating season, and are sloughed off when that period is at an end, which means, as one observer puts it, that "the Puffin displays his wedding garments on his beak." Puffins are not likely to be seen near land after the breeding season is over. They are skillful swimmers and expert divers; in their diving they often descend to a great depth, and they are exceedingly quick and sure in their motions under the surface. At their breeding places the birds are likely to appear with remarkable punctuality, and they disappear with their young with corresponding regularity. In fact this departure is methodical to the extent that young birds which have not got the full use of their wings are left behind when the time for migrating arrives. It seems probable that the birds remain mated for life.

On land the bird places the whole length of the foot and heel on the ground and proceeds with a waddling stride. Robbing a Puffin's nest is dangerous business when either of the birds is at home, for they fight desperately and can inflict ugly wounds with their powerful mandibles and sharp inner nails.

The birds show strong affection for one another. If one is shot and falls in the water, others are likely to alight near it, swim around it, push it with their bills, and display in many ways their distress.

From old records we learn that in various parts of the Puffin's European range it was the custom to salt down large quantities of the young birds, to be eaten especially in Lent. To be sure the bird wasn't actually fish, but it tasted enough like fish to satisfy adaptable consciences among the devout.

CASSIN'S AUKLET

Ptychoramphus aleuticus (*Pallas*)

A. O. U. Number 16

Other Name.— Sea Quail.

General Description.— Length, 9½ inches. Color above, blackish; below, whitish; bill, shorter than head, wider than broad at base, its upper outline nearly straight.

Color.— *Upper parts, blackish-plumbeous;* head, wings and tail, nearly black; a grayish shade extending around head, neck, fore-breast, and along sides of body, fading to white on abdomen; bill, black, yellowish at base; feet, bluish in front, blackish behind and on webs; iris, white; a touch of white on lower eyelid.

Nest and Eggs.— The single egg, chalky-white or faintly tinged with green or blue, unmarked, is deposited in a burrow in the ground or in a crevice in rocks on an island or coast adjacent to the sea.

Distribution.— Pacific coast of North America from Aleutian Islands to latitude 27° in Lower California; breeds locally throughout its range.

While the Cassin Auklet has been found living on some of the rocky islands from the Aleutians to Lower California, yet I have never found one of the birds nesting on the rocks off the Oregon coast.

During the summer of 1903, Mr. Herman T. Bohlman and I camped for five days and nights on Three Arch Rocks which contain the greatest colonies of sea birds off the Oregon coast. Again in 1914, we lived for four days and nights on these rocks and climbed from top to bottom studying the various birds that live there. We have yet to see our first Auklet about Three Arch Rocks. This has led me to believe that it is rather uncertain as to just where the bird may be found. Mr. L. M. Loomis found the birds nesting on the Farallons and Mr. Wil-

liam L. Dawson found them nesting on some of the rocks off the Washington coast.

Because of its plump shape and size, it has been called a "Sea Quail." In his study of Cassin's Auklet on one of the islands off the Washington coast, Mr. William L. Dawson speaks of spending the night on the slope of the island where the Auklets had their nests. The birds burrow in under the soil, like the Petrels and Puffins, and are largely nocturnal in their nesting habits. The old birds come in at night to change places in the burrows. The Auklet chorus of birds in the burrows, he says, reminds one of a frog pond in full cry. Although the Auklets are quiet in daytime, yet the tumult increases as the night progresses.

WILLIAM L. FINLEY.

CRESTED AUKLET

Æthia cristatella (*Pallas*)

A. O. U. Number 18

Other Names.— Snub-nosed Auklet, or Auk; Dusky Auklet; Crested Stariki; Sea Quail; Kanooska.

General Description.— Length, 9 inches. Color above, brownish-black; below, brownish-gray. Bill, shorter than head, with knob at base; a beautiful crest of from 12 to 20 slender black plumes springing from forehead, recurved gracefully over bill, about two inches long; a slender series of white filaments behind each eye, drooping downward and backward.

Color.— ADULTS: Brownish-black above, brownish-gray below; no white anywhere; bill, coral or orange, horn color at tip; feet, bluish-black; iris, white. YOUNG: Lacking bill plates, crests, and white filaments on side of head; a white spot below eye; iris, brown; otherwise as in adults.

Distribution.— Coasts and islands of Bering Sea and north Pacific, from Bering Strait south to Kodiak Island and Japan.

This is essentially a sea-bird of the far North, its normal habitat being the north Pacific Ocean and the islands of Bering Sea. In Yukon Harbor they have been seen in myriads. Their appearance there is thus described by Dr. Charles Townsend in a leaflet prepared for the National Association of Audubon Societies:

"The surface of the water was covered with them, and the air was filled with them. Large, compact flocks launched themselves into the air from the lofty cliffs, and careened toward the vessel with great speed and whirring of wings. Twilight did not come until after 9 o'clock, and during the long evening the birds were amazingly active. Flocks of them continued to come in rapid succession from the cliffs, many passing close to the ship at high speed and swinging about the harbor. After the anchor was dropped near the cliffs, a loud blast of the whistle made the Auklets still more abundant.

"These birds appeared to be nesting chiefly in crevices in the cliffs, although they could be heard under the boulders near the beaches. To discover the nesting localities is easy. One has but to walk along the great ridges of volcanic stones thrown up by the sea. The stones are rounded and sea-worn like pebbles, but they are gigantic pebbles and cannot readily be moved. The Auklets go far down among them, perhaps three or four feet, and can be heard chattering there during any part of the nesting-season. We found that a considerable part of the food of this and other kinds of Auklets consisted of amphipod crustaceans, or beach-fleas, as they are called, when found under bits of seaweed along the shore. The native Aleuts eat Auklets, just as

they do most other kinds of sea-birds and capture them with nets that are like a large dip-net with a long handle.

Drawing by R. I. Brasher

CRESTED AUKLET (⅔ nat. size)

A strangely ornamented bird

"We need not concern ourselves, I think, about the preservation of the Auklets. They dwell among the high cliffs and the boulder-strewn beaches of a thousand uninhabited islands, and know how to stow away their eggs so safely that neither natives nor blue foxes can get them easily."

LEAST AUKLET

Æthia pusilla (*Pallas*)

A. O. U. Number 20

Other Names.— Minute Auklet; Knob-nosed Auklet; Knob-billed Auklet; Choochkie.

General Description.— Length, 6½ inches. Color above, black; below, white; bill, shorter than head, with knob at base; no crest.

Description.— ADULTS IN SUMMER: Front, top, and sides of head, sprinkled with white delicate feathers; a series of exceedingly fine hair-like feathers from back of eye down back of head and nape; some white on shoulders and on tips of some secondaries; otherwise entire upper parts, glossy-black; throat and under parts, white clouded with dusky, usually more thickly across breast; bill, red, darker above at base; legs, dusky;

iris, white. ADULTS IN WINTER: Bristles of head, fewer and less developed; white of under parts, more extensive, reaching almost around neck; bill, brownish.

Nest and Eggs.— The single egg, chalky-white or faintly tinged with greenish or bluish, unmarked, is deposited in a burrow in the ground or in a crevice among rocks on an island or on a coast adjacent to the sea.

Distribution.— Coast and islands of the north Pacific; breeds from Bering Strait south to Aleutian Islands; winters from Aleutian and Commander islands south to Washington on the American side and to Japan on the Asiatic.

The Least Auklet is one of the commonest of the water fowl in Bering Sea. It congregates in countless thousands on the rocks in Bering Strait, making them look like great beehives. In the spring they are very playful, especially while they are in the water, where they chase each other in great apparent good nature, meanwhile keeping up an incessant but subdued chattering. Like the other Auklets, they build no nest, but lay a single egg deep in the crevice of a cliff, or among the rocks well below the surface, or in a burrow in the ground.

"A walk over their breeding grounds at this season," wrote Doctor Baird, "is exceedingly interesting and amusing, as the noise of hundreds of these little birds directly under foot gives rise to an endless variation of sound as it comes up from the stony holes and caverns below, while the birds come and go, in and out, with bewildering rapidity, comically blinking and fluttering. The male birds, and many of the females, regularly leave the breeding grounds in the morning, and go off to sea, where they feed on small water shrimps and sea fleas, returning to their nests and sitting partners in the evening." (*North American Birds.*)

ANCIENT MURRELET

Synthliboramphus antiquus (*Gmelin*)

A. O. U. Number 21

Other Names.— Gray-headed Murrelet; Black-throated Murrelet; Black-throated Guillemot; Old Man.

General Description.— Length, 10½ inches. Color above, dark slate; below, white; bill, small and short, *with no horny growth at base.*

Color.— ADULTS IN SUMMER: Head, black, sooty on chin and throat; a conspicuous white stripe over each eye to nape, spreading on sides and back of neck into a series of sharp white streaks; a trace of white on each eyelid; upper parts, dark slate, blackening on tail; under parts, white; sides of body, velvety-black, the black feathers lengthening behind and overlaying the white flanks, extending upward in front of wings, meeting that of nape and there mixing with the white streaks; bill, yellowish-white, black on ridge and base; feet, yellowish, webs, black; iris, dark brown. ADULTS

IN WINTER: Upper parts, darker, the slate obscured by dusky, especially on wing, tail-coverts, and rump; forehead, crown, and nape, sooty-black without white streaks; eyelids, sometimes largely white; no black on throat, but dusky mottling at base of bill; white of under parts extending nearly to eyes and far around on sides of nape.

Nest and Eggs.— The single egg, buff with markings of grayish-lavender and light brown, is deposited in holes or burrows in banks on the coast or on a sea island.

Distribution.— Coasts and islands of the North Pacific; breeds from Aleutian Islands to Near Islands and from Kamchatka to Commander Islands; winters from the Aleutians south to San Diego, California, and to Japan; accidental in Wisconsin.

The Ancient Murrelet is another of the diving birds which fairly swarm on many of islands along the southern coast of Alaska. It ranges as far south as California in summer, and then is common on the Commander Islands in the Bering Sea, where the natives call it the "Old Man," because of the curious feather arrangement on the sides and back of the head. These feathers are dropped as winter comes on, so that the significance of the popular name may not be apparent when the bird visits its southern feeding grounds.

The Ancient Murrelet is an expert diver, and swims very rapidly under water, where it pursues fish with such energy as sometimes actually to drive them to the surface.

BLACK GUILLEMOT
Cepphus grylle (*Linnæus*)
A. O. U. Number 27   See Color Plate 3

Other Names.— White-winged Guillemot; Sea Pigeon; Tysty; Geylle; Spotted Greenland Dove; White Guillemot; Scapular Guillemot.

General Description.— Length, 13 inches. Prevailing color, in summer, sooty-black; in winter, black and white; bill, slender and straight, *with no horny growth at base.*

Color.— Sooty-black; wings and tail, pure black; *wings with a large white mirror on both surfaces;* bill, black; mouth and feet, carmine, vermilion, or coral-red; iris, brown. This perfect dress is worn only two months. In August, wings and tail become gray, the white mirror is mixed with brown, head, neck all around, rump, and under parts, marbled with black and white, the bird looking as if dusted over with flour; back, black, the feathers white-edged; completion of the molt gives the following winter plumage: head and neck all around, rump, and under parts, pure white; back, hindneck, and head varied with black and white; wings and tail, black, the white mirror perfect.

Nest and Eggs.— EGGS: Deposited on the bare surface of the rock, in nooks and crannies of rocky islands on coast; 2 or 3, white or greenish-white, irregularly spotted and blotched with dusky and lavender shell markings.

Distribution.— Coasts of eastern North America and northwestern Europe, breeding from southern Greenland and Ungava to Maine; winters from Cumberland Sound south to Cape Cod; rarely to Long Island, N. Y., and New Jersey.

Winter   Summer

Drawing by R. I. Brasher

BLACK GUILLEMOT (½ nat. size)

Their black bodies, white-lined wings, and red legs make a color scheme well worth seeing

Along the coast of Maine the numerous rocky islands extending in an irregular line out to sea afford favorite nesting places for numerous sea-fowl, among which the Black Guillemot, or "Sea Pigeon," is by no means rare. Farther north they are more numerous and breed in numbers on Grand Manan Island, New Brunswick, at various places in the Gulf of St. Lawrence, and along the Labrador coast. In approaching their nesting islands one will observe what appear to be short, black Ducks swimming ahead of the boat, usually several together. One by one they will suddenly disappear, as with surprising swiftness they dive beneath the surface. Under water they are much at home, and by the use of wings, as well as legs, they take their submarine flight to a considerable distance before reappearing. Usually one does not see them again until they rise to the surface well beyond gunshot range. On taking wing they rise readily from the water. Their progress is swift, strong, and usually directed in a straight line. In flight they rarely rise more than a few feet above the water.

The Black Guillemot's nest is placed in the cleft of rocks well above the reach of high tides. While clambering over the great jumble of giant bowlders, that reach from the water to the higher ground on some of the Maine islands, I have often come upon these birds brooding their eggs or young. The first knowledge of their presence would be when one would spring out from among the bowlders and go dashing away to the sea. Their black bodies and white-lined wings, combined with the red of the dangling, wide-spraddled legs, made a color scheme well worth seeing. Hidden generally well from view is the nest, and often it would take a steam derrick to reach it. Not the slightest effort at nest building is attempted. The two handsomely spotted eggs are deposited on the bare rocky floor of the little cave. The young are covered with down, literally as black as the "ace of spades." The birds feed on various crustaceans and shell-fish which are secured by diving.

Many sea-birds of the North journey to southern waters to spend the winter, but the Sea Pigeon apparently sees no need for exerting itself to such an extent. In fact it can hardly be said to migrate at all, for it is rarely found south of Cape Cod, scarcely two hundred miles beyond its southernmost nesting grounds. At all times they are coast-wise birds, seldom being seen out of sight of land, and never under any circumstances going inland. T. GILBERT PEARSON.

PIGEON GUILLEMOT

Cepphus columba *Pallas*

A. O. U. Number 29

Other Name.— Sea Pigeon.

General Description.— Length, 13 inches. Prevailing color, in summer, sooty-black; in winter, black and white; bill, slender and straight, *with no horny growth at base.*

Plumage.— *White mirror of upper surface split by an oblique dark line* caused by extension of dark bases of greater coverts increasing from within outward until the outside ones are scarcely tipped with white; plumage and changes otherwise as in Black Guillemot.

Nest and Eggs.— Similar to those of the Black Guillemot.

Distribution.— Coasts and islands of the Arctic Ocean, Bering Sea and Cape Lisburne, and both coasts of the north Pacific from Bering Strait south to Santa Catalina Island, California, and to northern Japan.

Mr. Dawson says that the Pigeon Guillemot is "unquestionably the most characteristic water-bird of the Puget Sound region," and explains its sharing the popular name "Sea Pigeon" with the Bonaparte Gull as follows: "The Gulls are dove-like in posture (at least a-wing), and in their manner of flocking; while the Guillemot owes its name both to its plumpness and to its very unsophisticated, not to say stupid, appearance." (*Birds of Washington.*)

E. W. Nelson found this bird "the most abundant of the small Guillemots throughout the North, from Aleutian Islands to those of Wrangel and Herald, where we found it breeding abundantly during our visit there on the *Corwin.*" He notes that the birds are very conspicuous by reason of their white wing patches and bright red legs. When perched on the rocks they squat like Ducks, and when swimming they often paddle along with their heads below the surface.

For breeding operations a few pairs may take

possession of a group of small rocks, or a colony of several hundred may share cliffs with Cormorants, Tufted Puffins, and Glaucous Gulls. Mr. Finley observes (MS.) that off the Oregon coast these Guillemots nest in isolated places and not in colonies. "They like a crevice or a hole in the face of a cliff for a nest site." On land they have an awkward shambling gait, but in the water they are entirely at ease, and are swift swimmers and expert divers.

MURRE

Uria troille troille (*Linnæus*)

A. O. U. Number 30

Other Names.— Foolish Guillemot; Guillem, or Gwilym; Tinker; Tinkershire; Kiddaw; Skiddaw; Marrock; Willock; Scuttock; Scout; Strany; Lavy; Frowl.

General Description.— Length, 17 inches. Color above, brown; below, white. Bill, narrow and slender.

Color.— ADULTS IN SUMMER: *Head and neck all around, rich maroon-brown* shading on upper parts into dark slaty-brown; some feathers of back and rump with grayish-brown edges; secondaries, narrowly tipped with white; under parts, pure white; sides and flanks with dusky markings; bill, black, feet, dusky; iris, brown. ADULTS IN WINTER: White of under parts,

reaching bill, on sides of head to level of gape, extending further around on sides of neck, leaving only a narrow line of dark color; the two colors shading without sharp line of demarcation.

Nest and Eggs.— A single egg, remarkably variable in coloration, is laid on the rock of cliffs, without any attempt at nest building; it varies from white to dark green, spotted, blotched, and scratched with black, brown, and lilac over the entire surface.

Distribution.— Coasts and islands of North Atlantic; breeds in North America from southern Greenland and southern Ungava south to Newfoundland and Magdalen Islands; winters south to Maine.

The common Murre's natural habitat is the northern Atlantic Ocean, and various islands therein, but in winter it wanders southward as far as New England, and possibly to New York, though the records of its appearances there seem not to be entirely reliable. On the water this bird looks much like a Duck, though its neck is shorter and its bill more pointed than is charac-

MURRE (⅓ nat. size)

Drawing by R. I. Brasher

teristic in that family. In their nesting places on ledges of rocky islets they sometimes gather in such numbers as to present a seemingly almost solid mass of birds, while the eggs are found lying so close together that it is actually difficult to walk without treading upon them.

All the Murres are oceanic birds, only visiting the rocks during the breeding season, and found inland only when driven there by storms. Their food consists of fish and various crustaceans; this particular species is especially partial to the fry of herrings and pilchards, which are captured at night in the open sea.

Doctor Chapman remarks that "long-continued studies of Murres on the coast of Yorkshire warrant the belief that, although the eggs of no two Murres (or Guillemot as it is termed in England) are alike, those of the same individual more or less closely agree, and that the same bird lays year after year on the same ledge. Murres perch on the entire foot or tarsus, and when undisturbed usually turn their backs to the sea and hold their eggs between their legs with its point outward. When alarmed they face about, bob and bow and utter their low-voiced *murre*."

CALIFORNIA MURRE

Uria troille californica (*H. Bryant*)

A. O. U. Number 30a

Other Names.— California Guillemot; California Egg-bird; Farallon Bird.

General Description.— Similar to the common Murre, but averaging about an inch longer.

Nest and Eggs.— Like those of common Murre.

Distribution.— Coasts and islands of the north Pacific; breeds from Norton Sound and Pribilof Islands south to the Farallons, California; winters from the Aleutian Islands south to Santa Monica, California.

The California Murre is the most abundant sea-bird on the off-shore rocks of the Pacific from Alaska to the Farallons. It is readily

Photo by W. L. Finley   Courtesy of Nat. Asso. Aud. Soc.

AN INCUBATING CALIFORNIA MURRE

During incubation the single egg is held between the legs with its point outward. Photo taken on island off the coast of Oregon

recognized by its snow-white breast and sooty-brown back. Its legs are placed clear at the end of its body, so it does a good deal of its sitting standing up. Its attempt to walk is a very awkward performance resembling a boy in a sack race. But in water the bird is very expert. It uses its feet as propellers and its wings as oars, flashing under water with such swiftness that it can overtake and capture a fish.

The Murre is a creature of the crowd. To see this bird in great colonies and to watch its home life, one gets the idea that a Murre would die of lonesomeness if isolated. They huddle together in such great numbers on the narrow sea ledges that they occupy every available standing place. There is not the least sign of a nest. The female lays a single egg on the bare rock. One egg is all that can be attended to under the circumstances. One might wonder why the birds persist in crowding so close together. Neighbors always seem to be quarreling and sparring with their sharp bills. They rarely hit each other, because they are experts at dodging. The babble is continuous; everyone talks at the same time.

The peculiar top-shape of the Murre's egg prevents it from rolling. The practical value of this may be seen every day on the sloping ledges. We tried several experiments and the eggs were of such taper that not one rolled over the edge. When an egg starts down grade, it does not roll straight, but swings around like a top and comes to a standstill. The shells are also very tough and not easily broken.

One day we lay stretched out on a ledge just

above a big colony where we could watch the ordinary run of life and not disturb the birds in any way. When a Murre arrived from the fishing grounds, he alighted on the outer edge of the shelf. Then, like a man in a Fourth of July crowd, he looked for an opening in the dense front ranks. Seeing none, he boldly squeezed in, pushing and shoving to right and left. The neighbors resented such behavior and squawked and pecked at the new arrival. But he pressed on amid much opposition and com-

plaint until he reached his mate. They changed places and he took up his vigil on the egg. The mate, upon leaving the colony, instead of taking flight from where she stood, went through the former proceeding, often knocking over several neighbors who protested vigorously, jabbing at the parting sister. Arriving at the edge of the ledge, she dropped off into space. The continuous going and coming made an interesting performance for the onlooker.

WILLIAM L. FINLEY.

Photo by W. L. Finley and H. T. Bohlman

CALIFORNIA MURRES

Off Oregon coast on Three Arch Rocks Reservation

BRÜNNICH'S MURRE

Uria lomvia lomvia (*Linnæus*)

A. O. U. Number 31   See Color Plate 3

Other Names.— Franks' Guillemot; Thick-billed Guillemot; Thick-billed Murre; Brünnich's Guillemot; Polar Guillemot; Egg-bird.

General Description.— Length, 18 inches. Similar to common Murre in plumages and changes, but crown darker in contrast with throat and sides of neck; *bill, shorter and stouter* with cutting edge of upper jaw flesh-colored.

Nest and Eggs.— Indistinguishable from those of the Murre.

Distribution.— Coasts and islands of north Atlantic; breeds from southern Ellesmere Land, and northern Greenland to Hudson Bay and Gulf of St. Lawrence; resident in Greenland and Hudson Bay; south rarely in winter from Maine to South Carolina, and in interior to northern Ohio, central Indiana and central Iowa.

Brünnich's Murre comes as near being like the Antarctic Penguins as any other North American species. It is built primarily for swimming and diving, and is a poor walker, waddling awkwardly in an upright position.

Except as it may climb out of the cold water on a cake of ice, its only chance to exercise these poor gifts is during the short summer in the Far North on its breeding grounds. There the Murres, mingled with the other species, resort

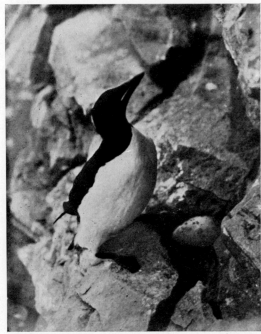

Photo by H. K. Job   Courtesy of Houghton Mifflin Co.

BRÜNNICH'S MURRE

Presently it will lift its egg onto its feet and hold it there for incubation

to precipitous shores or rocky islands, from the Gulf of St. Lawrence away up to northern Greenland. I have visited the colony on Great Bird Rock, Magdalen Islands. Here, in June, I found them standing in rows on the narrow ledges of the cliff, usually with back to the sea, each bird holding between its legs one large pear-shaped egg. These eggs have very hard shells, and are so shaped that they roll in a circle, which helps to prevent their falling off the cliff. They are colored a great variety of tints of green, blue, buff, whitish, and are so variously marked that it is impossible to find any two alike. Usually the Murres crowd upon these ledges as thickly as they can find room to stand or squat.

From these ledges they throw themselves with confident abandon, and, with exceedingly rapid wing beats, circle out over the sea and back again to the rock. Otherwise they alight on the water with rather a heavy splash, and are apt to dive forthwith. They can be seen here and there swimming about, distinguishable from Ducks by the fact that their posterior part floats rather high — reminding one of the ancient ships as described by Vergil, with "lofty sterns."

Their hoarse baritone voice is almost human, and they are supposed to say *murre*. When I first heard them on the rocky ledges close at hand, I was involuntarily startled, so much did it sound to me like someone calling my boyhood nickname, "Herb, Herb!"

Unless one can visit a breeding colony, about the only way to cultivate their acquaintance is to get offshore in winter, on the bleak, wind-swept ocean, not much further south than Nantucket shoals, or, better, the coast of Maine. Miles off Cape Cod in mid-winter, from fishing vessels I have seen them by hundreds. Flocks of them dotted the ocean in all directions, or moved in lines swiftly through the air, to plunge into the water and disappear like stones, presently to bob up many rods further off. Occasionally at the entrance of harbors, in bitter cold weather, I have seen them perched on some slanting pole or beacon, from which they would plunge directly into the water.

Though oceanic in habit, this particular species seems to have a peculiar faculty, as has the Dovekie, for getting into trouble by wandering from its real element. After winter storms they are liable to be found far inland, sometimes stranded in a snow bank out in some field, or on the ice of a pond or stream, vainly seeking to find water. In such cases they are emaciated and must perish, as they are unable to rise on wing from any surface except water. When word comes of a queer unknown bird which stands upright on the ice or in the snow, it is a likely guess to call it a Brünnich's Murre.

HERBERT K. JOB.

RAZOR-BILLED AUK

Alca torda *Linnæus*

A. O. U. Number 32   See Color Plate 3

Other Names.— Razor-bill; Tinker.

General Description.— Length, 18 inches. Color above, black; below, white. Bill, flatly compressed; tail, pointed.

Color.— Adults in Summer: Head and neck all around, and upper parts, black, more brownish on former, a slight greenish-gloss on latter; tips of secondaries and entire under parts from neck, white; a sunken line of white from eye alongside of forehead to bill; bill, black, crossed by a white line; feet, dusky; iris, brown. **Adults in Winter:** White extending to bill, invading sides of head to level of eyes and neck; no white line from bill to eye; color of upper parts, duller.

Nest and Eggs.— Usually one egg, sometimes two, is laid on the bare rock of cliffs or islands along the coast, very variable in shape and size of markings; white or bluish, spotted and blotched with sepia or black, these spots sometimes wreathed in a circle around the large end; in others diffused over entire surface.

Distribution.— Coasts and islands of the north Atlantic; breeds on American side from southern Greenland to Newfoundland and New Brunswick; winters from New Brunswick and Ontario to Long Island and rarely to North Carolina.

The Razor-billed Auk presents a striking and interesting appearance in the water, which it rides as buoyantly as a cork. Like all of its kind, it is exceedingly quick and clever at diving, a method of escape which it always adopts in preference to flight, when it can. It slips under the surface with hardly any perceptible or audible splash, and it is quite impossible to tell where it will reappear. When fairly submerged the bird swims — using both wings and feet — with astonishing speed and often descends to a considerable depth. It feeds largely upon fish and various small marine creatures, and takes virtually all of its food from the sea. When it chooses to take to its wings, it can fly with much rapidity. In summer it is decidedly gregarious and the flocks often are seen far from land. If then overtaken by heavy gales, large numbers of the birds are drowned.

As the breeding season approaches, the birds abandon temporarily their nomad sea life and gather in large flocks at established breeding places, preferably on cliffs overlooking the ocean, and containing an abundance of niches and recesses, where the single egg is laid, no nest being made. The incubating bird is very loath to leave the egg, and often when so engaged may be taken in the hand. There are many evidences that the birds mate for life.

Drawing by R. I. Brasher

RAZOR-BILLED AUK (⅛ nat. size)

It rides the ocean as buoyantly as a cork

GREAT AUK

Plautus impennis (*Linnæus*)

A. O. U. Number 33

Other Names.— Garefowl; Penguin; Wobble.

General Description.— Length, 30 inches. Color above, black; below, white.

Color.— Adults: Hood and entire upper parts including wings, black; ends of secondaries, white forming a traverse band; under parts, white extending to a point on throat; a white oval spot between bill and eye; bill, black with lighter grooves; feet, black; iris, brown.

Nest and Eggs.— Nest: Site probably similar to that of the Razor-billed Auk. **Egg:** 1, white or bluish-white, spotted and blotched with shades of umber-brown and sepia.

Distribution.— Formerly inhabited coasts and islands of the north Atlantic from near the Arctic Circle south to Massachusetts and Ireland, and probably south casually to South Carolina and Florida and the Bay of Biscay; now extinct.

The Great Auk was the most powerful and swiftest diving and swimming bird in North America. It had to be, as it could not fly. In order to survive it must be fast enough not only to pursue and overtake the swift-swimming fish in their native element, but also active enough to escape sharks and other predatory fish that otherwise might have exterminated it. Also it was obliged to follow the smaller migratory fish southward in winter and northward in spring.

It has been pictured often among the icebergs, but it was not a bird of the Arctic regions and was not found within the Arctic Circle. It is believed to have inhabited southern Greenland, but that was centuries ago when the climate of Greenland probably was warmer than it is now. In primitive times, when man was a savage, the Auk was safe upon its island home in the raging sea, which men in their frail canoes visited rarely and in small numbers; but civilized man, coming in large companies in ships that sailed the seven seas, armed with firearms, brought extermination to all flightless birds which came under his notice, and so the Great Auk was one of the first of the North American birds to become extinct in the nineteenth century, the century that will always be noted for its great destruction of birds and mammals at the hand of man.

The Great Auk had been known in Europe for centuries when it was first discovered in North America. This was in 1497 or 1498, when adventurous French fishermen began fishing on the banks of Newfoundland. The birds were taken there in such enormous numbers that it was unnecessary to provision the vessels, as the fleet could secure all the fresh meat and eggs needed by visiting the bird islands. Jacques Cartier, on his first voyage to Newfoundland in 1534, visited an " Island of Birds " which, from the course and distance sailed from Buena Vista, must have been what is now known as Funk Island, the last breeding place of the Great Auk in America, where the crews filled two boats with the birds in " less than half an hour " and every ship salted down five or six barrelfuls. He also found the Great Auk on the Magdalen Islands in the Gulf of St. Lawrence. The bird became known among the French fishermen as the *Pingouin* (Penguin). There were at least three Penguin islands about Newfoundland and another near the tip of the peninsula of Nova Scotia, while numerous birds apparently sum-

mered at the head of Buzzards Bay and about Cape Cod.

The Auk migrated from Labrador to Florida. It was common at Nahant, Mass., and about the islands in Massachusetts Bay in the early years of the nineteenth century and was taken now and then near Plymouth, but had disappeared at that time from the upper end of Buzzards Bay. When Audubon visited Labrador in 1832, he was told that fishermen still took great numbers from an island off the coast of Newfoundland, but, from all accounts, it seems probable that the bird was extirpated on the coasts of North America before 1840. Apparently the Great Auk was destroyed in America before it was extirpated in Europe, where the last recorded specimen was taken, off Iceland, in 1844.

Its destruction was accomplished first by the demand for the eggs and flesh for victualing fishermen and settlers, next by the demand for the feathers, and last by unrestricted shooting. When the supply of eider-down and feathers for feather beds and coverlets gave out, about 1760, because of the destruction of the breeding fowl along the coast of Labrador, some of the feather hunters turned to the Penguin islands off the coast of Newfoundland. Cartwright said (1775) that several crews of men lived all summer on Funk Island, killing the birds for their feathers; that the destruction was incredible; and that this was the only island that was left for them to breed upon. Nevertheless the species continued more or less numerous about the shores of Newfoundland until about 1823 and then gradually disappeared before continuous persecution. Dr. F. A. Lucas, who visited Funk Island in 1878, found such enormous numbers of the bones of this species that he concluded that "millions" must have died there. Today there are about eighty mounted specimens in existence and not many over 70 eggs preserved in museums and collections.

This Auk was readily alarmed by a noise, as its hearing was very keen, but it was not wary if approached silently. When on land it stood upright or rested on its breast, and its locomotion was slow and difficult, so that it might be easily overtaken and killed with a club. In the water, however, it was so swift that a boat propelled by six oars could not overtake one. It is believed to have fed mainly upon fish, but its habits never were studied and described, and, therefore, they are unknown.   EDWARD HOWE FORBUSH.

DOVEKIE

Alle alle (*Linnæus*)

A. O. U. Number 34   See Color Plate 3

Other Names.— Little Auk; Sea Dove; Alle; Rotch; Ice-bird.

General Description.— Length 8½ inches. Color above, black; below, white; head and bill, formed like those of a Quail.

Color.— ADULTS IN SUMMER: Head, neck all around, and upper parts, glossy blue-black; sides of head, neck, and throat, shaded with sooty-brown; three or four white streaks on shoulders; secondaries, tipped with white; under parts, pure white; bill, black; feet, flesh-color in front, black behind and on webs; iris, brown. ADULTS IN WINTER: White of under parts extending to bill, invading sides of head and neck and nearly meeting on nape; otherwise as in summer.

Nest and Eggs.— A single greenish-blue egg laid in crevices of rocky cliffs on islands or coasts near the sea.

Distribution.— Coasts and islands of north Atlantic; breeds from Kane Basin and Baffin Bay east to Franz Josef Land; winters from southern Greenland south to Long Island (N. Y.), and rarely to Delaware Bay and North Carolina; accidental near Melville Island, and in Wisconsin, Michigan, Ontario, and Bermuda.

The little Dovekies or "Sea Doves" breed along the coasts of Greenland and other sea islands of the Atlantic, north of latitude 69°, and in winter come down the coast where less ice abounds and where, consequently, food is more easily secured. New Jersey is about the usual limit of this species' southern journey. They stay in small flocks in the open sea and feed by diving. Apparently at this season they come on land but rarely.

Cape Hatteras, ornithologically, is a very interesting place. Here the warm waters of the Gulf Stream meet and neutralize the last remaining vestige of the cold bearing currents from the north. As the distribution of animal life is largely determined by climatic conditions, the North Carolina coast affected by these currents becomes the meeting place of many northward moving species that naturally inhabit warmer regions, and southward moving species from the cold countries to the north. The extreme southern migration of the Dovekie illustrates this interesting fact. A few miles north of Cape Hatteras I found, one December some years ago, one of these little wanderers. It was sitting on the beach in a tired-out condition and made but feeble attempts to escape when I took it in my hands. Then I discovered the cause of its emaciated condition: one foot was missing. Doubtless it had been bitten off by some fish. With its power of diving in the ocean thus reduced at least one-half, its chances for securing a livelihood were all but gone, and in the end the tide had cast it upon the shore. Within a few hours it died, despite the most energetic efforts to induce it to eat such food as was available.

The Eskimos kill many Sea Doves and use their feathered skins for making the bird-skin shirts with which they help ward off the biting frost of their country. The birds are taken in nets which the natives wield over the face of the cliff where the birds crowd together to breed.

"I have often thought," wrote Audubon, "how easy it would be to catch these tiny wanderers

Drawing by R. I. Brasher

DOVEKIE (½ nat. size)

These small Sea Doves manifest very little apprehension of danger from the proximity of man

of the ocean with nets thrown expertly from the bow of a boat, for they manifest very little apprehension of danger from the proximity of one, insomuch that I have seen several killed with the oars. Those which were caught alive and placed on the deck, would at first rest a few minutes with their bodies flat, then rise upright and run about briskly, or attempt to fly off, which they sometimes accomplished, when they happened to go in a straight course the whole length of the ship so as to rise easily over the bulwarks. On effecting their escape they would alight on the water and immediately disappear."

T. GILBERT PEARSON.

ORDER OF LONG-WINGED SWIMMERS

Order *Longipennes*

BIRDS of the order of Long-winged Swimmers are cosmopolitan in distribution and are generally seen on the wing over or near water. In the order are three families: Skuas and Jaegers, Gulls and Terns, and Skimmers. They resemble most nearly the Tube-nosed Swimmers of all the water birds, but the character of the nostrils plainly distinguishes them without reference to internal anatomy. These birds have the nostrils lateral and open. The wings are long and pointed. Usually the tail is long. The legs are comparatively free and project from near the center of the body; the thighs are bare for a short distance; the tarsi are covered with horny shields of varying sizes. The toes are four in number, but the hind one, which is elevated, is very small (sometimes rudimentary); the front toes are webbed. Their bills are strong and thick; the Skuas, Jaegers, and Gulls have hooked, hawklike bills; the Terns have sharply pointed ones; and those of the Skimmers are bladelike.

Although there is no sexual variation in coloration in the species included in this order, there are seasonal and age differences. Their voices are shrill or harsh. Fish is the main item of their diet.

The eggs are few, usually numbering but three. The young are covered with down when hatched, but are helpless and the parents care for them in and out of the nest for some time.

SKUAS AND JAEGERS

Order *Longipennes;* family *Stercorariidæ*

THE Skuas and Jaegers are closely related to the Gulls and Terns; in fact they are Gulls with habits and structure modified sufficiently to justify their inclusion in a distinct family, the *Stercorariidæ*, while still remaining in the same order, the Long-winged Swimmers. Not the least striking of these modifications is a well-developed thieving propensity, with the result that they are often and variously called "Robber Gulls," "Sea Hawks," "Teasers," and "Boat-swains." Generally they are aggressive and daring birds, graceful, skillful and powerful in flight, by reason of which they are able to overtake their weaker and more timid relatives and force them to disgorge their food, which the pursuer catches in its fall. Because of these practices they are often spoken of as parasites, but the practice itself is essentially predatory rather than parasitic. The birds' bad habits are not confined to this aërial robbery, however, for certain species are known actually to eat young birds and eggs, and even small mammals.

The Skuas and Jaegers have wings of only moderate length for this group, the primaries are unusually wide and are rounded at the ends. The tail is relatively very short, but is broad and nearly even, the middle pair of feathers being larger than the others in adults. The body is stocky and heavy and powerfully muscled. The claws are strong, sharp, and curved.

There is general tendency toward a sooty blackish coloration of the upper parts in the older birds with a gilding of the head and hindneck and a whitening of the shafts of the white feathers toward their bases. The young are smaller than the adults and are profusely streaked with rufous; several years are required to reach the color and dimensions of the adults.

[32]

POMARINE JAEGER *Stercorarius pomarinus* (Temminck) PARASITIC JAEGER *Stercorarius parasiticus* (Linnaeus)
LONG-TAILED JAEGER *Stercorarius longicaudus* Vieillot DARK PHASE
ADULT INTERMEDIATE LIGHT PHASE
IMMATURE *S. parasiticus* SKUA *Megalestris skua* (Brünnich)
All ⅙ nat. size

SKUA

Megalestris skua (*Brünnich*)

A. O. U. Number 35   See Color Plate 4

Other Names.— Sea Hawk; Sea Hen; Bonxie; Skua Gull.

General Description.— Length, 22 inches. Color, blackish-brown.

Plumage.— ADULTS: *Blackish-brown, varied above with chestnut and whitish* (each feather dark-colored with a spot of chestnut toward end, shading into whitish along shaft); on nape and across throat, reddish-yellow with narrow white streak on each feather; crown and sides of head, with little whitish; wings and tail, dusky, white for some distance from base — concealed on tail by long coverts, but showing on primaries as a conspicuous spot; bill, black with gray cere; feet, black; iris, brown. Another plumage, not known to be characteristic of age or season, is uniform sooty-blackish *with the white wing spots very conspicuous.*

Nest and Eggs.— NEST: A depression in the grass; lined with grass and moss. EGGS: 2 or 3, olive or drab, irregularly marked and blotched with dark olive-brown and sepia.

Distribution.— Coast and islands of the North Atlantic; breeds on Lady Franklin Island (Hudson Strait), in Iceland, and on the Faroe and Shetland islands; winters on fishing banks off Newfoundland and Nova Scotia; rarely south to Long Island, N. Y.; in Europe south to Gibraltar.

The Skua is one of the largest and strongest members of its rapacious genus, and is much given to robbing the smaller sea birds, in the manner of its relatives. It occasionally strays along the North American coasts as far south as the northern boundary of the United States. There are records of its having been taken at least three times off the coast of Massachusetts. A single individual was shot on the Niagara River in 1886, and another was killed in 1896 by colliding with the lighthouse at Montauk Point, Long Island, N. Y.

Little seems to have been set down concerning the habits of the bird, which, however, probably do not differ essentially from those of the Jaegers. It does not assemble in flocks. Seldom are even two pairs seen together. It is famed for its courage and daring in attacking and teasing Gulls and forcing them to give up the fish they have caught. Indeed, its scientific name is an apt characterization — *megalestris* is from two Greek words which, translated, are "large pirate craft." In flight it has a striking appearance.

POMARINE JAEGER

Stercorarius pomarinus (*Temminck*)

A. O. U. Number 36   See Color Plate 4

Other Names.— Gull Hunter; Sea Robber; Gull Chaser; Jaeger Gull.

General Description.— Length, 24 inches. Color above, brownish-black; below, white.

Description.—ADULTS IN BREEDING PLUMAGE: Crown brownish-black extending below eyes and on sides of lower bill; back, wings, tail, upper and under tail-coverts, deep brownish-black; under parts from chin and neck all around, pure white — the sharp feathers of back and neck, light yellow; bill, horn color shading to black; feet, black; iris, brown. NEARLY ADULT: A row of brown spots across breast; sides barred with white and brown. INTERMEDIATE STAGE: Entire breast, brown mottled with white; upper tail-coverts and some wing-coverts, barred with white; feet, blotched with chrome yellow. In breeding and nearly adult plumage the *two central tail-feathers project about four inches and are twisted at right angles to the shafts;* in the intermediate plumage the central tail-feathers project only one inch and are *not* twisted; these central feathers are *rounded at the tip.* YOUNG OF THE YEAR: Whole body traversely barred with dull rufous; on head, neck, and under parts this color prevails, the bands very numerous, about same width as the dark color; on flanks and under tail-coverts the bars are wider, paler and almost white; on back and wing-coverts, brownish-black, nearly uniform, predominates; primaries and tail-feathers, dusky, darker at tips; head and neck, mostly pale rufous with a dusky spot in front of eye; feet, bright yellow. These plumages are evidently progressive with age and are independent of sex and season, and different from the following: DARK PHASE:

Plumage, blackish-brown all over, shading into black on crown, lightening on abdomen; primaries, whitish at base; feet, blotched with yellow and dusky; middle tail-feathers projecting but half an inch.

Nest and Eggs.— Nest: On the ground in northern marshes, of grass and moss. Eggs: 2 or 3, olive, pale greenish, or brownish, spotted with dark brown.

Distribution.— Northern part of northern hemi-sphere; breeds from Melville Island and central Greenland south to northern Alaska, northern Mackenzie, and Baffin Land, and also on Arctic islands of eastern hemisphere; winters off Atlantic coast south to New Jersey; in fall migration common along the California coast; winters south to the Galapagos, Peru, Africa, and Australia; accidental in Nebraska; occurs irregularly on the Great Lakes.

My first experience with that bold maritime robber, the Pomarine Jaeger, was on a day late in August, many years ago, when I crossed some Cape Cod sand-dunes and came in sight of the sea. Flocks of Terns and small Gulls were hovering over the water in all directions. Over them were big dark-colored birds with long tails

On the fishing-banks out at sea, wherever the Shearwaters and Petrels gather, from August on through the autumn, I have usually found this Jaeger in attendance. With them are apt to be about as many Parasitic Jaegers and an occasional one of the Long-tailed species. The Jaegers are seen flying about, not close to the water like

Young—Dark Phase

Drawing by R. I. Brasher

POMARINE JAEGER (¼ nat. size)

A bold maritime robber

coursing about with strong, swift flight. Now and then one of these would select for its victim a Tern which had just caught a fish, and give chase. No matter how the unfortunate one might dart and dodge, the Jaeger followed every move, and by savage attacks finally compelled it to drop the fish. Then by a spectacular swoop the robber would seize the booty in mid-air. When no victims are available for a hold-up, the Jaeger turns scavenger and picks up dead marine life like a true Gull, but its preference is for depredation.

the others, but higher up, say fifty to seventy-five feet, as though to get a better view, to detect any weaker bird which makes a lucky strike. Though somewhat shyer than the rest, they are bold enough upon occasion, especially when eatables are being passed around. Sometimes I have brought them up quite close by making believe to throw something overboard. I have baited up numbers of them by throwing out fish livers, and made the most of the opportunity in securing photographs. At close range it was fascinating to study the different individuals as they appeared, owing to their great variations in plumage, all the way from the sooty phase to that of the adult with white under parts.

Jaegers are Arctic-breeding birds, not nesting in colonies, like the Gulls and Terns, but in

scattered pairs. Such destructive birds would hardly make good colonizers. They are said to be great nest-robbers, and woe to the bird which leaves eggs or young exposed to these savages.

HERBERT K. JOB.

Photograph by H. K. Job   Courtesy of Houghton Mifflin Co.

POMARINE JAEGER

In quest of a victim

PARASITIC JAEGER

Stercorarius parasiticus (*Linnæus*)

A. O. U. Number 37   See Color Plate 4

Other Names.— Skait-bird; Boatswain; Marline-spike; Teaser; Dung Hunter; Man-o'-war; Richardson's Jaeger; Black-toed Gull; Arctic Hawk Gull.

General Description.— Length, 20 inches. Color above, brownish-black; below, white. *Two middle tail-feathers, narrow and pointed, as well as elongated.*

Color.— ADULTS IN BREEDING PLUMAGE: Crown and back of head, crested, the feathers sharp and stiff; crown and whole upper parts, slaty brownish-black, shading into black on wings and tail; chin, throat, sides of head, neck all around, and under parts, pure white, the sharp feathers on back of neck, light yellow; under tail-coverts, dusky; bill, horn color, darker at end; feet, black; iris, brown. NEARLY ADULT: Under parts, white but mottled everywhere with dusky patches, heaviest across breast, on sides, and under tail-coverts; center line of throat and abdomen, nearly pure white; feet, with small yellow blotches or not; otherwise as in breeding plumage. DARK PHASE: Entire plumage, dusky, darker and more slate-colored above, lighter and browner below; crown, black; back of head and neck, yellow; wings and tail, black; feet, black. YOUNG OF THE YEAR: Entire plumage, barred with rufous and

brownish-black; yellowish-rufous prevails on head and neck with dark shaft line on each feather; these shaft lines enlarge until between shoulders they occupy the whole of each feather except a narrow rufous border; on breast rufous becomes almost white, with traverse bars of brown, this pattern continuing over the entire under parts; primaries, dusky, narrowly tipped with rufous.

Nest and Eggs.— NEST: A depression in the ground near water, sparsely lined with grass and dead leaves. EGGS: 2 or 3, olive, greenish, gray, or brown, marked and blotched with shades of brown and pale lavender over entire surface.

Distribution.— Northern part of northern hemisphere; breeds from northwestern Alaska, Melville Island, and northern Greenland south to Aleutian Islands, central Mackenzie, central Keewatin, and on Arctic islands of Siberia and of northern Europe south to Scotland; winters from Aleutian Islands south to California, from New England coast southward to Brazil, in Australia, and from the coast of Europe south to the Cape of Good Hope; casual in interior to the Great Lakes, Missouri, Kansas, and Colorado.

As its name implies, the Parasitic Jaeger is a robber and lives largely on what it can take by force from its smaller brethren. It is large, and very strong and swift in flight, and the Eskimos call it "the cannibal" because, they say, once upon a time it killed and devoured men. It is much swifter and quicker than the Pomarine species, which it attacks and drives away, but it is less graceful on the wing. According to Edward W. Nelson, these birds bully and rob the Gulls and Terns, forcing them to disgorge fish which they have caught, and swooping below them snatch the food as it falls, very much in the manner of the Bald Eagle robbing the Fish Hawk.

These Jaegers often hunt in pairs and will then attack and rob even the Glaucous-winged Gull, which could make short work of its tormentors if it could only get at them. "But the parasites are too adroit, too elusive, and too desperately persistent," says Mr. Dawson. "The Gull hates to do it, but also he hates to be buffeted and hustled away from the fishing-grounds. 'Here, take it, you scum, and be off with you!'"

LONG-TAILED JAEGER

Stercorarius longicaudus *Vieillot*

A. O. U. Number 38   See Color Plate 4

Other Names.— Arctic Jaeger; Gull-teaser.

General Description.— Length, 23 inches. Color above, deep purplish-slate; below, white deepening into slate. During breeding season, crowns have slight crests. This is a smaller bird than the Parasitic Jaeger, the greater length being due *to the extremely long tail-feathers*.

Color.— ADULTS IN BREEDING PLUMAGE: Lores and side of head above eye to nape, brownish-black; neck all around light straw-yellow; above with wing and tail-coverts, deep purplish-slate, deepening on primaries, secondaries, outside tail-feathers, and ends of central pair into lustrous *brownish-black*; chin, throat, and upper breast, white gradually shading into the dark slate of abdomen and under tail-coverts; bill, dusky with black tip; feet, grayish-blue; toes, webs, and claws, black; iris, brown. IMMATURE: Changes of plumage identical with those of previous species. DARK PHASE: Very rare.

Nest and Eggs.— NEST: Depression in the ground, scantily lined with dry grass and leaves. EGGS: 2 or 3, dark greenish, thickly spotted and blotched with brown.

Distribution.— Northern part of northern hemisphere; breeds on Arctic islands of Europe and Asia, and coasts of Kotzebue and Norton sounds, northern Mackenzie and northern Hudson Bay to northern Greenland; winters south to Gibraltar and Japan; in migration not rare off New England coast; casual on the Pacific coast south to California; accidental in Manitoba, Iowa, Illinois, and Florida.

Nelson describes the Long-tailed Jaeger as "the most elegant of the Jaegers in its general make-up, and especially when on the wing. At this time, the bird shows all the grace and ease of movement which characterize such birds as the Swallow-tailed Kite, and other species with very long wings and slender bodies. It appears to delight in exhibiting its agility, and two or more frequently perform strange gyrations and evolutions during their flight as they pass back and forth over the low, flat country which they frequent. It is, like the Parasitic Jaeger, found more plentifully along the low portions of the coast than at sea, and is very numerous along the coast of Norton Sound."

Like the other members of the genus, this Jaeger is a persistent and merciless robber of the smaller Gulls, swooping down on them and forcing them to disgorge fish or mollusks they have taken, and capturing the food as it falls. Flocks of Kittiwakes are likely to be accompanied by one or more of these Jaegers industriously engaged in this brigandism.

The species may be readily identified by the marked elongation of the central tail-feathers.

GEORGE GLADDEN.

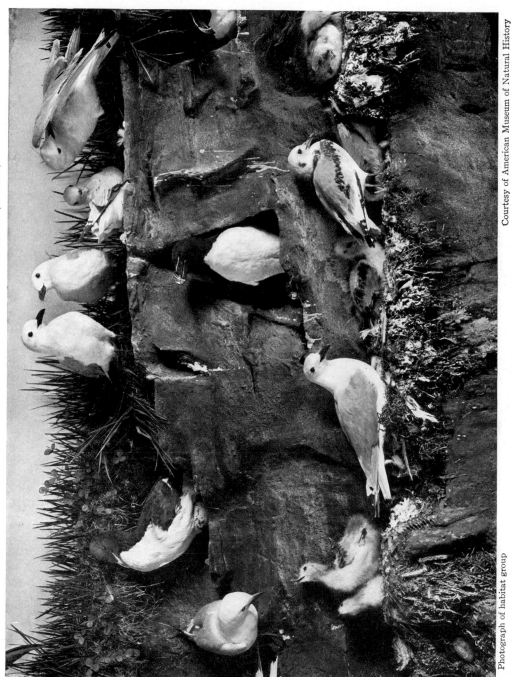

Kittiwake (summer)

Photograph of habitat group

Courtesy of American Museum of Natural History

A SMALL CORNER OF BIRD ROCK

Brünnich's Murre   Kittiwake (summer)   Razor-billed Auk   Kittiwake (winter)

GULLS

Order Longipennes; family Laridæ; subfamily Larinæ

THE Gulls comprise the subfamily *Larinæ* of the Gull and Tern family (*Laridæ*) which is part of the order of long-winged swimmers (*Longipennes*). There are about fifty species of Gulls, some of which are often found far inland, but most of which show an especial fondness for the seacoasts and their immediate vicinity. As a rule they are larger than their allies, the Terns, from whom they differ also in generally having almost square tails, though there are exceptions to this rule in the form of Terns with nearly square tails and of Gulls with tails which are more or less forked. An invariable difference, however, is in the structure of the upper bill, which is ridged and hooked at the end in Gulls and virtually straight in Terns. When hunting food, Gulls usually fly with their bill nearly on a line with the body, while Terns carry theirs pointed downward. Again, the Gulls alight freely on the water to feed, whereas the Terns hover and plunge for their food.

The Gulls show considerable variation in color, and some seasonal changes in plumage which have caused confusion in identifying species. " The predominating color of the adult birds," says Stejneger, " is white with a gray mantle, varying in shade from the most delicate pearl-gray to dark blackish-slate or nearly black, and the head is often more or less marked with black in summer. The seasonal change is not great, and affects chiefly the color of the head, which, in species with black heads, turns white in winter, while the White-headed Gulls usually get that part streaked with dark during the same season."

All of the species are web-footed and swim readily; they show little skill in diving, however, and the living fish they prey upon are chiefly the kind which come near the surface of the water, like the herring. On the wing they show perfect ease, and remarkable quickness and cleverness in their maneuvering, especially in the wind. It is certain, too, that they are capable of very long flights.

Gulls are markedly gregarious, and this instinct is especially in evidence during the breeding season, when several species may congregate on favorite nesting ledges to the number of thousands, if not millions. Their nests are composed usually of seaweeds and moss, and the eggs, usually no more than two or three, range in color from bluish-white to brownish, with blotches and spots of black, brown, or purplish.

Flocks of Gulls resting lightly on the waters of our harbors or following the wake of water craft are a familiar sight, but not every observer of the graceful motions of the birds is aware of the fact that Gulls are the original " white-wings." As sea scavengers they welcome as food dead fish, garbage, and offal of various sorts, and their services in cleaning up such material are not to be regarded lightly. It will surprise many to learn that certain Gulls render important inland service, especially to agriculture. At least one species, the California Gull, is extremely fond of field mice, and during an outbreak of that pest in Nevada in 1907–8 hundreds of Gulls assembled in and near the devastated alfalfa fields and fed entirely on mice, thus lending the farmers material aid in their warfare against the pestiferous little rodents. Several species of Gulls render valuable service to agriculture by destroying insects also, and in spring hundreds of Franklin's Gulls in Wisconsin and the Dakotas follow the plowman to pick up the insect larvæ uncovered by the share.

That at least one community has not been unmindful of the substantial debt it owes the Gull is attested in Salt Lake City, where stands a monument surmounted by bronze figures of two Gulls, erected by the people of that city "in grateful remembrance" of the signal service rendered by these birds at a critical time in the history of the community. For three consecutive years — 1848 to 1850 — black crickets by millions threatened to ruin the crops upon which depended the very lives of the settlers. Large flocks of California Gulls came to the rescue and devoured vast numbers of the destructive insects, until the fields were entirely freed from them. It is no wonder that the sentiment of the people of Utah, as reflected through their laws, affords Gulls the fullest protection. It would be well

RING-BILLED GULL
Larus delawarensis Ord
ADULT IN SUMMER   IMMATURE

HERRING GULL
Larus argentatus Pontoppidan
IMMATURE   ADULT IN SUMMER

GREAT BLACK-BACKED GULL
Larus marinus Linnaeus
IMMATURE   ADULT IN SUMMER

GLAUCOUS GULL
Larus hyperboreus Gunnerus
END OF SECOND YEAR   ADULT IN SUMMER
IMMATURE

All ½ nat. size

if such sentiment prevailed elsewhere throughout the United States.   However, within the last few years much progress has been made in protecting these most beautiful dwellers of coasts and marshes.

IVORY GULL

Pagophila alba (*Gunnerus*)

A. O. U. Number 39   See Color Plate 6

Other Name.— Snow-white Gull.

General Description.— Length, 18 inches. White.

Color.—ADULTS: Entire plumage, *pure white;* shaft of primaries straw yellow; bill, dull greenish, yellow at tip and along cutting edges; feet, black; iris, brown; eyelids, red. YOUNG: Front and sides of head, dusky-gray; neck all around with irregular spotting of brownish-gray; shoulders and wing-coverts with brownish-black spots, thicker on lesser coverts; tips of primaries and tail-feathers with dusky spots.

Nest and Eggs.— NEST: In niches of cliffs; constructed of grass and seaweed, and lined with moss and a few feathers. EGGS: 2 to 4, olive-buff, spotted with different shades of brown and gray.

Distribution.— Arctic seas; breeds from Melville Island and northern Baffin Land to northern Greenland and Arctic islands of eastern hemisphere; winters in the extreme north, rarely south to British Columbia, Lake Ontario, and Long Island, N. Y.; in Europe south to France.

The first word of the scientific name of the Ivory Gull expresses its chief characteristic, just as the second word—*alba,* the Latin for " white " — is descriptive of its plumage. *Pagophila* is from two Greek words meaning " ice " and " loving." Hence this beautiful snow-white Gull is a rare visitant to the temperate zone of this continent from its home in the Arctic seas. The only verified record of the appearance of the bird in New York seems to be that furnished by William Dutcher of one shot in Great South Bay, L. I., near Sayville, in January, 1893. Another observer reports having seen a single member of the species near Mt. Sinai Harbor, in Suffolk County, N. Y. In summer it occurs frequently on the Arctic islands of the eastern hemisphere, and in winter it ranges southward to France. The greenish-yellow beak and the black legs are in striking contrast to its beautiful snow-white plumage. It differs from other Gulls in the comparative shortness of its beak, and slightly tapering tail.

The Ivory Gull is a glutton whenever it can obtain the flesh of seals or the blubber of whales. It will watch a seal-hole in the ice, waiting for the seal, whose excrement it devours.

KITTIWAKE

Rissa tridactyla tridactyla (*Linnæus*)

A. O. U. Number 40   See Color Plate 6

Other Names.— Common Kittiwake; Kittiwake Gull; Pick-me-up; Coddy-Moddy; Tarrock.

General Description.— Length, 18 inches. Color, white with pale grayish-blue mantle. *Hind toe, absent or rudimentary;* tail, slightly notched.

Color.—ADULTS IN SUMMER: Head and neck all around, under parts, and tail, pure white; mantle, pale grayish-blue; wing-coverts and secondaries similar, latter white on tips; *primaries, blackish-blue* with white oblong spaces on inner webs, the second, third and fourth with white tips; *feet, blackish;* bill, *light yellow* tinged with olive; iris, brown; eyelids, red. ADULTS IN WINTER: Back of head, nape, and sides of breast, shaded with color of back; a dusky patch behind eye and a small black crescent in front of eye; bill, dusky-olive; otherwise as in summer. YOUNG: Eye-crescent and spot behind eye as in winter adult plumage; a broad bar across back of neck, lesser and middle wing-coverts, inner secondaries, and a terminal bar on tail, black; first four primaries with outer webs, outer half of inner webs and ends for some distance, black; the rest, pearly-white.

Nest and Eggs.— NEST: On rocky ledges overlooking the water; made of grass and seaweed. EGGS: 2 or 3, sometimes 5, buff, brownish-gray, or greenish-

gray, irregularly spotted with shades of brown and lavender.

Distribution.— Arctic regions; breeds from Wellington Channel and northern Greenland south to Gulf of St. Lawrence, and from Arctic islands of Europe and western Siberia to southern France; winters from Gulf of St. Lawrence south to New Jersey, and casually to Virginia, Bermuda, and the Great Lakes; accidental in Missouri, Colorado, and Wyoming.

The graceful and industrious little Kittiwake has several interesting and characteristic traits. It pursues its prey after the manner of the Terns, hovering over the water and plunging head foremost into the sea, with all of the dash and vigor of a Kingfisher. These Gulls are often seen following right whales apparently to get the fragments of fish rejected or dropped by those monsters. Observers who have watched the birds doing this say that they act as if they knew when the whales must rise to breathe.

The Kittiwake feeds mainly on fish, but will take almost any animal or vegetable refuse it can find. For drinking it prefers salt water to fresh, and it is often seen sleeping peacefully, floating on the great rollers, with its head tucked under its wing — literally " rocked in the cradle of the deep." It is a great wanderer, and de-

cidedly democratic in its disposition, for it is often found in the company of other Gulls, Terns, and various other sea-birds.

It takes its vernacular name from a fancied resemblance between its cry and the syllables " kit-ti-wake." In its scientific name, *Rissa* is its Icelandic name, and *tridactyla* is from the Greek, meaning " three-toed," and refers to an anatomical peculiarity of the species.

The Pacific Kittiwake (*Rissa tridactyla pollicaris*) is a geographical variation of the Common Kittiwake. The two differ but very little. The former occurs off the coasts of the north Pacific, Bering Sea, and the adjacent Arctic Ocean, breeding from Cape Lisburne and Herald Island south to the Aleutian and Commander Islands, and wintering from the Aleutian Islands south to northern Lower California.

Photograph by H. K. Job   Courtesy of Outing Publishing Co.

KITTIWAKE

In its nest on a cliff

GLAUCOUS GULL

Larus hyperboreus *Gunnerus*

A. O. U. Number 42   See Color Plate 5

Other Names.— Burgomaster; Burgomaster Gull; Ice Gull; Harbor Gull; Blue Gull.

Length.— 30 inches.

Color.— ADULTS IN SUMMER: *Mantle, pale blue-gray; rest of plumage, entirely white;* bill, chrome yellow, more waxy on end with a bright vermilion spot at angle; legs, pale flesh color; iris, light yellow. ADULTS IN WINTER: Similar to summer plumage, but head and hindneck tinged with pale brownish-gray. YOUNG: Upper parts, *whitish mottled with raw umber, pale reddish-brown, and dusky,* this coloration heaviest on back; under parts, nearly uniform pale brown; wings and tail, barred with same; bill and legs, pale flesh color, the former black-tipped; iris, brown.

Nest and Eggs.— NEST: In tussocks of grass; constructed of seaweed and dry grass. EGGS: 2 or 3, white to dark grayish-brown, blotched with brown and brownish-black.

Distribution.—Arctic regions; breeds from northwestern Alaska, Melville Island, and northern Greenland, south to Aleutian Islands, northern Mackenzie, and central Ungava, and on Arctic islands of eastern hemisphere; winters from the Aleutians and Greenland south to Monterey, California, the Great Lakes, and Long Island, N. Y., and casually to Bermuda, North Carolina, and Texas; in Europe and Asia south to the Mediterranean, Black, and Caspian seas, and Japan.

Under one of its popular names, the " Burgomaster Gull," the Glaucous Gull was made famous, or rather infamous, by Celia Thaxter's poem, which described its rapacious habits. This poem found its way into many school reading books of a generation ago. It gives a vivid and substantially accurate picture of the appearance and activities of a group of sea birds, and portrays one of the characteristics of the Burgomaster. Indeed, according to other observers, the bird not only robs smaller Gulls and other sea birds of the fish they catch, but eats their eggs and young and sometimes the adult birds themselves. It is recorded that a member of Ross's expedition to the Arctic regions shot one of these Gulls which, upon being struck, disgorged a Little Auk it had just devoured, and when dissected was found to have another member of the same species in its stomach.

Fishing fleets are likely to have the company of one or more of these Gulls, on the watch for any offal that may be thrown overboard. Under such conditions it has often been caught with a hook and line with a fish as bait. Though naturally timid and suspicious, its fondness for offal is likely to overcome its caution, and cause it to enter bays and even inland waters. Several specimens have been taken in the lower Hudson River and in New York Bay, and individuals have been seen in the Great Lakes.

A curious trait of this Gull is its apparent disinclination to alight in the water. In its natural habitat it alights generally on the highest point of an ice hummock. It displays none of the affection for its kindred which is characteristic of most of the Terns and Gulls, and will promptly desert either young or mate when they are in danger.

GREAT BLACK-BACKED GULL

Larus marinus *Linnæus*

A. O. U. Number 47   See Color Plate 5

Other Names.— Black-backed Gull; Saddleback; Coffin-carrier; Cobb; Wagell.

General Description.— Length, 30 inches. Color, white with a deep slate mantle.

Color.—ADULTS IN SUMMER: *Mantle, deep dark slate with a purplish tinge;* secondaries, broadly tipped with white; primaries, black, white-tipped; rest of plumage, pure white; bill, chrome yellow, tip wax yellow with a large spot of bright vermilion on angle; legs, pale flesh color; iris, lemon-yellow; eyelids, vermilion. ADULTS IN WINTER: Similar to summer plumage, but head and neck streaked with dusky. YOUNG: Above, dull whitish, mottled with brown and pale chestnut; wing-coverts and secondaries, dull brown with light edges; primaries, plain dusky, tipped with white; tail,

brownish-black, fading to white at base, imperfectly barred with brown; forehead, crown, and under parts in general, dull whitish, mottled on abdomen with brown and dusky; throat, usually immaculate but sometimes like breast with faint brownish streaks.

Nest and Eggs.— NEST: Usually on small island; large and bulky; constructed of dry grasses and well-cupped. EGGS: 2 or 3, pale olive-gray, blotched with dark brown and black, with some purplish spots.

Distribution.— Coasts of North Atlantic; breeds from North Devon Island and central Greenland south to Nova Scotia, and to latitude 50° on European coasts; winters from southern Greenland south to the Great Lakes and Delaware Bay (casually to Florida), and the Canaries; accidental in Bermuda.

John Maclair Boraston, an English ornithologist, included the following characterization of the Great Black-backed Gull in his book *Birds by Land and Sea:*

"A staider and more deliberate flight marks the movements of the Great Black-backed and as he passes slowly before you, his eye on a level with your own, the brow seems to beetle in a set frown, and the glass catches the expression of the deeply set eye. It seems an old eye, wise, authoritative. And, in fact, the bird may have been old when you were a child, for it requires four years for a Great Black-back to acquire all the marks of maturity, and its lifetime may well

pleasure is aroused, he will return again and again to swoop at you with menacing cry. 'The sea is mine,' he seems to say; 'and the smitten rocks. Get back to your brick-and-mortar cages with their glass peep-holes.' A century of the sea may well give a sense of prescriptive right."

This beautiful and dignified bird is frequently seen as a winter visitant off the shores of Long Island (between September and March) and on the Great Lakes. Its breeding places are confined to the Atlantic coast. It is very shy but exceedingly noisy. William Brewster says that he identified four distinct cries: "a braying *ha-*

Drawing by R. I. Brasher

GREAT BLACK-BACKED GULL (⅛ nat. size)

Four years are required for this Gull to attain maturity

be a century. It will take offence at your presence more readily than the other Gulls, and as it passes, utters a low *Ha-ha-ha-ha!* and sails on solemnly leaving you admonished. If his dis-

ha-ha, a deep *keow, keow,* a short barking note and a long drawn groan, very loud and decidedly impressive." The *keow* cry suggests the note of the Green Heron.

HERRING GULL

Larus argentatus *Pontoppidan*

A. O. U. Number 51   See Color Plate 5

Other Names.— Common Gull; Harbor Gull; Sea Gull; Lake Gull; Winter Gull.

General Description.— Length, 24 inches. Color, pure white with grayish-blue mantle.

Color.—Adults in Summer: Head, neck, tail, and under parts, pure white; *mantle, grayish-blue;* outer primaries, dusky with white spots and tips; center ones, color of mantle with *black subterminal bar and* *narrow white tips;* rest of primaries and secondaries, with white tips; bill, chrome yellow with red spot at angle; feet, brownish flesh color; iris, yellow. ADULTS IN WINTER: Similar to summer plumage, but head and neck streaked with dusky, and yellow of bill duller. YOUNG: Dull whitish, varied everywhere with shades of brown and dusky; tail, plain brown; primaries and secondaries, brown with white tips; bill, pale flesh color, dusky at end; legs, flesh color; iris, brown. There is much variation in the amount of dusky color in individuals; young of the year are sometimes almost entirely sooty-brown; this changes with the gradual acquisition of lighter tips and edges of the feathers, finally reaching the perfect adult plumage in three years.

Nest and Eggs.— NEST: Sometimes on the ground, occasionally in trees; ground nests usually mere depressions with scant nesting material; tree nests bulky and well constructed of strongly interwoven grass and moss. EGGS: 3, light bluish or greenish-white to dark olive-brown, irregularly blotched, spotted, and scrawled with dark brown and black.

Distribution.— Northern hemisphere; in America breeds from south-central Alaska, across British America to Cumberland Sound, south to British Columbia, across the United States on about the parallel 43° to Maine, and in Europe south to northern France and east to White Sea; winters from northern border of United States southward to Lower California and western Mexico, and from Gulf of St. Lawrence and the Great Lakes south to the Bahamas, Cuba, Yucatan, and coast of Texas, and in Europe to Mediterranean and Caspian seas.

The most abundant Gull along the Atlantic coast of the United States is the familiar Herring Gull. It is the species we find following the coast-wise ships looking eagerly for any scraps of food that are thrown overboard from the cook's galley. At low tide we may find them, often by hundreds, standing on the exposed bars and mud flats. They come into the harbors and fly about the piers. They wander far up the rivers and are continually met with even on the smaller lakes of the interior. Their food consists largely of fish, and the fact that some denizen of the deep may have been dead many days before the waves cast it upon the beach makes no difference with them. They are as fond of carrion as is a Vulture. One peculiar habit they have is the breaking of clam shells in a most unusual manner. When the water is low they sail over the mud flat until a clam is discovered. Dropping down they grasp it in their feet and fly away to a portion of the beach where the sand is packed hard and here from a height of forty or fifty feet they let it fall. I have seen one repeat this performance fourteen times before the shell broke and allowed it to enjoy the feast it so much craved.

Young

Drawing by R. I. Brasher

HERRING GULL
(⅛ nat. size)

The most abundant Gull along the Atlantic coast of the United States

Adult

A pair of adults

Courtesy of Outing Publishing Co.

Young gull

Alighting at nest

HERRING GULLS

Nest and eggs

[44]

Herring Gulls breed on the rocky islands off the coast of Maine and thence northward. Frequently they assemble in very large numbers at this season. Probably 10,000 nest annually on Great Duck Island and the colony on the island of No-Man's-Land, Maine, has of recent years been even larger. The nests are made of grass and are often hidden in clumps of grass, by the side of logs or among piles of bowlders. Within a few days after hatching the young are able to run about and when a visitor walks through a breeding colony at this time the young birds go scuttling away in every direction like so many dirty little sheep. Although hard to catch they at once become docile when picked up. I have sometimes amused myself by laying them on their backs where they will often remain perfectly still until a row of half a dozen have thus been assembled.

Apparently these Gulls are their own worst enemies, as hundreds of young are annually killed by the old birds, who peck them on the head. Unfortunately the young appear to be unable to distinguish between parent and neighbors, and when an old one alights nearby they come up trustingly in quest of food; frequently swift death is their reward.

Formerly hundreds of thousands of this species were killed in summer for the millinery trade; but the Audubon Law now makes this a misdemeanor in every State where they are found, and wardens employed by the National Association of Audubon Societies to-day guard all the important breeding colonies in the United States.

There are nesting communities of them at various places in the interior as, for example, Lake Champlain, Moosehead Lake, and the Great Lakes. A very similar subspecies known as the Western Gull (*Larus occidentalis*) inhabits the Pacific coast of North America.

T. GILBERT PEARSON.

CALIFORNIA GULL

Larus californicus *Lawrence*

A. O. U. Number 53

General Description.— Length, 23 inches. Color, pure white with pearly-blue mantle.

Color.—ADULTS IN SUMMER: Mantle, pearly-blue; outer primaries, black with white spots and tips, the

black grading to a narrow bar on sixth primary; secondaries, white-tipped; rest of plumage, pure white; bill, chrome yellow, a vermilion spot at angle below with a small black spot above; feet, dusky *bluish-green;*

Photo by W. L. Finley and H. T. Bohlman

CALIFORNIA GULLS

They generally nest in colonies on the inland lakes of western United States webs, *yellow;* iris, brown; eyelids, red. ADULTS IN WINTER: Similar to summer plumage, but head and neck streaked with dusky and bill much duller. YOUNG: Dull whitish, mottled with dusky on head, neck, rump, wing-coverts, and secondaries; back, grayish-blue, feathers with lighter edges; bill, dull flesh color; terminal half, dusky.

Nest and Eggs.— NEST: On the ground; constructed of small sticks and grass. EGGS: Usually 3 or 4, some-

times 5, pale bluish-white to brownish-clay color, blotched with dark brown and black zigzag markings.

Distribution.— Western North America; breeds from east-central British Columbia and Great Slave Lake south to northeastern California, northern Utah, and northern North Dakota; winters from its breeding range southward to Lower California and western Mexico; accidental in Kansas, Texas, Colorado, Alberta, and Hawaii.

RING-BILLED GULL

Larus delawarensis *Ord*

A. O. U. Number 54   See Color Plate 5

Other Names.— Common Gull; Lake Gull.

General Description.— Length, 20 inches. Color, pure white with pale bluish-gray mantle. Easily confused with the Herring Gull.

Color.—ADULTS IN SUMMER: Mantle, pale bluish-gray; first primary, black, white spot near end; second, plain black; third, black with gray space on inner web; next three, black-tipped; rest of primaries and secondaries, color of mantle; rest of plumage, pure white; bill, greenish-yellow with a *broad band of black encircling it at angle;* feet, greenish-yellow; iris, pale yellow; eyelids, red. ADULTS IN WINTER: Similar to summer plumage, but head and neck behind *spotted* with dusky. YOUNG: Above, mottled with brown and grayish-blue; wing-coverts, mostly dusky margined with lighter; secondaries and primaries, with a subterminal

brownish area shading forward into gray; tail, with a broad subterminal band of dusky and indistinctly barred with brown; below, faintly mottled with brownish; bill, flesh color, dusky on terminal half; legs, dull greenish-yellow; iris, brown.

Nest and Eggs.— NEST: In the grass in marshes; built of dead reeds. EGGS: 2 to 3, bluish-white to dark brown, spotted and blotched with different shades of brown and lavender.

Distribution.— North America at large; breeds from southern British Columbia across British America to southern Ungava, south to Oregon, Colorado, North Dakota, central Wisconsin, central Ontario, northern New York (casually), and northern Quebec; winters from northern United States southward to Bermuda, the Gulf coast, Cuba, and southern Mexico.

Photo by H. K. Job   Courtesy of Houghton Mifflin Co.

RING-BILLED GULLS RETURNING TO NEST

The versatility of the Gull shows his degree of intelligence. He is equipped for life on the water. His webbed feet are for swimming, but he doesn't seem to care whether nature equips him for the sea or not. His taste often runs to angle-worms instead of sardines. As the notion takes him, he will take up quarters about a pig-pen or a garbage pile, follow the plow as a Blackbird does, picking up angle-worms, or he will sail along in the wake of a vessel for days at a time to satisfy his taste for scraps.

The California and Ring-billed Gulls generally nest together in big colonies on the inland lakes through the western part of the United States. In many places, these birds are of great economic importance. I have seen them spread out over the fields and through the sagebrush and get their living by catching grasshoppers. In Utah, the Gull lives about the beet fields and alfalfa lands and follows the irrigating ditches. When the fields are irrigated and the water rushes along, seeping into holes and driving mice from their burrows, the Gulls flock about and gorge themselves on these rodents.

After the nesting season, large flocks of California and Ring-billed Gulls often collect along the southern coasts to spend the winter. While at Santa Monica, California, during the winter of 1905 and 1906, I often watched the flocks of Gulls returning every evening from far inland where they had been skirmishing during the day. I often saw them about the gardens and in

the fields. A few miles from the ocean is the Soldiers' Home at Sawtelle. The garbage is hauled two or three times a day over to the pig-pens. When the dump wagon reaches the pens, the driver not only always finds himself besieged by a lot of hungry porkers, but a flock of Gulls

Courtesy of Nat. Asso. Aud. Soc.

NEST AND EGGS OF CALIFORNIA GULL

is always at hand to welcome his arrival. They sit around on the ground or fences waiting patiently. The Gulls and pigs eat together. The Gull doesn't care if his coat gets soiled, for he returns to the shore each evening and takes a good bath before bedtime.

WILLIAM L. FINLEY.

HEERMANN'S GULL
Larus heermanni *Cassin*
A. O. U. Number 57

Other Name.— White-headed Gull.

General Description.— Length, 20 inches. Head, white; body, bluish-gray.

Color.—ADULTS: Head all around, pure white, shading on neck into bluish-ash of under parts and into the *dark bluish-slate of upper parts;* rump and upper tail-coverts, clear ash; primaries, black with narrow white tips; tail, black narrowly tipped with white; *bill, bright red, black on terminal third;* feet, dusky-red; iris, brown; eyelids, red. YOUNG: Head and throat, mot-

tled with dusky and dull white; upper tail-coverts, gray; tail, broadly white-tipped; otherwise similar to adult plumage.

Nest and Eggs.— NEST: Probably similar to others of the genus. EGGS: Dull yellowish-drab, scatteringly marked with spots of brown and lilac.

Distribution.— Pacific coast of North America; breeds in Lower California and western Mexico; migrates north to southern British Columbia; winters from northern California southward to Guatemala.

As Mr. Dawson says, " Heermann's Gull is an inveterate loafer and sycophant. Of southern blood (we have just learned that he is bred on the islands off the coast of Mexico) he comes north in June only to float and loaf and dream throughout the remainder of the season. Visit

the ' Bird Rocks ' of Rosario Straits early in July and you will find a colony of Glaucous-wings distraught with family cares and wheeling to and fro in wild concern at your presence, while upon a rocky knob at one side, a white-washed club room, sit half a thousand Heermanns, impassive, haughty, silent. If you press inquiry they suddenly take to wing and fill the air with low-pitched mellow cries of strange quality and sweetness. And go where you will at that season, the Heermann's Gull is guiltless of local attachments — in the North." (*Birds of Washington.*)

Another observer notes that these Gulls display considerable intelligence in their pursuit of herring, when the fish are traveling in schools. The birds approach these schools from the rear along in the direction the herring are swimming until the fish come to the surface, when the birds renew their diving captures.

The systematic robbery of the Pelicans, an amusingly impudent performance, is also described by Mr. Dawson. "Often a long train of Pelicans is seen, as the tide is rising, slowly wandering around the bay, each one attended by one or more of these Gulls which are usually some distance behind. Whenever a Pelican awkwardly plunges into the water and emerges with

Photo by W. L. Finley and H. T. Bohlman

HEERMANN'S GULLS

They are inveterate loafers, and, while other Gulls are engaged with family cares, they stand on one side, impassive, haughty, silent

and take the fish near the surface by diving for them. As the herring discover their pursuers they sink some distance, but the school continues to travel in the same direction. The Gulls seem to know this, for after having reached the head of the school, they circle to the rear, and follow its enormous scoop net full of fish, its parasites are sure to be ready and fearlessly seize the fish from its very jaws, the stupid bird never resenting the insult, or appearing to take the least notice of the little pilferers which it could easily rid itself of by one blow, or even swallow alive."

LAUGHING GULL

Larus atricilla *Linnæus*

A. O. U. Number 58   See Color Plate 6

Other Name.— Black-headed Gull.

General Description.— Length, 16 inches. Color, white with dark slate-gray mantle and almost black hood.

Color.—ADULTS IN SUMMER: *Hood, dark slaty-black* extending further on throat than on back of head; a white spot above and below eye; neck all around, rump, tail, tips of secondaries and primaries, and entire under

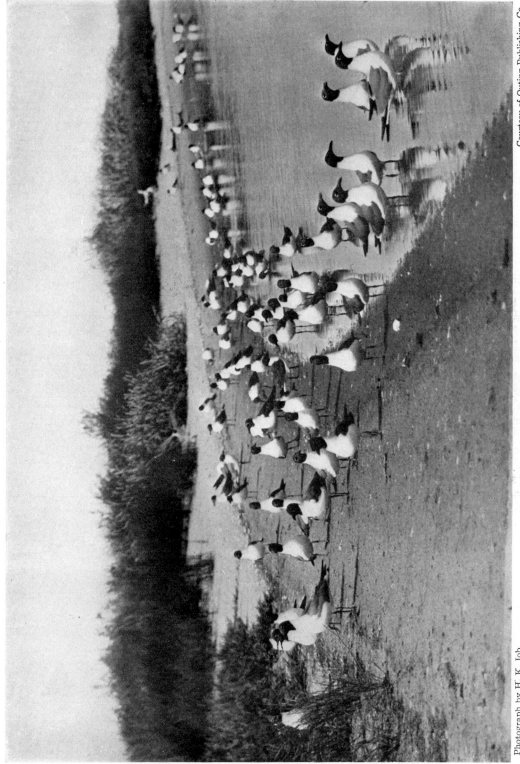

Photograph by H. K. Job

Courtesy of Outing Publishing Co.

LAUGHING GULLS

On beach, Louisiana.   Everywhere they add life, beauty, and interest to the scene parts, white, the latter with a rosy tinge; *mantle, dark slate-gray; outer six primaries, black;* bill, deep carmine; feet, black; iris and edge of eyelids, carmine. ADULTS IN WINTER: Under parts, without rosy tint; head, white, mottled with dusky; bill and feet, dull. YOUNG: Mantle, variegated with light grayish-brown; primaries, brownish-black, lighter on tips; secondaries, dusky on outer webs; tail, with a broad terminal band of dusky with narrow white tips; upper tail-coverts, white; bill and feet, brownish-black tinged with red.

Nest and Eggs.— NEST: On the ground in marshes; constructed of seaweed, sedges, and eelgrass. EGGS: 2 to 5, from dull grayish to dark olive, heavily marked with spots and splashes of brown, black, chestnut, and lavender.

Distribution.— Tropical and temperate coasts of North America; breeds from Maine (rarely) and Massachusetts (abundantly but local) south on the Atlantic and Gulf coasts to Texas, the Lesser Antilles, and Venezuela; winters from Georgia and Gulf coast south to western Mexico, Chile, and Brazil; casual in Colorado, Nebraska, Wisconsin, Ontario, and Iowa.

The Laughing Gull is well named, for seemingly it laughs. No great stretch of the imagination is required to assume that its loud cries are those of real mirth. It is a handsome creature in the breeding season, with its dark mantle, black head, and white breast faintly tinged with the color of the rose.

It breeds normally along most of the Atlantic coast of the United States. Until recent years it has been almost extirpated by constant persecution on the New England coast but now, under protection, its numbers are increasing. It nests on sandy islands, often among high grasses or ivy vines, and in the north it builds a substantial warm nest of grasses and weeds, but in the south a mere hollow in the sand often suffices. In pleasant warm weather the birds are seen to leave their nests, trusting apparently to the heat of the sun, but in cool or stormy weather the female incubates closely. The young leave the

nest soon after they are hatched and run about on the sandy soil, squatting and hiding in the thickest cover at the first alarm. Meanwhile the parents wheel high overhead, uttering their notes of apprehension. These birds are very gregarious and breed, as well as feed, in flocks.

Their food is largely composed of marine objects picked up on bars, beaches, flats, in the beds of estuaries and even at times in the salt marshes but ever near the sea. Audubon tells how the Laughing Gull robs the Brown Pelican

Photo by Herbert Mills   Courtesy of Nat. Asso. Aud. Soc.
NEST AND EGGS OF LAUGHING GULL
Passage Key, Florida

in Florida. Waiting until the Pelican dives and comes to the surface the Gull alights upon its head and snatches the small fish from its enormous bill. Sometimes this Gull follows schools of porpoises for the small fish that they drive to the surface. Everywhere it adds life, beauty, and interest to the scene.

EDWARD HOWE FORBUSH.

FRANKLIN'S GULL

Larus franklini *Richardson*

A. O. U. Number 59

Other Names.— Prairie Pigeon; Franklin's Rosy Gull.

General Description.— Length, 14 inches. Color, white with dark bluish-slate mantle and dark slate hood.

Color.—ADULTS IN SUMMER: *Hood, dark slate* extending around upper part of neck as well as on

head; *eyelids, white;* mantle, dark bluish-slate; outer primaries, with dusky bars near tip, this color graduating from about 2 inches in width on first to a small bar on sixth; primaries and secondaries, white-tipped; tail, pale grayish-blue, the three outside pairs of feathers, white; neck all around, rump, and whole under parts, white, the latter with rosy tint; *bill, carmine crossed with black near end;* legs, dusky-red. ADULTS IN WINTER: Similar to summer plumage, but without hood; a few slaty feathers around eyes and on sides of head; no rosy tint below; bill and feet, dull. YOUNG: Traces of hood; outer 5 or 6 primaries, wholly black; mantle, gray or brown, varied with bluish-gray, according to age; tail, ashy-white with a broad black subterminal bar; under parts, white; bill, dusky, paler at base below; feet, flesh color; iris, dark brown.

Nest and Eggs.—NEST: On the ground among standing rushes and grass of marshes bordering lakes or rivers; constructed of dead rushes. EGGS: 3, varying from dull white to olive-drab, marked with bold blotches and zigzag lines of umber-brown and sepia.

Distribution.— North and South America; breeds from southwestern Saskatchewan and southwestern Keewatin to South Dakota, Iowa, and southern Minnesota; winters from the Gulf coast of Louisiana and Texas southward to Peru and Chile; very rare on the Atlantic coast; accidental in Utah, Ontario, Ohio, Virginia, and the Lesser Antilles.

A typical scene of the interior prairie region, say in the Dakotas or Manitoba, is the farmer plowing up the rich black soil, on a cold windy day in early spring, followed almost at his heels by a troup of dainty white birds which are picking up the worms and grubs exposed to view. especially if one be curious to know whither they are roaming. Obviously, however, they are flying either to or from their nesting-ground.

In their breeding habits they are about as distinct and spectacular as any other North American species. Selecting some marshy lake, where

Photograph by H. K. Job ·   Courtesy of Outing Publishing Co.

FRANKLIN'S GULLS

On nesting ground

He calls them "Prairie Pigeons," a pretty and appropriate title, though in reality they are Franklin's Gulls. Sometimes they have been called the Rosy Gull, because when the feathers of the under parts are opened up there is seen to be a faint rosy flush, as delicate as that of the tea-rose.

This Gull is as typical of the prairie as is the Western Meadowlark or the Prairie Horned Lark, though in a different way. I should characterize it as the "courser" of the prairies. Bands of them are usually seen flying steadily along in a line or some regular formation, uttering flute-like cries, perpetually on the move. To a degree they strike one as birds of mystery, reeds or rushes grow from water, thousands of them will come together and build semi-floating nests of dead stems, partly buoyed by the vegetation and filled in from the bottom. If a person wade or push a boat to the edge of the colony, the air is full of indignant and screaming birds, always graceful and beautiful, no matter how excited they become. The nests are only a few feet apart, each containing two or three typical gull-like eggs by the last week of May. If the intruder keeps quite still, one or both of the owners may finally alight and stand on the nest, but neither will incubate as long as anyone is in sight. The downy young swim from the nests soon after they are hatched, and in a colony in

Photo by H. K. Job   Courtesy of Outing Pub. Co.

FRANKLIN'S GULL

Dropping down among the reeds to its nest

late June and July the aquatic vegetation seems alive with paddling puff-balls.

In their feeding habits during the warmer part of the year they are largely insectivorous. Out in the marshy lakes they feed a great deal upon nymphs of the dragon-fly, and on any insects or larvæ locally available. On the plowed fields they find many injurious grubs and cut-worms. Later they are active in pursuit of grasshoppers.

Their flocking is very spectacular, both when they are preparing to leave in the fall, and when they arrive in spring. In selected places, especially near the nesting-grounds, the prairie is sometimes fairly white with them.

Gulls are supposed to be chiefly maritime birds, but this species is a seeming exception. In fact the Rosy Gulls are rarely seen either on the Atlantic or the Pacific coast of the United States, though in winter some of them at least come out along the Gulf coast, and follow it down into South America. But it would seem hard to one who has known it in the sloughs and on the prairies to picture it flying over the ocean, where it could easily be mistaken for the Laughing Gull.   HERBERT K. JOB.

BONAPARTE'S GULL

Larus philadelphia (*Ord*)

A. O. U. Number 60   See Color Plate 6

Other Names.— Bonaparte's Rosy Gull; Black-headed Gull; Sea Pigeon.

General Description.— Length, 14 inches. Color, white with pale bluish-gray mantle and dark slate colored head.

Color.—ADULTS IN SUMMER: *Head, dark slate* reaching further in front than behind; *a white patch above and another below eye;* mantle, pale grayish-blue; most of *primaries with black tips;* neck all around, tail, and under parts, pure white, latter rose-tinted; *bill, black;* gape and eyelids carmine; feet, coral-red; webs, vermilion. ADULTS IN WINTER: *No hood;* crown and back of head, mottled with dusky; back of neck with tint of color of mantle; *a crescent before eye and patch on side of head, deep slate;* bill, light-colored at base below; feet, flesh color. YOUNG: No mottling on crown; a patch of dusky on side of head; wing-coverts and shoulders, dusky-brown with lighter edges; pri-

maries and secondaries, dusky tipped; tail white with a subterminal dusky bar; bill, dull flesh color; feet, light flesh color; iris, brown.

Nest and Eggs.— NEST: On the ground in marshes, usually on elevated hummocks; constructed of small sticks and dead grasses. EGGS: 3, olive-gray with a wreath of dark and light brown spots around large end and some scattered markings of the same color over whole surface.

Distribution.— North America in general; breeds from northwestern Alaska and northern Mackenzie south to British Columbia and Keewatin; winters from Maine to Florida; on the Pacific coast from southern British Columbia to Lower California and western Mexico, and on the Gulf coast to Texas and Yucatan; in migration west to Kotzebue Sound and east to Ungava; casual in the Bahamas and Bermuda; accidental in Europe.

Bonaparte's Gull is one of the smaller American Gulls, and unlike most of that family is sometimes found in flocks which often resort to plowed fields and swamps where the birds feed on insects and earth-worms. Its favorite haunts, however, are coasts, rivers, and lakes, where it feeds much after the manner of the Herring Gull.

Along the seacoast the Bonapartes are decidedly gregarious and often associate with Terns and other Gulls. Unlike their relatives, however, they are not given to following ferryboats and other craft from which offal and garbage are thrown overboard. In these surroundings their diet is chiefly marine worms and crustaceans

SABINE'S GULL   ADULT IN SUMMER
Xema sabini (J. Sabine)
LAUGHING GULL   ADULT IN SUMMER
Larus atricilla Linnaeus
KITTIWAKE
Rissa tridactyla tridactyla (Linnaeus)
ADULT IN SUMMER
IMMATURE

IVORY GULL
Pagophila alba (Gunnerus)
IMMATURE
All ⅛ nat. size

BONAPARTE'S GULL
Larus philadelphia (Ord)
ADULT IN SUMMER
IMMATURE

ADULT IN SUMMER

which they find on tide flats, in channels, and on kelp-beds.

A peculiarity of this bird's flight, which is graceful and fairly swift, is that each stroke of the wings swings the body slightly upward. Its maneuvers on the wing are often very skillful, especially a trick it has of suddenly stopping its progress and sweeping backward and downward to inspect an object seen on the surface of the water. In general its flight is more like that of the Terns than the Gulls.

BONAPARTE'S GULL (⅓ nat. size)

Although a shore bird, it is often found in plowed fields feeding on earthworms

Drawing by R. I. Brasher

SABINE'S GULL

Xema sabini (*J. Sabine*)

A. O. U. Number 62   See Color Plate 6

Other Names.— Hawk-tailed Gull; Fork-tailed Gull.

General Description.— Length, 14 inches. Color, white with bluish-gray mantle and dark slate hood. *Tail, forked with the feathers rounded*, not pointed, at the ends.

Color.—Adults in Summer: Heads with hoods of dark slate *bounded behind by a narrow border of black;* mantle, bluish-gray; edge of wing, black; *five outer primaries and their coverts, black* with small white tips; *rest of primaries, white;* outer secondaries, white; the gray of mantle extending diagonally across to end of inner secondaries; neck, tail, and entire under parts, white, the last with rosy hue; bill, black to angle, yellow, chrome, or orange from angle to tip; gape, vermilion; feet, black; iris, reddish; edges of eyelids, orange. Adults in Winter: Entire head, white with some dark feathers on crown and sides; bill, duller; no rosy hue; otherwise as in summer plumage. Young: Head, back of neck, and upper parts in general, transversely barred with slate-gray and dull whitish; under parts, white; tail, white with a bar of black one inch wide on middle feathers, this color narrowing outward; bill, dusky flesh color; legs, flesh color.

Nest and Eggs.— Nest: A depression in moss or sand, lined with fine dry grass. Eggs: 2 or 3, deep olive-brown obscurely spotted and blotched with darker shades of the same.

Distribution.— Arctic regions to South America; breeds on the coast of Alaska from Kuskokwim River to Norton Sound, and in northern Mackenzie, northern Keewatin, and northern Greenland, and on Taimyr Peninsula in northwestern Siberia; in migration on both coasts of United States and casual in interior; winters along the coast of Peru.

Sabine's Gull is essentially an Arctic species, though it occasionally wanders as far south as the North Atlantic States and has been taken as a straggler on Long Island, on the Great Lakes, and on Great Salt Lake, Utah. In any of its plumages it may readily be recognized by its forked tail — whence one of its names. The normal diet of this Gull appears to be composed partly of marine insects, most of which probably are obtained on beaches where they are left by receding waves. The species seems first to have been described by Sabine, from specimens taken by his brother, a member of the Northwest Expedition of 1818, on one of a group of rocky islands off the coast of Greenland.

GEORGE GLADDEN.

TERNS

Order *Longipennes;* family *Laridæ;* subfamily *Sterninæ*

DISTRIBUTED throughout the world are over fifty species of Terns, ten occurring regularly in North America. These birds belong to the family *Laridæ* which includes the Gulls, and is part of the order of Long-winged Swimmers. All of the species are exceedingly graceful and expert on the wing, and some show extraordinary endurance in flight. This is true especially of the Arctic Tern, whose journey from the Arctic to the Antarctic and back each year, is one of the most astonishing known feats in the bird world.

The Terns are often called "Sea Swallows," and for obvious reasons, as several of the species are not unlike large Swallows both in appearance and in flight. They are generally smaller than the Gulls, and their bodies are more elongated, but in coloration they more or less resemble their larger relatives, whom they also resemble in their food and feeding habits, with the exception of their diving practices. The Terns hover and plunge for their food, while the Gulls alight on the water to feed. Because of this characteristic, Terns have often been called "Strikers."

Again like the Gulls, the Terns are decidedly gregarious and often breed in colonies of thousands on ledges; some of the species occasionally place their nests on the limbs of large forest trees. Generally the nests on the grounds are little more than mere depressions, and often they are placed so close together that in walking through a nesting place, it is difficult to avoid treading upon either the eggs or the young. When hatched, the young are covered with down of a mottled pattern, and, although sometimes they will enter the water of their own accord and swim about, they are dependent upon their parents until they acquire the power of flight.

GULL-BILLED TERN

Gelochelidon nilotica (*Linnæus*)

A. O. U. Number 63   See Color Plate 7

Other Names.— Marsh Tern; Egyptian Tern; Nuttall's Tern; Anglican Tern; Nile Tern.

General Description.— Length, 13 to 15 inches. Color, white with light bluish-gray mantle. Bill, *stout and short, and curved over at tip.*

Color.—ADULTS IN SUMMER: *Crown and crest, glossy greenish-black,* extending to level of eyes, leaving only a narrow white line on upper side of bill; mantle, light grayish-blue; primaries, grayish-black but heavily silvered, appearing much lighter; tail, color of mantle fading to pure white at base; chin, throat, neck all around, and under parts, pure white; *bill, black,* usually with narrow yellow tip; legs, greenish-black; iris, brown. ADULTS IN WINTER: The forehead and fore-part of crown, white; black restricted to hind head and nape; side of head and a spot in front of eye, gray; otherwise similar to summer plumage.

Nest and Eggs.— NEST: A mere depression among the reeds of marshes; sometimes on sandy shores. EGGS: 3, olive-buff irregularly marked with umber-brown, blackish, and lavender.

Distribution.— Nearly cosmopolitan; breeds in North America, on coasts of Texas, Louisiana, North Carolina, Virginia (formerly to New Jersey), and in the Bahamas; wanders casually to Maine and Ohio; winters in southern Mexico, Central America, and all of South America; breeds also in Europe, Asia, and Australia, wintering to northern Africa.

It seems clear that the Gull-billed Tern is decreasing rapidly in numbers. Once common — or at least not actually rare — along the Atlantic coast, it now, according to Dr. Chapman, seldom, if ever, breeds north of Cobb's Island, Va., where it was found nesting in great numbers by Dr. Ridgway and Dr. Henshaw in 1879. Here Dr. Ridgway noted especially its cry, which he described as a chattering laugh, wherefore he thought it might well be named the Laughing Tern — its scientific name literally means "laughing swallow of the Nile." The same

observer noted that the bird showed much more courage in defending its nest than do other Terns; it swooped downward and straight at the intruder, often nearly striking him with its bill, and in its attempt to change its course the rush of the air through its wings made a booming sound not unlike that produced by the Night-hawk when it checks its downward plunge.

This bird differs superficially from its kind in having a shorter and comparatively heavy bill, and a shorter and less distinctly forked tail. It is also less excitable than the Common Tern.

CASPIAN TERN

Sterna caspia *Pallas*

A. O. U. Number 64   See Color Plate 8

Other Names.— Imperial Tern; Caspian Sea Tern.

General Description.— Length, 20 to 23 inches. Color, white with grayish-blue mantle. Tail, *slightly* forked with outer feathers pointed; wings, long and slender.

Color.— ADULTS IN SUMMER: Crown, glossy greenish-black; a white spot on lower eyelid; mantle, grayish-blue, but so heavily silvered when new as to appear light gray; rest of plumage, pure white; *bill, bright vermilion;* feet, black; iris, brown. ADULTS IN WINTER: The crown is broken by white and some dusky feathers show on wing-coverts.

Nest and Eggs.— NEST: A mere hollow scooped in dry sand. EGGS: 2 or 3, pale olive-buff, rather evenly marked with spots of dark brown and lavender.

Distribution.— Nearly cosmopolitan; breeds in North America at Great Slave Lake, Klamath Lake, Oregon, on islands of northern Lake Michigan, on coast of southern Labrador, and on coasts of Texas, Louisiana, Mississippi, South Carolina and (formerly) Virginia; winters from coast of central California to Lower California and western Mexico, and on the South Atlantic and Gulf coasts; casual in migration north to Alaska, James Bay, and Newfoundland.

Photo by W. L. Finley and H. T. Bohlman

COLONY OF CASPIAN TERNS

FORSTER'S TERN

Sterna forsteri *Nuttall*

A. O. U. Number 69   See Color Plate 7

Other Names.— Havell's Tern (immature) ; Sea Swallow.

General Description.— Length, 15 inches. Color, white with pale grayish-blue mantle. *Tail, forked for half its length.* Not distinguishable from either the Common Tern or the Arctic Tern except with specimens in hand.

Color.— Adults in Summer: Crown, glossy black not extending below eye; mantle, pale grayish-blue; primaries strongly silvered; entire under parts and rump, white; *the two long outside tail-feathers, white on outer web, dusky gray on inner; bill, orange-yellow,* terminal half, black with the extreme tip yellow; feet, bright orange; iris, brown. Adults in Winter: Crown variegated with white; nape, dusky; a distinct black bar on sides of head embracing eyes; outside tail-feathers, shorter than in summer; bill, dusky except at base below; feet, dusky yellowish.

Nest and Eggs.— Nest: In marshes; constructed of dead reeds and stems of water plants and lined with finer reeds. Eggs: 2 or 3, varying from pure white or pale green to warm brownish-drab irregularly spotted with brown, umber, and lilac.

Distribution.— North America at large; breeds in California, Oregon, Nevada, southwestern Saskatchewan, and Manitoba south to northern Colorado, northern Nebraska, northeastern Illinois and southern Ontario, and on the coasts of Texas, Louisiana, and Virginia; winters from southern California, Gulf of Mexico, and South Carolina southward to Guatemala; rare as far north as Massachusetts; casual in Brazil.

The Caspian Terns nest in colonies through the lake region of southern Oregon. They gather on one of the tule islands. We found two of the largest colonies on Lower Klamath and Malheur lakes, where these birds were living near a colony of California and Ring-billed Gulls. When we first visited Lower Klamath Lake, in 1905, we found these Gulls and Terns together with White Pelicans, Farallon Cormorants, Western Grebes, and Great Blue Herons, gathered in what might have been called one immense colony in the tules on the northwest side of the lake. Since that time, however, owing to disturbance, the birds have scattered; the Gulls, Terns, and Grebes have moved their colonies to other parts of the lake.

As one cruises about these lakes, he sees the graceful little Black and Forster's Terns flitting along over the surface, dropping here and there to pick up a bit to eat. The Caspian Tern is much larger than these two and is sometimes mistaken for a Gull. However, the exceedingly long wings, jet-black cap, and deep-red beak are

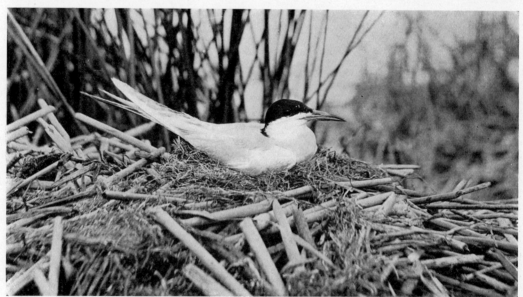

Photo by W. L. Finley and H. T. Bohlman

FORSTER'S TERN

On nest built on a muskrat house

the distinguishing features of this bird. We soon learned to recognize their harsh call note, for each morning they came flying over the camp, crying *Crack-a-day-o! Crack-a-day-o!*

Forster's Tern is readily recognized by its deeply forked tail; the outer feathers are very long and narrow. As it flits along over the water, its sharp bill is ever pointing downward and its eyes are watching the surface of the water. Because of its beautiful velvety plumage, the long pointed tail- and wing-feathers of this bird were formerly a much-sought adornment for women's hats.

While the Black Tern resembles Forster's Tern somewhat in size, yet Nature has made a striking difference in its dress. It can never be mistaken when once seen, for its fore parts are pure black and the wings and tail slaty-gray. This bird and the Forster Tern differ in their nesting habits from the Caspian, because they do not crowd together in a colony. They are sociable, however, and like company. The nests of both these birds are often a little floating mass of vegetation on the surface of the water, or oftentimes the nest is placed on a muskrat house. Where one nest is found, a few others are likely to be somewhere around in the same locality. I have at times found nests that contained eggs of both Forster's and Caspian Terns.

A peculiar habit of these swallow-like birds tended greatly toward their destruction at the hands of plume hunters. When a hunter shot one of them and it fell wounded to the surface, all the other Terns nearby would be attracted to the bird on the water and they hovered about and served as easy marks for the plumer.

By building a blind in which to hide nearby a colony of Caspian Terns on Malheur Lake, we had a splendid chance to study the home life of these birds. There were several hundred nesting close together, yet housekeeping was in no sense a communal matter. Each bird had its own particular nest spot and the invasion of that place by any other Terns meant a challenge for fight. When the Terns had young, their greatest anxiety seemed to be to keep them crouching low in the nest, so that they would not run away and get lost in the crowd. If a young bird did start to run out of the nest, he was immediately pounced upon by his own parents and pecked and beaten until he dropped flat to the ground or hid in the leaves. If a young bird ran to a neighboring nest or old bird for protection, he received a fusillade of blows that knocked him over. A young bird, therefore, that wandered from his own nest spot was likely to be pecked and beaten to death.

WILLIAM L. FINLEY.

ROYAL TERN

Sterna maxima *Boddaert*

A. O. U. Number 65   See Color Plate 8

Other Name.— Cayenne Tern.

General Description.— Length, 20 inches. Color, white with very pale bluish-gray mantle. A prominent glossy greenish-black crest on back of head.

Description.— ADULTS IN SUMMER: Crown, glossy greenish-black *not extending below eyes;* mantle, very pale bluish-gray, shading to white on rump and ends of inner secondaries; first five primaries with grayish-black spaces toward tips; rest of primaries and most of secondaries, pale pearl-blue; sides of head, chin, throat, rump, tail, and under parts, white; tail, forked for half its length; *bill, orange-red;* feet, blackish; iris, brown. ADULTS IN WINTER: Forehead, white; most of crown, variegated with black and white, the black ex-

tending forward on side of head as far as eye; tail, tinged with color of mantle and darkening toward tip into a deeper gray; less forked than in summer.

Nest and Eggs.— NEST: A hollow in the sand. EGGS: 2 or 3, whitish to yellowish-drab, blotched with dark umber, sepia, and lavender.

Distribution.— Tropical coasts north to United States; breeds in West Indies and on south Atlantic and Gulf coasts from Virginia to Texas; wanders casually to Massachusetts; not rare in summer from San Francisco Bay southward to western Mexico; winters from southern California and Gulf of Mexico south to Peru and Brazil, and on west coast of Africa from Gibraltar to Angola.

Because of its large size and conspicuous reddish bill the Royal Tern is one of the most striking birds to be seen along our southern coast. They may easily be distinguished from the smaller Gulls by the manner in which they hold their heads while in flight. A Gull's bill points forward on a plane with its body, while a Tern carries its bill pointed directly downward

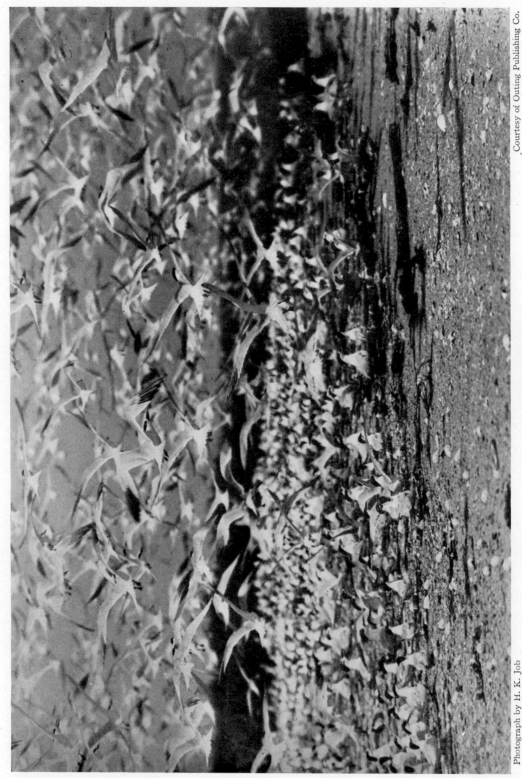

Courtesy of Outing Publishing Co.

Photograph by H. K. Job

ROYAL AND CABOT'S TERNS

Air full of them — Battledore Island, Louisiana

like a mosquito. Their food consists chiefly of small fish which they gather by plunging directly into the water, usually from a height of several yards. So much force is put into the blow that the bird often disappears beneath the surface. In Florida these Terns often rob the slow-moving Brown Pelican of his hard-earned prey. They are distinctively birds of the salt water and rarely come inland. They seldom appear in small harbors, and we never find them flying about wharves and fish factories as we do the Gulls.

Like most sea-birds the Royal Terns assemble in colonies to rear their young. Their eggs are laid on the bare sandy islands with no attempt at concealment. No other birds in North America make their nests so near together; in fact, when they are incubating it is often difficult, at a little distance, to see the ground between them, so closely do they sit.

A few years ago I visited a colony nesting on Royal Shoal Island in Pamlico Sound, North Carolina, where probably there were some four thousand eggs scattered about on the sand among the shells. A high tide sometime before had washed at least a thousand of these from their resting places and left them in a great windrow along the beach. The bereaved birds had then moved over to higher ground on the other side of the egg area and scratched out new nesting places. In doing this they took possession of a plot of ground already occupied by a colony of Black Skimmers. They simply kicked the Skimmer's eggs away or covered them with sand and at once took up the duties of incubation serenely indifferent to the mild protestations of the discomfited Skimmers. Usually other species of Terns, and frequently Skimmers and Oyster-catchers, breed on the islands occupied by the Royal Terns but never, so far as I have observed, within the actual boundaries of their colony. The one exception to this is the rare Cabot's Tern which their big neighbors seem to have taken under their special protection. The two species fly together, feed together, nest together, and — perhaps — die together.

The Royal Terns were largely exterminated in many sections of their range by the gunners of the millinery trade some years ago, but under the protection of the wardens of the Audubon Society they are again increasing in numbers. Their chief breeding places today are on the islands off the coast of Virginia, North Carolina, South Carolina, and Louisiana.

T. GILBERT PEARSON.

CABOT'S TERN

Sterna sandvicensis acuflavida *Cabot*

A. O. U. Number 67

Other Names.— Sandwich Tern; Kentish Tern; Boys' Tern; Ducal Tern.

General Description.— Length, 16 inches. Color, white with light bluish-gray mantle and tail.

Color.— ADULTS IN SUMMER: Crown and crest, glossy greenish-black extending below eyes but leaving a space alongside of bill white to the end of the feathers; mantle, light bluish-gray shading on rump and upper tail-coverts into pure white; first four outer primaries with black space near ends; tail, color of mantle; *bill, black, the tip* for about one-half inch *bright yellow;* feet, blackish; iris, brown. ADULTS IN WINTER: Crown, white varied with black shaft lines; crest, brownish-black; outside tail-feathers, shorter than in summer; yellow tip of bill less in extent and duller; otherwise as in summer. YOUNG: Forehead, crown, and nape, brownish-black variegated with white, upper parts, marked everywhere with irregular spots and transverse bars of dusky; primaries, as in adult; tail-feathers, tipped with dusky; bill, smaller and weaker, brownish-black, the extreme point only, and sometimes not that much, yellow.

Nest and Eggs.— NEST: On sandy shores, in colonies. EGGS: 2 or 3, creamy or buffy, irregularly spotted and scrawled with dark brown, chestnut, black, and lavender.

Distribution.— North and South America; breeds from North Carolina to Florida and Texas; winters from the Bahamas, Florida, and Louisiana south to Central America, Greater Antilles, Colombia, and Brazil; accidental in Ontario, Massachusetts, New Jersey and Lesser Antilles.

The Cabot's Tern in flight at a distance resembles its more famous relative the Arctic; however, it is a more stoutly built bird; also its tail is relatively shorter, while its head-feathers form a crest, which the bird can make quite conspicuous when it is angry or excited. In diving for its prey it often disappears entirely beneath the surface, and apparently descends to a much greater depth than do other Terns. When breeding in colonies, the Cabot's Terns often place their nests so close together that it is difficult to avoid stepping on them while one is exploring the premises.

Some ornithologists attribute the remarkable variation in the coloration of this Tern's eggs to the fact that they are incubated alternately by the male and the female, one bird being ready to cover the eggs the instant the other leaves them. Under these conditions the law of natural selection cannot operate in such a way as to eliminate an egg of conspicuous coloration, which is true of many Terns' eggs.

There is apparently reliable evidence that these Terns mate for life, and return year after year to the same nesting region, though not necessarily always to the same spot. English observers have noted that the birds change their actual breeding ground from time to time, though apparently the same general colony is likely to return to the same island.

Photo by H. K. Job

CABOT'S TERNS AND EGGS

Breton Island Reservation

COMMON TERN

Sterna hirundo *Linnæus*

A. O. U. Number 70   See Color Plate 7

Other Names.— Sea Swallow; Wilson's Tern; Summer Gull; Mackerel Gull; Lake Erie Gull; Bass-gull; Red-shank.

General Description.— Length, 15 inches. Color, white with mantle of pale pearl-blue.

Color.— Adults in Summer: Crown, lustrous greenish-black extending to lower level of eyes; mantle, pale pearl-blue deepening on back, ending abruptly on rump which, together with upper tail-coverts, is pure white; throat, chin, and sides of head, pure white shading insensibly to a much paler tone of color of mantle on entire under parts; outer primaries, grayish-black strongly silvered; secondaries, pure white shading to grayish-blue on end; *outer pair of tail-feathers, grayish-*

Plate 7

ARCTIC TERN ADULT IN SUMMER
Sterna paradisaea Brünnich
GULL-BILLED TERN ADULT IN SUMMER
Gelochelidon nilotica (Linnaeus)
LEAST TERN *Sterna antillarum* (Lesson)
IMMATURE ADULT IN SUMMER

SOOTY TERN ADULT IN SUMMER
Sterna fusca Linnaeus

FORSTER'S TERN
Sterna forsteri Nuttall
ADULT IN SUMMER

BLACK SKIMMER
Rynchops nigra Linnaeus
ROSEATE TERN ADULT IN SUMMER
Sterna dougalli Montagu

All ⅕ nat. size

IMMATURE
COMMON TERN
Sterna hirundo Linnaeus
ADULT IN SUMMER IMMATURE

blue on inner webs, grayish-black on outer; rest of tail-feathers with inner webs, pure white, outer webs, pearl-gray; *bill, vermilion on basal half; rest, black with yellow on extreme tip;* feet, coral-red; iris, deep brown. ADULTS IN WINTER: Forehead and most of crown, white; under parts, nearly pure white; bill and feet, duller; otherwise as in summer. IMMATURE: Similar to winter adults, but back mottled or washed with light brownish and bill brownish.

Nest and Eggs.— NEST: A hollow in the sand; composed of a few bits of grass and dry seaweed. EGGS:

3, greenish-white to deep brown, spotted and blotched with brown, black, and lavender.

Distribution.— Northern hemisphere, northern South America, and Africa; breeds from Great Slave Lake, central Keewatin, and southern Ungava south to southwestern Saskatchewan, northern North Dakota, southern Wisconsin, northern Ohio and North Carolina; winters from Florida southward to Brazil; casual in migration on Pacific coast from British Columbia to Lower California. In eastern hemisphere, breeds in Europe and Asia and winters in India and Africa.

The level rays of the rising sun, coming up from the other side of the world, stream over the heaving sea, lighting up an islet where the surf beats unceasingly upon shifting sands. This islet of recent origin has risen from the sea, thrown up by the surging tempestuous waters of the Atlantic and is destitute of all vegetable life. As our boat lands through the plunging surf a cloud of white birds rises and storms about us with harsh resounding cries. *Tee'-arr, tee'-arr* they call with many variant sounds until all blend in one great monotone of angry entreaty. As we leave the beach a troop of downy young rises and moves toward the farther shore, augmented as it goes by others lying hidden behind every

stone or shell or bunch of sea-drift until it seems like a feathered army marching in one continuous front across the isle. As they reach the farther shore they do not hesitate, but throw themselves into the surf, only to be tossed back again drenched and soggy upon the streaming sands. Stand back now, lie quietly down, and watch them swimming, tumbling in the surf, returning to the island, solicitously guarded by their watchful parents. We have found a colony of Common Terns! Now we see that there are many eggs laid on the bare sand or in slight hollows where a few stones or bits of seaweed have been collected by the parent birds.

Where nesting material is plentiful this Tern

COMMON TERN (½ nat. size)
It is useful to the fisherman, guiding him to schools of edible fish

sometimes builds a substantial nest of sticks, seaweed, and grasses, placing it just above high-water mark along the beach. At times it nests in thick grass on high islands, and on the Magdalen Islands Maynard found it breeding on the tops of grass-topped rocks 200 feet above the sea. The eggs are commonly laid in May or June but many are deposited as late as July. In New England, however, most of the young are able to fly early in August; and then the families join in flocks, leave their breeding places and forage over the country. At this season and in September some of them frequently go up the rivers and sometimes to inland ponds, where they probably find small fry in the warm waters.

In fishing they usually fly with the bill pointing downward, and, when they observe their prey, dive like a flash to the surface, often immersing the head but seldom going entirely under water. Several naturalists have followed the lead of Giraud in asserting that this bird, though web-footed, never dives and rarely swims, appearing to avoid the water, except as it is obliged to descend to the surface to procure food. It is true that it does not, like Gulls, rest often on the surface but in hot weather near its breeding grounds small parties may be seen floating on the waves bathing and throwing the spray about with the abandon and enjoyment of the true waterfowl — and they swim exceedingly well.

These birds are useful to the fishermen as they serve to mark the presence of schools of edible fish. These fish drive the small fry to the surface, the telescopic eyes of the Terns mark the disturbance from afar and when the fishermen see the gathering, plunging flocks they put off

Photo by O. E. Baynard   Courtesy of Nat. Asso. Aud. Soc.

EGGS OF COMMON TERN

A hollow in the sand, a few bits of grass and dry seaweed, and the nest is ready for the three eggs

in their boats, well knowing that their work lies there.

This Tern feeds largely on small fry, shrimps and other small crustacea but also at times on grasshoppers and many flying insects.

EDWARD HOWE FORBUSH.

ARCTIC TERN

Sterna paradisæa *Brünnich*

A. O. U. Number 71   See Color Plate 7

Other Names.— Common Tern; Sea Swallow; Paradise Tern; Crimson-billed Tern; Long-tailed Tern; Short-footed Tern; Portland Tern; Pike's Tern.

General Description.— Length, 14 to 17 inches. Color, pale bluish-gray, lighter below.

Color.— ADULTS IN SUMMER: Crown, lustrous greenish-black encroaching on lores so as to leave only a slender white line of feathers on upper side of bill; mantle, pale bluish-gray; under parts, a little lighter shade of color of back, fading into white on chin, throat, and edges of black cap, *ending abruptly at under tail-coverts which are pure white;* outer primaries, silvery-gray; inner webs, mostly white; inner primaries, color of back, broadly tipped with white; tail, very long, pure white, with outer web of outside feather grayish-black; *bill, carmine;* feet, coral-red; iris, brown. ADULTS IN WINTER: Forehead, white; crown, white with narrow black shaft lines, widening behind and merging into solid black on nape; a dark stripe on side of head; under parts, nearly white; otherwise as in summer. IMMATURE: Like winter adult, but tip of bill black.

Nest and Eggs.— Not distinguishable from those of the Common Tern.

Distribution.— Nearly cosmopolitan; breeds from Massachusetts north to northern Greenland, across Arctic regions to northern Alaska, and in entire Arctic regions of Europe and Asia; winters in Antarctic Ocean, south to latitude 74°; in migration, Pacific coast south to southern California, and Atlantic coast south to Long Island; accidental in Colorado.

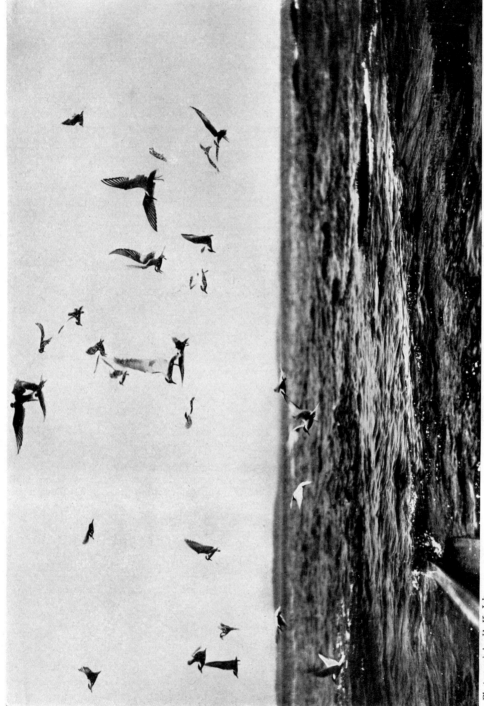

ARCTIC TERNS

Feeding near breeding colony, Matinicue Rock, Maine

Photograph by H. K. Job

The world's migration champion is the Arctic Tern. It deserves its title of "Arctic," for it nests as far north as land has been discovered; that is, as far north as the bird can find anything stable on which to construct its nest. Indeed, so arctic are the conditions under which it breeds that the first nest found by man in this region, only 7½° from the pole, contained a downy chick surrounded by a wall of newly fallen snow that had to be scooped out of the nest by the parent. When the young are full-grown the entire family leaves the Arctic and several months later they are found skirting the edge of the Antarctic continent.

What their track is over that 11,000 miles of intervening space no one knows. A few scattered individuals have been noted along the United States coast south to Long Island, but the great flocks of thousands and thousands of these Terns which range from pole to pole have never been noted by an ornithologist competent to indicate their preferred route and their time schedule. The Arctic Terns arrive in the Far North about June 15, and leave about August 25, thus staying fourteen weeks at the nesting site. They probably spend a few weeks longer in the winter than in the summer home, and this would leave them scarcely twenty weeks for the round trip of 22,000 miles. Not less than 150 miles in a straight line must be their daily task, and this is undoubtedly multiplied several times by their zigzag twistings and turnings in pursuit of food.

The Arctic Tern has more hours of daylight and sunshine than any other animal on the globe. At the most northern nesting site the midnight sun has already appeared before the birds' arrival, and it never sets during their entire stay at the breeding grounds. During two months of their sojourn in the Antarctic the birds do not see a sunset, and for the rest of the time the sun dips only a little way below the horizon and broad daylight is continuous. The birds therefore have twenty-four hours of daylight for at least eight months in the year, and during the other four months have considerably more daylight than darkness.

WELLS W. COOKE, in *Bird Migration*.

ROSEATE TERN

Sterna dougalli *Montagu*

A. O. U. Number 72   See Color Plate 7

Other Names.— Graceful Tern; McDougall's Tern.

General Description.— Length, 15 inches. Color above, pearly-gray; below, delicate rose-pink.

Color— ADULTS IN SUMMER: Crown, glossy black reaching to lower border of eyes; mantle, delicate pale pearly-gray; neck all around and *entire under parts, a delicate rose pink;* primaries, grayish-black strongly silvered; *long tail-feathers, white on both webs;* bill, black, extreme tip, yellow, reddish at base; feet, vermilion; iris, brown. ADULTS IN WINTER: Forehead and cheeks, white; crown, hind head, nape, and sides of head, dusky mottled with white above; below, pure white without rosy tinge; lesser wing-coverts, brownish; tail, less forked, pearly-gray like back; bill, dull black with yellow tip and brown base. IMMATURE: Similar to winter adult.

Nest and Eggs.— Nesting similar and eggs indistinguishable from those of the Common Tern except by comparison.

Distribution.— Temperate and tropical regions; breeds locally from Sable Island to Long Island, N. Y., and from the Bahamas to the Lesser Antilles and Venezuela; formerly from Maine to Florida; rare migrant in Central America; winters from the Bahamas to Brazil; accidental in Ohio; occurs on the coasts of a large part of the eastern hemisphere.

The Roseate Tern is the embodiment of symmetry and grace — its flight the poetry of motion. Its elegant form tapers and swells in lines of beauty. Its lustrous plumage reflects the yellow rays of the sun and the pale refracted light of sea and sands in evanescent pink and rosy tints. These are seen in perfection only in the living bird and fade when the light of life fades from its eyes. The stuffed and distorted specimen on the museum shelf has lost the grace, beauty, and color of the living thing and remains but a sorry travesty of the life that is gone. It seems a bird of ethereal origin, fitted only for the balmy airs of tropic isles but it follows north the coast of both hemispheres and is found in Maine on one side of the Atlantic and in Scotland on the other.

Years ago, when fashion called for its plumage and there was none to save, this bird was almost exterminated on the Atlantic coast. The adults were shot on their breeding grounds and the young left to starve in the nests, but now, under protection, they are beginning to increase and may be found breeding with the Common Terns on isolated islands off the New England coasts. This Tern keeps mostly to the sea and its bays, sounds, and estuaries. Its nest is built often among low vegetation and the young can hardly be distinguished from the downy chicks of the Common Tern. The adult birds, however, are quite different from that species, a little slower and more graceful in flight. They may be readily identified by the black bill, the long graceful white tail, the rosy appearance of the breast and other under parts, and their incisive notes. When excited, they call *hoyit, hoyit,* ending with a prolonged cry, but the alarm note commonly heard is *cac, cac.* In the latitude of New England, about the first of August, the young are well able to fly, and they join the wandering flocks which visit the shores, far and near, before the southern migration begins.

EDWARD HOWE FORBUSH.

LEAST TERN

Sterna antillarum (*Lesson*)

A. O. U. Number 74   See Color Plate 7

Other Names.— Silver Ternlet; Sea Swallow; Little Striker; Little Tern; Minute Tern.

General Description.— Length, 9 inches. Color above, pale grayish-blue; below, satiny-white.

Color.—ADULTS IN SUMMER: Crown, glossy greenish-black with *a narrow white crescent with horns reaching above eyes and extending to bill,* but separated from white of cheeks by a dusky line through eye to bill; entire upper parts, including tail, *pale grayish-blue reaching to the black cap* and fading on sides of head and neck into satiny-white of all under parts; two outer primaries, black with white space on inner webs; rest of primaries, a darker shade of color of back; *bill, yellow tipped with black; feet, orange yellow;* iris, brown. ADULTS IN WINTER: Forehead, lores, and crown, white, the latter with black shaft lines; back of head and nape, dusky, connecting with a narrow streak through eye; hindneck, white; mantle, darker than in summer; edge of wing and a band along forearm, grayish-black; most of primaries, plain dusky.

Nest and Eggs.— NEST: In pebbly depression or on the dry sand of beaches. EGGS: 1 to 4, from pale greenish to dull drab, spotted over entire surface with splashes and dots of different shades of clear brown and some lavender.

Distribution.— Tropical and temperate America; breeds on coast of southern California and on Gulf coast from Texas eastward; also northward to Missouri (formerly Iowa) and northwestern Nebraska; has occurred in Wisconsin and South Dakota; breeds also from the coasts of Massachusetts, Virginia, North Carolina, and Florida south to the Bahamas, West Indies, British Honduras, and Venezuela; now rare everywhere; in migration occurs on the coasts of Lower California and western Mexico; winters from Gulf coast to Venezuela and Peru.

Unquestionably the most dainty of all the American sea-birds is the Least Tern. This petite little creature is adorned with a pair of silvery-gray wings that carry it on long voyages up and down the coast. From its winter home in the tropics it comes north in spring to California and Massachusetts and in both States it finds a summer home. A few pass up the Mississippi valley and it has been recorded as far north as South Dakota. Thirty years ago they swarmed literally by thousands in our Atlantic waters near the shore-line but the feather-hunters made sad work of them. There is a record of ten thousand having been shot for their feathers on Cobb Island, Virginia, in a single season. This was of course done in the summer and the orphaned young were left to perish on the beaches.

At one time large colonies existed in the sounds of North Carolina; but their numbers became so reduced that when the Audubon Society wardens were first established in that territory, in the spring of 1903, only sixteen eggs were laid in the bird colonies that year. They have responded splendidly to protection and although many years must elapse before we can hope to have them as abundant as formerly they are nevertheless increasing in a most encouraging way.

Like the other members of this family they prey mainly upon small fish which they capture by a swift plunge from the air. They do not confine themselves entirely to this diet, however, and often catch such insects as are found flying over the marshes.

Least Terns are usually seen in small scattered

flocks. They are very sympathetic and solicitous about the welfare of their fellows that chance to get into trouble. Any old Tern hunter will tell you that, if one be shot down, its friends will at once come and fly anxiously about emitting their little squeaky cries of anxiety. It was thus often possible to bag almost the entire company. When a flock was seen and the gunners found difficulty in obtaining the first bird to serve as a decoy, they were induced often to approach the boat by the simple expedient of tying a handkerchief to a stick and throwing it into the air. The sight of this object, which at a distance somewhat resembles a falling Tern, usually brought the birds on the run.

Like many other Terns the nest of this species is merely a slight depression hollowed out in the sand. The eggs are usually two in number, although as many as four are found at times. If not disturbed these Terns sometimes become quite tame and on more than one occasion I have been privileged to walk within fifteen feet of a resting bird before it took flight. Mated birds are very attentive to each other, and one of the most charming sights of a visit to a Least Tern colony is to see one of these little, gentle creatures feed his mate as she sits brooding her eggs on the shimmering sandy shore.

T. GILBERT PEARSON.

Drawing by R. I. Brasher

LEAST TERN (⅔ nat. size)
The most dainty of all the American sea-birds

BLACK TERN

Hydrochelidon nigra surinamensis (*Gmelin*)

A. O. U. Number 77   See Color Plate 8

Other Names.—American Black Tern; Short-tailed Tern; Semipalmated Tern; Surinam Tern.

General Description.— Length, 9 inches. Upper parts, leaden-gray; head and under parts, black. Bill, very sharp and slender, shorter than head; wings, long and pointed with no distinct markings; tail, short and but slightly forked; feet, webbed only to middle of toes.

Color.— ADULTS IN SUMMER: *Head and neck and entire under parts as far as the tail-coverts, jet black;* under tail-coverts, pure white; on back of neck and between shoulders the black shades into leaden-gray, which color extends over entire upper parts to the ends of tail-feathers; primaries, grayish-black; outer secondaries similar, inner secondaries like back; shoulder of wing, narrowly white-bordered; *bill, black;* gape, carmine; feet, dark red-brown; iris, brown. ADULTS IN WINTER: Forehead, sides of head, neck all around and entire under parts, pure white; crown, mixed gray and white, darker on nape with a dusky stripe above and another behind eye; upper parts, pale lead-gray; many feathers with white edges.

Nest and Eggs.— NEST: On dead reeds in marshes; a careless structure of a few dead sedges and grass. EGGS: 2 to 4, pale brownish-olive heavily marked with blotches and spots of light brown and sepia.

Distribution.— North and South America; breeds from southwestern British Columbia, Great Slave Lake, southern Keewatin, and western Ontario south to inland lakes of California, Nevada, Colorado, northern Missouri, and northern Ohio; rare on east coast of United States in autumn; winters from Mexico to Panama, Peru, and Chile; accidental in Alaska, Nova Scotia, and New Brunswick; casual in West Indies and the Bahamas.

Plate 8

CASPIAN TERN
Sterna caspia Pallas
IMMATURE   ADULT IN SPRING

ROYAL TERN
Sterna maxima Boddaert
ADULT IN WINTER   ADULT IN SPRING

All ⅙ nat. size

BLACK TERN
Hydrochelidon nigra surinamensis (Gmelin)
ADULT CHANGING TO WINTER PLUMAGE
ADULT IN SPRING   IMMATURE

The Black Tern is a species of really unique personality, and might be characterized as the "aquatic swallow" of the sloughs of the northwest. It may be recognized as the dark gray bird with black under parts, in general form and motions not unlike a Purple Martin, which may be seen flitting about over the prairies, especially in the vicinity of wet grounds or sloughs, pursuing insects like any Swallow. In late summer and early autumn these birds gather into large loose flocks, and are very much in evidence. Where the Franklin's Gull is found, the Black Tern hardly can fail to be present, though, as the Tern is much more widely distributed, the converse is not true.

persistent attacks. On one occasion they hit me so hard on the top of the head that, even though I wore a cloth cap, their blows gave me a severe headache. After hatching, the young do not remain long in the frail nests, but quickly take to the water, and swim about through the aquatic vegetation, watched over by their parents, and brooded from time to time wherever they may crawl out upon any convenient spot.

As far as is definitely known, these Terns breed only in the western interior of the United States and Canada. On one occasion, however, when I landed on a low sandy island on the Atlantic coast, near Cape Charles, Virginia, I was surprised to find a considerable number of them,

Drawing by R. I. Brasher

BLACK TERN (⅓ nat. size)

A Tern with many Swallow habits

Here, in these sloughs and marshes, it breeds in abundance, and is one of the last of all to deposit its eggs — about the middle of June. The nest is the merest apology for such, being a slight depression, lined with a few wet stems, on some little hummock of mud or débris which may happen to project from the water. Sometimes the nests are partly floating, but heavy rains must work havoc with them. Two or three eggs are laid.

The parents are very solicitous when their home is approached. They dart about screaming and make angry swoops at the head of the intruder, in fact often striking hard with their bills. More than once I have suffered from their

all in full adult plumage, with black breasts. They were with other species of Terns, and acted exactly as on their western breeding-grounds, hovering over me screaming, and dashing furiously at my head. Unfortunately there had been a high storm tide, which had destroyed every nest on this barren sand bar, including those of Forster's Terns and those of Black Skimmers. Both of these latter had constructed new nests and were resentful of intrusion. Where the Black Terns hovered there were little hollows in the sand, lined with grass, smaller than those of the other Terns, just the size that the species constructs in the West. It was unfortunate that I could not return to the island later, as I am positive they must have been breeding there, and this is the only case thus far known

Photo by H. K. Job   Courtesy of Doubleday, Page & Co.

NEST OF BLACK TERN

The merest apology for a nest, being a slight depression, lined with a few wet stems, on some little hummock which may happen to project from the water

of any evidence of their breeding on the Atlantic coast.

On another occasion also I witnessed a peculiar happening with the species. It is well known that they do not breed until two years old and in full plumage. In their second summer they are in an immature, white-breasted phase. In winter all migrate down into Central and South America, and only a comparative few of the immature plumaged birds of a year old are observed in our borders. In June, 1915, while cruising along the western coast of Louisiana, I saw great clouds of rather small birds, resembling in the distance flights of Golden Plovers such as I had seen many years ago, performing evolutions high in the air, and then settling down on the shores of a sandy inlet back of the outer beach. We managed to land and cross to it, and were amazed to find there swarms of Black Terns, nearly all in the one-year-old plumage, with a very few adults intermingled, fairly covering the flats for probably a couple of miles. There must have been tens of thousands of them, and their identity was proved by collecting a few. This would indicate that the young remain well to the south, not migrating north to any considerable extent until fully mature.

HERBERT K. JOB.

NODDY

Anoüs stolidus (*Linnæus*)

A. O. U. Number 79

General Description.— Length, 16 inches. Color of head and neck, gray; of body, brown. Tail, rounded, the *central* feathers longest.

Color.— Forehead, white; crown, leaden-gray; sides of head and neck all around, bluish-slate with a dark spot in front of eye; rest of plumage, deep brown blackening on wings and tail; bill, black; feet, dark reddish-brown; iris, brown.

Nest and Eggs.— NEST: In low bushes; constructed of sticks, leaves, and grass. EGGS: 1, warm buff, spotted and blotched with reddish-brown and lavender, chiefly around large end.

Distribution.— Tropical coasts. Breeds on Florida Keys, the coast of Louisiana, and in the Bahamas and West Indies; winters south to Brazil and Tristan da Cunha Island.

SOOTY TERN

Sterna fuscata *Linnæus*

A. O. U. Number 75   See Color Plate 7

Other Names.— Egg Bird; Wide-awake.

General Description.— Length, 15 to 17 inches. Color above, black; below, white.

Color.—ADULTS: Entire upper parts, black with a slight greenish-gloss; a white crescent on forehead extending above eyes, separated from white cheeks by a

black band from eye obliquely downward and forward to bill; sides of head to eyes, half way around neck, and entire under parts, white; primaries and secondaries, black, lighter on inner webs of former, white on inner webs of latter; long outside tail-feathers, white; bill and feet, black; iris, red. YOUNG: Entire plumage, smoky-brown, grayish on abdomen; upper wing-coverts and shoulders, tipped with white giving a spotty appearance; feathers of back, rump, and upper tail-coverts, margined with dull rufous; primaries and tail, black, the latter but little forked; bill, black above, dull reddish below; eyes and feet, dusky-red.

Nest and Eggs.— On sandy beaches 1 to 3 eggs are dropped with slight attempt at a nest; the eggs are creamy or buff, sparsely spotted and splashed with light brown, Vandyke brown, and lavender.

Distribution.— Tropical and subtropical coasts, except Pacific coast of South America; breeds from Florida, Louisiana, and Texas throughout the Bahamas, West Indies, and tropical islands of the Atlantic; rarely north to Maine; winters from the Gulf coast to Brazil and the Falkland Islands.

As there is more or less similarity in the appearance, habits, and habitat of the Noddy and Sooty Terns it becomes proper as well as convenient to treat the two species together. For most of the following facts, we are indebted to John B. Watson's carefully prepared monograph, "The Behavior of Noddy and Sooty Terns," this being one of the *Papers from the Tortugas Laboratory of the Carnegie Institution of Wash-*

fool, and that it is applied to the Tern in question because of the bird's tameness or stupidity, especially when on the nest. How much justification there is for this explanation will appear from Mr. Watson's description of the Noddy's conduct during the nidification period. As he shows, the name undoubtedly has reference to the bird's curious nodding habit, of which he gives the following description:

Drawing by R. I. Brasher

NODDY (¼ nat. size)

It greets a stranger bird with a nod of the head

ington. Mr. Watson remarks that "extended statements of the instincts and habits of these birds are not extant." The habit of the birds of assembling on islands has been noted by various naturalists and travelers, but nearly all information concerning them has to do with their traits during the nesting season, and little is known of the remainder of their lives. What Mr. Watson records concerning their domestic conduct should, however, receive the careful attention of all who are interested in these comparatively little known birds.

Certain of the dictionaries inform the readers that the word "Noddy" means simpleton or

"This nodding reaction is one of the most interesting and ludicrous acts of the Noddy Tern. It is quite elaborate. Two birds will face each other, one will then bow the head almost to the ground, raise it quickly almost to a vertical position, and then quickly lower it. He will repeat this over and over again with great rapidity. The other bird goes through a similar pantomime. If a stranger bird alights near a group, he salutes those nearest, and is in turn saluted by them. During the pantomime a sound is rarely heard."

Mr. Watson observed these singular birds on Bird Key, a very small coral island about sixty-five miles west of Key West. The Terns arrived for the nesting season during the last week of April. It was observed that their food consisted of small fish of various kinds; that they never swam or dived, and that they never touched the water except when drinking, bathing, or fishing. They drank sea water, which they took on the wing by dipping the opened beak into the sea. They bathed by dipping the breast and head, and did not immerse the whole body. Frequently they followed schools of minnows which were driven to the surface by larger fish, and which they caught with their bills. This fishing was done by groups of Noddies and Sooties to the number of from fifty to one hundred.

formance. It is begun by the male, who nods vigorously to the female. She responds by thrusting her bill down his throat while he regurgitates the fish he has caught. Then the male flies away to return presently with a stick, and the nest-building operation is begun without further ceremony. The nest is made of dead branches, or seaweed, or a combination of both, and it may be lined with shells, upon which the eggs are laid. The building may be done jointly by both sexes or, apparently, by either working chiefly unassisted. It is far from true that the brooding bird displays indifference when an intruder approaches, says Mr. Watson. On the contrary,

Photograph by H. K. Job   Courtesy of Outing Publishing Co.

SOOTY TERN ON NEST

Mr. Watson noted that the Noddies left the island at about daybreak, fished for about two hours, and then returned to relieve their mates, who thereupon flew out to sea for their turn at fishing. Before the single egg is laid the male Noddy does all of the fishing and feeds the female. After the egg is laid the birds relieve each other at intervals of about two hours. During the laying and brooding season the male Sooty probably stays out over the water all day, but during the laying season he returns at night to feed the female, while in the brooding season he relieves the female. It seems probable that the birds feed within fifteen knots of the shore.

The courtship of the Noddy is a curious per-

though they may permit a very close approach, even to within handling distance, they strike savagely with their sharp beaks, and Mr. Watson says he has been attacked by the flying birds with such spirit that his hat was knocked off and his scalp cut by their bills. Incubation requires from thirty-two to thirty-five days, and the parents share the labor of feeding the young. The Noddies made use of nests of the previous season, by adding new material; and that this operation, apparently, was repeated several times seemed probable to Mr. Watson, as some of the nests were very large and bulky. But he found no proof that the same pair actually returned to the same nest. Often the birds built in low bushes, but in no instance was the nest placed directly on the ground, for it was noticed that even nests which seemed to be so placed were in reality resting on a worn-down turf of grass.

The nest of the Sooty Tern, on the other hand, was at the most no more than a shallow oval depression, hollowed out of the sand by the bird's claws. Sometimes this nest was fashioned under bayberry bushes, and occasionally a rim of leaves was gathered about the edge, but these leaves were only such as the bird could reach while she was covering the eggs. These birds have very definite ideas about their property rights, according to Mr. Watson. That is, they evidently consider a plot of ground from fourteen inches to two feet square within which their nest is placed as their private premises, and they will leave their eggs or even their young to drive away any other bird that comes within their domains. This jealousy causes almost constant commotion and uproar in the colony; for, if a bird upon returning to its mate does not alight literally within its own yard, and attempts to walk to its own nest, it will be set upon by every other bird through whose premises it passes. Against human intruders, however, it defends its

home somewhat less vigorously than does the Noddy. The birds share incubation, and sometimes one will brood the eggs for two days in succession before being relieved. They never

Photo by Herbert Mills   Courtesy of Nat. Asso. Aud. Soc.

A NODDY NESTING UPON THE BARE GROUND

Only a few sticks have been gathered around the rim of the nest

rest or swim on the water and, apparently, get so little sleep that they are called the "Wide-awake Terns."

SKIMMERS

Order *Longipennes;* family *Rynchopidæ*

THE Skimmers constitute a single family, *Rynchopidæ*, which includes five species. Like the Loons and Grebes, they evidently are very old forms, as their fossil remains have been found in Patagonia in the strata of the Tertiary Period. In several respects they strongly resemble the Terns, but they differ from them and from all other birds in the curious structure of the bill, which is long, and much compressed laterally, the lower mandible, which is much longer than the upper, being as thin as a knife-blade. The upper mandible is peculiar in that it is movable. These differences are plainly modifications which fit the bird for its method of capturing its food (shrimps, small fish, and other animal forms) by skimming the surface of the water with the lower mandible, the upper being kept slightly raised meanwhile. This manner of feeding is suggestive of that of the whales. They hunt their food in companies and are partially nocturnal in their habits.

The birds generally are pure white below, and black, with some white tipping of the feathers on the upper parts. Their bodies are from sixteen to about twenty inches long, their wings slender and long, the tail short and slightly forked; the feet are small with the webs between the middle and the inner toes deeply notched.

Skimmers build no nest, but lay three or four eggs in a slight hollow in the sand. The Black Skimmer is the only member of the family which occurs in America.

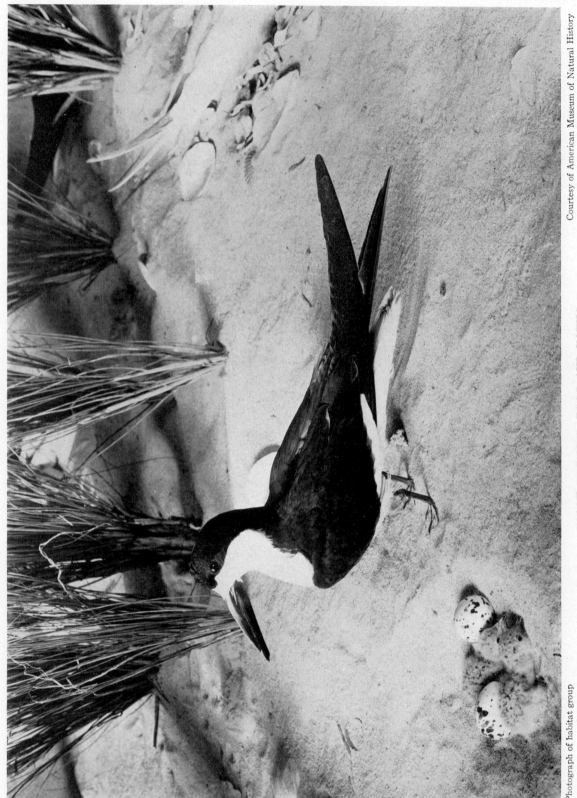

Photograph of habitat group

Courtesy of American Museum of Natural History

BLACK SKIMMER, EGGS, AND YOUNG

BLACK SKIMMER

Rynchops nigra *Linnæus*

A. O. U. Number 80   See Color Plate 7

Other Names.— Cutwater; Scissorbill; Shearwater; Storm Gull.

General Description.— Length, 16 to 20 inches. Color above, black; below, white.

Color.— Crown, sides of head to below eyes, back of neck, and entire *upper parts, glossy black*; forehead, sides of head below eyes, sides of neck, and whole under parts, pure white with a rosy tint in spring; tips of inner four primaries and secondaries, white; tail, white, the central feathers black; basal half of bill, carmine, rest black; feet, carmine; iris, brown. DOWNY YOUNG: Sand-colored.

Nest and Eggs.— EGGS: Deposited on the bare sand; 4, white to pale buff, spotted and blotched with dark browns and black and some lavender.

Distribution.— Tropical and temperate America; strictly maritime; breeds from Virginia (formerly New Jersey) to the Gulf coast and Texas; rarely north to the Bay of Fundy; winters from the Gulf coast to Colima, Mexico, and Costa Rica; casual in West Indies.

Five species of the Skimmer family inhabit the warmer portions of the earth. One of these, the Black Skimmer, reaches the shores of the United States and is distributed along the Gulf of Mexico from Texas to Key West, and northward along the Atlantic coast to Virginia. It is a large, long-winged bird, black above and white beneath. The bill of this bird is most unique, both mandibles being thin and flat like a knife-blade, and come together edgewise, and not like a duck's bill. The under one is an inch or more longer than the upper, and this is pushed forward under the surface of the water as the Skimmer with open mouth flies along the sea looking for the small marine animal-life upon which it feeds. In search of food they often follow along the narrow creeks through the marshes and at times enter the outer bays and river-mouths. They never go inland, nor do they travel very far to sea. When Skimmers first appear in spring along our southern beaches they come in flocks of hundreds or even thousands. At this season they are very restless and the flocks are continually taking flight from one beach or bar to another, and their shouts fairly drown the roar of the surf.

They are more or less gregarious throughout the summer, and assemble in colonies to rear their

Photograph by H. K. Job   Courtesy of Outing Publishing Co.

BLACK SKIMMERS

On Battledore Island, Louisiana

young. Their nesting places are situated on sand spits running out from shore or on small isolated islands of sand and sea-shells. The nest is a simple, unlined hollow in the sand which the bird makes by turning its body around many times. The eggs vary from three to five in number and are variously spotted and blotched, no two being exactly alike. If the nests are robbed, a second nest is soon made and another clutch of eggs is laid. Very often groups of breeding Skimmers assemble on the same sandy shore where Terns are nesting, but use a territory more or less separated from that occupied by the Terns. They are poor fighters and are little disposed to defend aggressively their rights.

For this reason, and also because they begin to lay well after their neighbors have taken up their household duties, they are forced to take such accommodations as the Terns may deign to leave them. If you approach one of their nesting places the Skimmers will leap into the air and bear down upon you with hoarse cries, but I have never had one come near enough actually to strike me.

One of the local names for these birds is "Shearwaters." Along the Virginia coast they are known as "Storm Gulls." They are never shot for food, but their eggs are regularly taken by fishermen unless the colonies are carefully guarded.   T. GILBERT PEARSON.

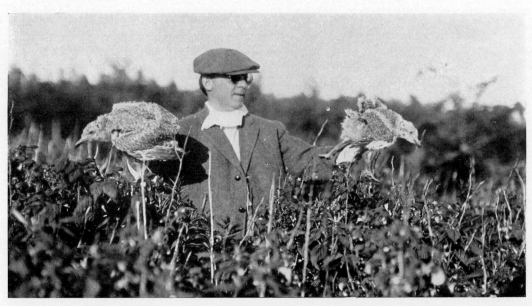

T. GILBERT PEARSON HUNTING YOUNG HERRING GULLS HIDING IN THE WEEDS
Little Duck Island, Maine

ORDER OF TUBE-NOSED SWIMMERS

Order *Tubinares*

NOSTRILS opening through tubes are the distinguishing characteristic of this group of birds. Not only is the order cosmopolitan in distribution, but many of the species are found throughout the world. Two families—the Albatrosses and the Fulmars, Shearwaters, and Petrels—represent the order in North America. In the first of these families the tubes enclosing the nostrils are separated and placed one on either side of the bill; in the other the tubes are connected and are on top of the bill.

An unusual range in size is exhibited by the Tube-nosed Swimmers: the Storm Petrel is the smallest of the natatorial birds, while the Giant Albatross is unsurpassed in wing expanse in the entire bird kingdom. They are unequaled in the power of flight. As a rule they keep far off shore, only visiting land for the purpose of reproduction. They live practically in the air, flying low over the water and snatching their food of marine life and oily matter from the surface of the sea. So far as is known, but one egg is laid each season; some species nest in a burrow, but others lay the egg on the ground. The young are covered with down when hatched, generally of a sooty or gray color, but are helpless and in need of the parents' care for some time.

Birds of this order have no bright markings in their plumage and are usually gray, or black, and white. There are no sexual variations in coloration and the seasonal differences, if any, are undetermined. The plumage is very compact and oily. The wings are long, narrow, and pointed, and the tail rather short. The bill is hooked and enlarged at the tip, the upper mandible being longer than the lower and curved downward. The covering of the bill is in several horny plates, showing seams between. The three front toes are webbed and the hind toe, when present, is small and elevated.

ALBATROSSES

Order *Tubinares;* family *Diomedeidæ*

FEW birds make a stronger appeal to the imagination than do the Albatrosses, with their complete mastery of an art which has been a profound mystery to man until very recent years, and in which he can never hope to be more than a clumsy tyro in comparison with these great conquerors of the air. Much mystery has been made of the evident ease with which these great birds follow a rapidly moving ship for hours or even days at a time, with seldom or never an apparent movement of their wings. But an Albatross is not a supernatural creature and therefore cannot defy the laws of physics. Hence it is obvious that the bird must move as the result of the action of some motive force— either the pressure of the wind on its wings or the movement of the wings themselves. On this interesting subject we have a pretty definitely expressed opinion from a trained naturalist, the late Henry N. Moseley, one of the party of scientists who circumnavigated the globe in the *Challenger* expedition of 1872–1876.

"I believe," wrote Moseley, "that Albatrosses move their wings much oftener than is suspected. They often have the appearance of soaring for long periods after a ship without flapping their wings at all, but if they be very closely watched, very short but extremely

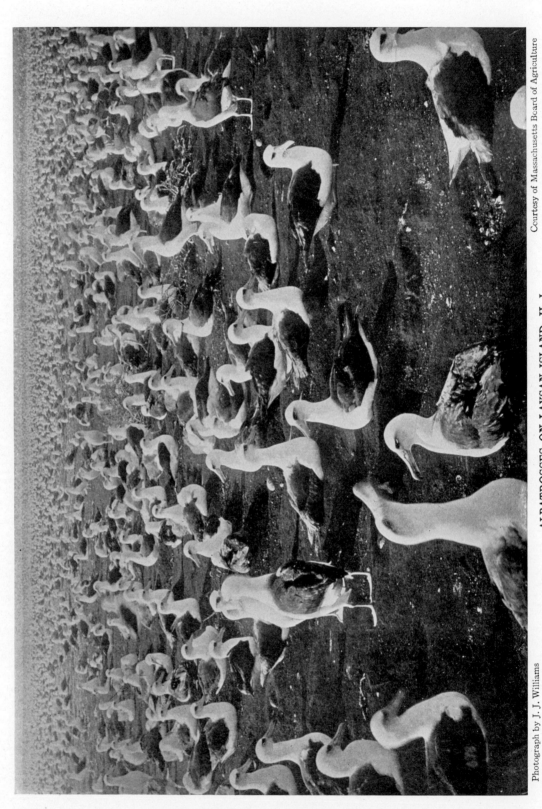

Photograph by J. J. Williams

ALBATROSSES ON LAYSAN ISLAND, H. I.

quick motions of the wings may be detected. The appearance is rather as if the body of the bird dropped a very short distance and rose again. The movements cannot be seen at all unless the bird is exactly on a level with the eye. A very quick stroke, carried even through a very short arc can, of course, supply a large store of fresh momentum. In perfectly calm weather, Albatrosses flap heavily." (*Notes by a Naturalist.*)

Professor Hutton's description (in the *Ibis*) of the flight of the Albatross is probably as accurate as any:— " With outstretched, motionless wings he sails over the surface of the sea, now rising high in air, now with a bold sweep, and wings inclined at an angle with the horizon, descending until the tip of the lower one all but touches the crests of the waves as he skims over them. Suddenly he sees something floating on the water and prepares to alight; but how changed he now is from the noble bird, but a moment before all grace and symmetry. He raises his wings, his head goes back and his back goes in; down drop two enormous webbed feet straddled out to their full extent, and with a hoarse croak, between the cry of a Raven and that of a sheep, he falls ' souse ' into the water. Here he is at home again, breasting the waves like a cork. Presently he stretches out his neck, and with a great exertion of his wings runs along the top of the water for seventy or eighty yards, until, at last, having got sufficient impetus, he tucks up his legs, and is once more fairly launched in the air."

Moseley's statement that Albatrosses flap heavily in calm weather should set at rest the oft-reported assertion that they never move their wings in flight, while the observation that there is actually some occasional movement even when the wings seem to be motionless must, of course, be accepted as entirely accurate, even though that acceptance necessarily destroys the cherished notion that the bird has and exercises supernatural powers. But even after it has been explained in perfectly cold-blooded scientific language, there should be enough of the truly remarkable left in the flight of the Albatross to create a profound impression upon any mind which does not insist upon seeing the supernatural where it does not exist. These notions of the supernatural are, of course, especially prevalent among sailors, who are famous for the variety and picturesqueness of their superstitions. And we are indebted to their Albatross superstition for having inspired Samuel Taylor Coleridge to write "The Rime of the Ancient Mariner," which, so Swinburne says,"for melody and splendor it were hardly rash to call the first poem in the language."

About sixteen species of the Albatross are known, and all are essentially birds of the subtropical or southern tropical seas, although the Black-footed and Laysan species sometimes wander as far north as Alaska, and either is occasionally seen off the Pacific coast of the United States. Though their wings when extended may measure twelve feet, or even more, their bodies rarely weigh more than eighteen pounds. The food of these great birds consists of fish, cuttlefish, jellyfish, offal, and refuse thrown overboard from the ships they follow. Such matter they seize eagerly, a habit which is taken advantage of by brutal or thoughtless persons who catch the bird by trolling with a long line and a hook baited with meat or fish.

BLACK-FOOTED ALBATROSS

Diomedea nigripes *Audubon*

A. O. U. Number 81

Other Name.— Goony.

General Description.— Length, 30 to 36 inches. Color above, dark chocolate-brown; below, gray. Tail, short; wings, very long and when folded reaching to or beyond tip of tail.

Color.— ADULTS: Top of head and upper parts, dark chocolate-brown; leaden-gray below whitening on front of head and at base of tail; a spot in front of eye and streak above it, black; feathers of upper parts with paler edges; bill, dusky; *feet, black*. YOUNG: Similar to adult, but less white on face, and upper tail-coverts dusky.

Nest and Eggs.— NEST: On the ground, usually on isolated islands of the ocean; there is little attempt at nest building, the single egg being surrounded merely by seaweed.

Distribution.— North Pacific; breeds on islands northwest of Hawaii and on Marshall Islands; occurs off the coast from southern Alaska to California and western Mexico, and off coasts of China and Japan.

I have a distinct picture in mind, when out on the Pacific, of a big dark long-winged bird coasting down the troughs of the waves and aëroplaning over the mountainous crests. I scarcely ever saw the bird light and feed on the water, yet of course, it follows the ship for scraps. The bird is more a part of the sea than the Gull. It curves in great circles over the maddened sea purely for

the love of flying. I asked its name of one of the sailors and he called it a " Goony." I told him it was a Black-footed Albatross.

The Albatross will always be known in English literature through Coleridge's poem, " The Ancient Mariner." What a lesson against the wanton killing of a friendly bird!

WILLIAM L. FINLEY.

LAYSAN ALBATROSS

Diomedea immutabilis *Rothschild*

A. O. U. Number 82.1

General Description.— Length, 3 feet. Color above, smoky-brown; color below, white. Tail, short; wings, very long and when folded reaching to or beyond tip of tail.

Color.— Head, neck, lower rump, and under parts, white; back and shoulders, smoky-brown; wings and their coverts, blackish-brown; tail, black shading to

white at base; bill, gray, blackish at tip, yellow at base below; feet, fleshy-pink; iris, brown.

Nest and Eggs.— The single egg is deposited on the ground on Laysan and adjacent islands of the North Pacific.

Distribution.— Laysan and Midway islands to San Geronimo and Guadalupe islands, Lower California.

The Laysan is the Albatross whose ruthless slaughter and narrow escape from complete extinction constitute an episode revealing the most heartless and hideous brutality ever perpetrated by man upon the bird-world, which is saying much. The island of Laysan, which gives its name to this beautiful and interesting species of one of the most wonderful of all the birds, lies in the Pacific Ocean about 700 miles west by north of Honolulu. It is barren, except for a scanty growth of shrubs, and therefore has never been inhabited by man, but for a great many years had been the home and breeding place of the Laysan Albatross, the Black-footed Albatross, the Sooty, White, Noddy, and Hawaiian Terns, the Bonin Petrel, two species of Shearwater, the Red-tailed Tropic-bird, two species of Booby, and the Man-o'-war-bird. A photograph of the island, taken in 1909, shows a great plain, about a mile in area, not only covered, but actually crowded, chiefly with Laysan Albatrosses.

For several years guano had been shipped from this island, and the Albatrosses were robbed more or less persistently of their eggs, but were not otherwise seriously molested. Then came the episode referred to above, which is described by Dr. William T. Hornaday in his book *Our Vanishing Wild Life:*

" At last, however, a tentacle of the feather trade octopus reached out to Laysan. In an evil moment in the spring of 1909, a predatory individual of Honolulu and elsewhere, named Max Schlemmer, decided that the wings of those Albatrosses, Gulls, and Terns should be torn off and sent to Japan, whence they would undoubtedly be shipped to Paris, the special market for the wings of sea-birds slaughtered in the Pacific. Schlemmer the Slaughterer bought a cheap vessel, hired twenty-three phlegmatic and cold-blooded Japanese laborers, and organized a raid on Laysan. With the utmost secrecy he sailed from Honolulu, landed his bird-killers upon the sea-bird wonderland, and turned them loose upon the birds. For several months they slaughtered diligently and without mercy. Apparently it was the ambition of Schlemmer to kill every bird on the island.

" By the time the bird butchers had accumulated between three and four carloads of wings, and the carnage was half finished, William A. Bryan, professor of zoölogy in the College of Honolulu, heard of it and promptly wired the United States Government. Without the loss of a moment the Secretary of the Navy dispatched the revenue cutter *Thetis* to the shambles of Laysan. When Captain Jacobs arrived he found that in round numbers about three hundred thousand birds had been destroyed, and all that remained of them were several acres of bones and dead bodies, and about three carloads of wings, feathers and skins. The twenty-three Japanese poachers were arrested and taken to Honolulu for trial, and the *Thetis* also brought away all of the stolen wings and plumage, with the exception of a shedful of wings that had to be left behind on account of lack of carrying space."

In 1911, the Iowa State University sent to Laysan a scientific expedition under charge of Professor Homer R. Dill. His report on the conditions he found is a terrible indictment, from which the following may be quoted: " An old cistern back of one of the buildings tells a story of cruelty that surpasses anything else done by these heartless, sanguinary pirates, not excepting the practice of cutting wings from living birds and leaving them to die of hemorrhage. In this dry cistern the living birds were kept by hundreds to slowly starve to death. In this way the fatty tissue lying next to the skin was used up, and the skin was left quite free from grease so that it required little or no cleaning during preparation. Many other revolting sights, such as the remains of young birds that had been left to starve, and birds with broken wings and deformed beaks were to be seen. Killing clubs, nets, and other implements used by these marauders were lying all about.

" This wholesale killing has had an appalling effect upon the colony. It is conservative to say that fully one-half the number of birds of both species of Albatross that were so abundant in 1903 have been killed. The colonies that remain are in a sadly decimated condition."

The prompt and effective interference of the Government was due to the fact that in February, 1909, President Roosevelt issued an executive order creating the Hawaiian Island Reservation for Birds, which includes Laysan Island and

several other islands and reefs. But for that interference, the Laysan Albatross might have been reduced to a point which would have seriously threatened it with extermination.

Scientifically the Albatross is best known through Mr. Walter K. Fisher's photographs and descriptions. In May, 1902, he visited the Island of Laysan, where he found the Black-footed and Laysan Albatrosses breeding in great numbers. His account of their nesting habits, courting antics, and peculiar dances is well worth reading.

In the *Auk* for January, 1904, he writes: " The Albatross lays one egg on the ground, usually in a slightly raised mound with a shallow basin in the top. . . . The egg is laid about the middle of November. . . . The young are not hatched until February, and then begin the six months of hard work to feed the hungry babies. They grow slowly, for birds, and it is not till the last of July that the most venturesome follow their parents on short flights to the sea. A few weeks later all are on the wing, and with the old birds they scatter far and wide over the Pacific."

Speaking of the peculiar dance of the Albatrosses, Mr. Fisher says, " The old birds have an innate objection to idleness, and so for their diversion they spend much time in a curious dance, or perhaps more appropriately a ' cakewalk.' . . . At first two birds approach one another, bowing profoundly and stepping heavily. They swagger about each other, courtesying solemnly, then suddenly begin to fence a little, crossing bills and whetting them together, sometimes with a whistling sound, meanwhile pecking and dropping stiff little bows. All at once one lifts its closed wing and nibbles at the feathers beneath, or rarely, if in a hurry, quickly turns its head. The partner during this short performance assumes a statuesque pose, and either looks mechanically from side to side, or snaps its bill loudly a few times. Then, the first bird bows once, and pointing its head and beak straight upward, rises on its toes, puffs out its breast, and utters a prolonged nasal *Ah-h-h-h*, with a rapidly rising inflection and bovine quality. . . . Often both birds raise their heads in air and favor the appreciative audience with that ridiculous and indescribable bovine groan. . . . Occasionally while ' cake-walking ' one will lightly pick up a straw or twig, and present it to the other, who does not accept the gift, however, but thereupon returns the compliment, when straws are promptly dropped, and all hands begin bowing and walking about as if their very lives depended upon it." GEORGE GLADDEN.

FULMARS, SHEARWATERS, AND PETRELS

Order *Tubinares;* family *Procellariidæ*

THE Fulmars, Shearwaters, and Petrels are the family *Procellariidæ* and with the Albatrosses form the order of Tube-nosed Swimmers. As the name of the order indicates, its chief point of difference from all other orders is the tubular form of the nostrils. Other characteristics are: the bill, hooked and enlarged at the tip and with the upper section longer than the lower and with the covering in several horny sections; the tail, rather short with twelve or fourteen feathers; the wings, usually long and pointed; and the hind toe, either small or lacking, and, if present, elevated. The plumage is compact and oily and shows a tendency toward uniformity in coloration. Often the bodies of the birds in this family are so fat that they can be used for illumination.

Over the oceans of the world are distributed nearly one hundred members of this family. About thirty-five are of regular or accidental occurrence in North America. Not a member is ever found inland unless driven there by a storm. Neither do any of them frequent the shores except for the purpose of reproduction. They spend practically all their time on the wing, and gather their food of marine animals and oily matter from the surface of the water.

So far as is known, the members of this group lay only a single egg. The Fulmars nest in colonies, like the Gulls, on the small islands near the shores of the North Pacific and North Atlantic. Of the nesting habits of the Shearwaters, very little is known; some breed on the islands of the North Atlantic, and it is probable that others breed on the islands of the southern hemisphere, coming north as the southern winter sets in. Some of the Petrels breed in the northern hemisphere and others in the southern. The species in this group concerning whose nesting habits we do know something usually deposit the lone egg in a burrow or a cavity. The young when hatched are covered with down, usually of a grayish color, and are cared for in the nest. At first they are fed by regurgitation on an oily fluid.

FULMAR

Fulmarus glacialis glacialis (*Linnæus*)

A. O. U. Number 86

Other Names.— Fulmar Petrel; Molly Hawk; John Down; Sea Horse; Mollimoke; Mallemuck; Noddy.

Length.— 18 to 20 inches.

Color.— LIGHT PHASE: Mantle, pale bluish-gray restricted to back and wings or extending also on head and tail; primaries and secondaries, dark ashy-brown; a dark spot in front of eye; rest of plumage, pure white; bill, yellow, tinged with green above and below; feet, pale gray; iris, brown. DARK PHASE: Entire plumage, smoky-gray, paler below; feathers of upper parts, with darker margins; primaries, ashy-brown; bill, dull yellow; feet, dusky-gray; iris, brown.

Nest and Eggs.— The single white egg is deposited in a crevice of the rock.

Distribution.— North Atlantic; breeds from northern Greenland to Cumberland Sound, and east at least to Franz Josef Land; ranges north to latitude 85° and west to Melville Island; winters south to fishing banks off Newfoundland and to Georges Bank off Massachusetts, rarely to New Jersey.

The Fulmar is a circumpolar bird of the northern hemisphere. It breeds in countless numbers in Greenland, Franz Josef Land, Baffin Bay, Iceland, Spitzbergen, St. Kilda, and other regions throughout the northland. It is one of the largest of its family in the northern hemisphere, and an untrained or careless observer might mistake it for a Gull, but its peculiarly constructed bill separates it distinctly from that family, and puts it among the so-called "Tube-nosed Swimmers." Moreover, its flight is much more like that of the Albatross and differs sharply from that of the Shearwaters and Petrels. As Percy R. Lowe says (in *Our Common Sea-birds*): "With outspread wings, stretched stiff as a board, it will remain poised and balanced against a strong half-gale, or glide through the air with wonderful grace by the minutes together, now skimming over the crests of the waves or following down into their deep troughs, now stopping to alight, feet first, on the surface, in order to pick up some scrap food or some mollusk which it has espied. In coloration, too, the Fulmar approaches more nearly to the Albatross than to the rest of its family," while in nesting habits it " seems intermediate between the Albatross, which nests on the flat oceanic islands in the open, and the true Petrels, which nest in holes or burrows in the ground or loose rocks."

Another peculiarity of this bird is that it is almost voiceless. Even when its nesting places are invaded and hundreds or even thousands of the Fulmars take to their wings, they sail about in utter silence, like so many ghosts of birds. They are strictly pelagic in their habits except during the breeding season. On the ocean they are much given to following whaling ships for the blubber and oily scraps thrown overboard. This food they seem never to eat while on the wing, but invariably to devour it while floating on the surface of the water, after the practice of the Albatross. To the crews of the whalers and sealers the bird is well known, and to them it owes the names of " Mollimoke " and " Noddy."

GREATER SHEARWATER

Puffinus gravis (*O'Reilly*)

A. O. U. Number 89

Other Names.— Hagdon; Hag; Haglet; Wandering Shearwater; Common Atlantic Shearwater; Cinereous Puffin.

General Description.— Length, 18 to 20 inches; spread of wings, 36 to 45 inches. Color above, dark brown; below, white.

Color.— Upper parts, dark brown, shading on head to grayish-brown; usually lighter on hindneck, darkest on inner secondaries and rump, the feathers of back, rump, and wing-coverts edged with pale brownish-ash; crown, uniform brown extending on sides of head to level of gape, with line of demarcation from white

Drawing by R. I. Brasher

GREATER SHEARWATER (⅓ nat. size)

One of the " stiff-winged " flyers of the ocean

of throat distinct; upper tail-coverts, white with dusky bars or centers; primaries, brownish-black, lightening toward base; entire under parts, white with large dark brown patches on sides and flanks; *under tail-coverts, dark grayish-brown* with white tips; tail, brownish-black; bill, dusky horn color; feet, yellowish flesh color; iris, brown.

Nest and Eggs.— Little is known concerning its

nesting; it is supposed to breed in a burrow on islands of the north Atlantic, laying a single white or yellowish-white egg.

Distribution.—Atlantic Ocean, from Arctic circle south to Cape Horn and Cape of Good Hope; occurs off the eastern coast of North America from June to November; occasionally visits the British Isles during the autumn months.

From the firm deck of a great ship out under the vast circle of the sky, surrounded by the heaving, racing ocean swells, the heart sickens at the thought of being left there alone. But to the Shearwater this is home. It needs no companionship and seeks none. On long slender wings, extending some three feet, it goes on, almost ever on, upon its lonely course. A series of rapid beats give it momentum for a prolonged

Photo by H. K. Job   Courtesy of Outing Pub. Co.
GREATER SHEARWATER
Off the coast of Massachusetts

glide upon stiffly extended pinions, even into the very teeth of the gale. Tipping to one side, the better to trim sail, it skims along never to reach a destination, for it seems always going, never arriving.

Such is the rather large gray sea-bird with white breast which we may meet from late spring to advanced autumn well off our Atlantic shores, hardly nearer than where land appears only as a distant haze. Though this is the most common of our Shearwaters, few of our human kind are privileged to enter its select social circle. Deep-water fishermen know the birds well, calling them "Hags" or "Haglets." Floating offal or grease thrown from the vessel, especially when anchored on the fishing-grounds, sometimes draws quite a concourse. At such times they can be enticed very close, and can even be caught

with hook and line and be drawn squealing and fighting upon deck, from the hard surface of which they are unable to take wing.

In calm weather they can be seen resting on the water, and it is one of the few occasions when they seem really social, sitting around and chattering to one another. At such times they take to wing with some difficulty, for want of wind, and I have almost run them down by steering straight for them.

Their food, besides floating animal or vegetable matter, consists of various marine organisms, particularly small fish. The appearance of a school of the latter will quickly, as though by magic, draw a crowd, even though few or none may have been previously noticed. They plunge headlong into the water and flap about as though mad, or else remain on wing and patter with their feet over the surface. The frightened fish submerge, and immediately each bird is off on its lonely wanderings.

No one has yet discovered the breeding haunts of this singular creature, but they are undoubtedly on some desolate Antarctic island where, in a burrow or a hole in the rocks, the female deposits one large white egg, after the usual Shearwater manner. The southern summer, when they nest, is our northern winter. When nesting time is over, and the only bond but death strong enough to keep them quiet is relaxed, they renew their roaming. Oceans are hardly wide enough to circumscribe their energy, and thus, driven by the returning wanderlust, they visit us during our warmer months.

The best places to find Shearwaters, as well as the other "ocean wanderers," apparently are the fishing "banks," where fishing vessels congregate. I have found them in considerable numbers five to ten miles or more southeastward off Chatham, Mass., and off Cape Sable, Nova Scotia. Fishermen report them abundant on Georges, Grand, and other banks. Though seen from May or June to November, the period of July to September seems to represent the height of their season with us.   HERBERT K. JOB.

SOOTY SHEARWATER

Puffinus griseus (*Gmelin*)

A. O. U. Number 95

Other Names.— Black Hag; Black Hagdon; Dark-bodied Shearwater.

General Description.— Length, 16 to 18 inches; spread of wings, 40 inches. Plumage, dark sooty-brown above and below.

Color.— *Uniform dark sooty-brown, blackening on wings and tail;* more sooty-gray below with paler throat; bill, dusky-bluish horn, the tube, ridge, and bill blackish; inside of leg and upper side of feet, flesh color; outside of outer toe and under side of feet, blackish.

Nest and Eggs.— NEST: Probably a burrow in the ground on sea islands of the South Atlantic, a single white egg being deposited at the end of the burrow.

Distribution.— Oceans of southern hemisphere; occurs in summer on the Pacific coast from southern Alaska to Lower California, and on the Atlantic coast from Gulf of St. Lawrence to South Carolina.

Photograph by H. K. Job — Courtesy of Doubleday, Page & Co.

SOOTY SHEARWATER (foreground) AND GREATER SHEARWATER

CORY'S SHEARWATER

Puffinus borealis *Cory*

A. O. U. Number 88

General Description.— Length, 20 inches; spread of wings, 40 to 45 inches. Color above, brownish-ash; below, white.

Color.— Upper parts, brownish-ash; feathers of back, with pale tips; those on nape and sides of neck narrowly tipped with white; the ash on sides of head and neck and white of under parts gradually mingle; *tips of upper tail-coverts, white;* under eyelid, white in contrast with ashy-gray of head; wings and tail, brownish-gray; sides and flanks, tinged with ash; under tail-coverts, white, the longest tinged near ends with ash which extends nearly to tips of the longest tail-feathers; bill, greenish-black, yellow at base and on tip; feet, greenish-black; iris, brown.

Nest and Eggs.— Unknown but probably similar to others of the genus.

Distribution.— Coasts of Massachusetts, Rhode Island, and Long Island (August to November).

Somewhat smaller than the Greater Shearwater, the Sooty Shearwater very closely resembles it in habits and flight, but differs from it markedly in plumage, which at a distance looks as black as that of a Crow. It would seem decidedly strange that this bird escaped entirely the notice of Wilson, Nuttall, and Audubon, but for the fact that even now its nesting habits are unknown, nor have its nest and eggs been discovered.

Cory's Shearwater is even more a stranger; it has been seen only off the Atlantic coast between Massachusetts and Long Island, from August to November.

WILSON'S PETREL

Oceanites oceanicus (*Kuhl*)

A. O. U. Number 109

Other Names.— Common Stormy Petrel; Mother Carey's Chicken; Long-legged Storm Petrel.

General Description.— Length, 7 inches. Color, dark sooty-brown. *Legs, long and stilt-like; tail, square.*

Color.— Body, dark sooty-brown; wings and tail, black; wing-coverts, pale gray; upper and under tail-coverts, sides of rump, and base of tail, white; bill and feet, black, *latter with a large yellow spot on webs;* iris, brown.

Nest and Eggs.— NEST: In burrows or in crevices on Antarctic islands in February. EGGS: 1, white.

Distribution.— South polar regions north to Labrador and British Isles; common off the north Atlantic coast of America from May to September; accidental in Ontario.

Nearly everyone who crosses the Atlantic or makes a coasting voyage must have noticed those tiny dark-colored birds about the size of Swallows, with a conspicuous patch of white on the rump. On rapidly fluttering wing they circle about the vessel, or wander irregularly over the waves. At times they hover at some particular spot, pattering their feet in the unstable element while a-wing. These are Petrels, often called "Mother Carey's Chickens." They are so distinct from all other birds that no one who gets a fair look could possibly mistake them. The first ones are sighted several miles off shore, and they are quite inclined to follow vessels far out on the open ocean. They are birds whose home is on the ocean waves. Some of their scientific Latin names appropriately describe them as "runners on the sea."

Two species represent their kind on our Atlantic coast. One is slightly the larger with a forked tail, and is known as Leach's Petrel. The other, which has the tail square or slightly rounded at the end, is Wilson's Petrel. It is the species mostly seen off shore during our summer season. Like their relatives the Shearwaters, they breed on the far southern islands of the

Drawing by R. I. Brasher

WILSON'S PETREL (⅓ nat. size)

Its home is on the ocean's waves

Antarctic, nesting in February and laying a single white egg in a burrow. For a winter tour they wander thousands of miles and enjoy our northern summer, from about June to October.

Being summer tourists with us, they are better known than though they came with Boreas, and for the same reason it is this species which is generally observed in summer south of the latitude of Maine, as the other species is a northern breeder. Excursionists from New York City to the lower bay often see these birds in considerable numbers. One year, on July 13, a roasting hot day ashore, I was refreshed and delighted with the constant sight of these Petrels from the steamer flying between the heated wilderness of bricks and the New Jersey shore resorts. Sometimes I have almost lived with them while fishing offshore from Chatham, Mass. It was more fun than fishing to throw out fish liver, which floats, and draw the Petrels by scores around the stern. Especially on calm days they would come up so close that I have seen them caught by hand. It afforded splendid opportunity to watch them at close range as they emulated the Apostle Peter, from whom they are named because of their curious propensity to "walk" on the water. When caught they proved very unapostolic, and vomited up liver or ejected thus or from their nostrils some dark yellow, strongly scented oil. As they flew and fed so close at hand, their pretty little twittering was very noticeable.

The marvel of these birds is their well-nigh ceaseless activity. On a very few occasions, when the weather was calm and lowery, especially before storm, I have seen flocks of them huddled together upon the ocean "floor." At other times, one sees only that eternally restless

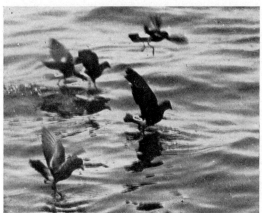

Photo by H. K. Job   Courtesy of Houghton Mifflin Co.

WILSON'S PETRELS

"Walking" on the water

wandering, quartering over the ocean to pick up oily refuse or small marine life. When waves rage and break, they evidently must remain on the wing day and night. This is a life only for those to whom weariness is foreign.

HERBERT K. JOB.

LEACH'S PETREL

Oceanodroma leucorhoa (*Vieillot*)

A. O. U. Number 106

Other Names.— Common Fork-tailed Petrel; Leach's Fork-tailed Petrel; White-rumped Petrel.

General Description.— Length, 8 inches. Color, brownish-black. *Legs, short; tail, forked,* outer feathers more than ½ inch longer than middle pair.

Color.— Brownish-black, grayer on wing-coverts and below; primaries, black; upper tail-coverts, pure white; bill and feet, black; iris, brown.

Nest and Eggs.— NEST: In burrows on the ground. EGGS: Single, white, unmarked, or wreathed with fine light red spots around the larger end.

Distribution.— Both coasts of North America; breeds from the Aleutian and Copper islands, Bering Sea, south to Sitka, and from southern Greenland south to Maine and the Hebrides; casual in migration south to Virginia.

Leach's Petrel and Wilson's Petrel are supplementary each of the other. The former breeds north, the other south, but the latter meets its relative in the summer near its breeding grounds. The fact that I have never been able — perhaps partly from lack of abundance of opportunity — to meet any Petrels off our Atlantic coast in winter makes me wonder whether some day Leach's may not be found to return the compli-

ment and visit its relative in its remote southern home.

All the Petrels I have identified off southern New England shores in summer have been Wilson's, which is natural enough, since Leach's is not known to breed south of Maine. There and northward I have found it nesting. Hundreds of them resort to the same barren islands. In the turf each pair digs a little burrow the size of a rat-hole, and about the middle of June each hole contains a single fragile white egg. As we land there is not a sign of a bird. But sometimes we can smell the peculiar odor like that of the oil they eject, characteristic and persistent and which lasts in mounted specimens for years.

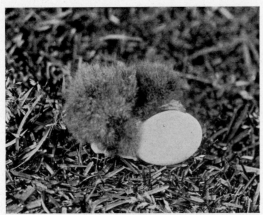

Photo by H. K. Job

LEACH'S PETREL

Young and egg removed from burrow

Presently we notice the little holes, which run almost horizontally, just below the roots of the grass. A hand inserted up to the elbow lands in a little chamber where the brooding bird is now imprisoned. At the beginning of the breeding season I have found both male and female in the burrow; later, only one, which may be of either sex, as both sexes incubate. The other partner is supposed to be out at sea, but it is a curious fact that in daytime no Petrels are seen in the vicinity of the islands where they breed. Nor have they been proved to remain in other burrows or hide in holes of the rocks. After dusk the Petrels emerge from their burrows, and there are lively times. Dark forms dart around like bats, twittering, and also uttering a singular little plaintive " song," as it may well be called.

Where animals, such as dogs or cats, are kept by fishermen or lighthouse keepers on islands, I have found that they make a regular practice of digging out and eating Petrels, until the colonies are depleted or exterminated. Such practices should be prevented.

Later in the summer, investigation of the holes reveals the presence of soft, fuzzy young, covered with thick coats of gray down, lighter in color than the parents. I have found them as late as September without a single feather — perhaps the result of robbery of the nests. Such occurrences might have given rise to an old superstition that Petrels hibernate. Winter apparently drives them at least further south than our bleak north Atlantic coast.

Once I tried to make a captured Petrel of this species sit for its picture. Its ceaseless activity was something astonishing. No wonder it can outlast gales and billows in many a test of endurance.   HERBERT K. JOB.

FORKED-TAILED PETREL

Oceanodroma furcata (*Gmelin*)

A. O. U. Number 105

Description.— Length, 9 inches. General color, *light bluish-gray*, fading to white on chin, throat, and under tail-coverts; bend of wing and space around eye, dusky; bill and feet, black. Tail, slightly forked; bill, small and weak.

Nest and Eggs.— NEST: A hole in a bank; thinly lined with dry grass and fine roots. EGGS: Single, dull white with minute dark specks evenly dusted over the large end.

Distribution.— North Pacific and adjacent Arctic Ocean; breeds from Commander and Aleutian islands south to islands off Oregon; in migration occurs on both shores of Bering Sea north to Kotzebue Sound; wanders south to San Pedro, California.

KAEDING'S PETREL

Oceanodroma kaedingi *Anthony*

A. O. U. Number 105.2

Description.—Length, 8 inches. General color, *sooty-black;* upper tail-coverts and side of under coverts, white; wing-coverts, brownish; bill and feet, black. Tail, slightly forked; bill, small and weak. Similar to the Forked-tailed Petrel, but smaller in size and darker in color.

Nest and Eggs.— NEST: A burrow in a bank or under a pile of stones; lined with grass, pieces of bark, or chips of wood. EGGS: Single, white.

Distribution.— Pacific coast of North America; breeds on islands off Washington, Oregon, and California from Cape Flattery south to the Farallons; in migration south to Guadalope, Socorro, and Clarion islands.

On Three Arch Rocks off the Oregon coast, we found both the Forked-tailed and the Kaeding Petrels nesting. The latter birds, however, were far more abundant than the former. One might remain about these rocks for a month, climbing over them every day, and not know that a Petrel is there, for they are never seen flying about the rocks in daytime.

We climbed to the grassy slope on the north side of the outer rock. My first acquaintance with these two birds was when I dropped on my knees and dug out a single white egg. Then, as I dug a little farther, I saw a Kaeding's Petrel that had crawled back in the extreme corner to hide.

The Petrel nestling is a fluffy ball of down. One parent stays in the burrow with the nestling during the day, while the other is far out on the ocean. The parent feeds the young by thrusting the beak down his mouth and injecting into it a yellowish fluid. Both old birds are experts at this. If you take one out of the burrow, he will immediately " play Jonah " in your direction with surprising power of projection. A dose of rancid fish oil shot up your sleeve is not pleasing to your nerves or your nostrils.

I shall never forget the evening we made a dangerous trip to the top of the rock and hid on the north slope. As it grew dark, the Petrels began coming in to the island like a swarm of bats. Those in the burrows came chittering out to meet them. The ground beneath seemed full of squeakings and the air full of soft twittering and whistlings until it felt uncanny. We frequently felt the breath of swift wings, but it was like a fantasy, for not a bird could be seen, nor even a shadow. How one of these Petrels could find his own home and his mate in an acre of nesting holes hidden all about in the grass and in the darkness of night is one of those mysterious things that we cannot solve.

WILLIAM L. FINLEY.

STORM PETREL

Thalassidroma pelagica (*Linnæus*)

A. O. U. Number 104

Other Name.— Mother Carey's Chicken.
General Description.— Length, 5½ inches. Color, brownish-black. *Legs, short; tail, square.*
Color.— Glossy brownish-black, browner below; *upper tail-coverts, white with black tips;* under tail-coverts, streaked with white; bill and feet, black; iris, brown.

Nest and Eggs.— NEST: Holes excavated by the bird under rocks. EGGS: One, white.
Distribution.— Easterly parts of the Atlantic Ocean south to the Mediterranean and west coast of Africa; occasionally found on the Newfoundland Banks and off the coast of Nova Scotia; breeds on islands off Great Britain.

LEAST PETREL

Halocyptena microsoma *Coues*

A. O. U. Number 103

Other Name.— Wedged-tailed Petrel.
General Description.— Length, 6 inches. Color, brownish-black. *Tail, rounded.*
Color.— Lustrous brownish-black, without any white, darker on upper parts, blackening on wings and tail, slightly grayer on greater wing-coverts; bill and feet, black; iris, brown.

Nest and Eggs.— The single egg, white with a ring of black specks at end, is laid in a crevice of rocks, not in a burrow.
Distribution.— Eastern Pacific Ocean; breeds on islands off Lower California; south in migration to western Mexico, Panama, and Ecuador; occasionally found north of breeding range.

What the Wilson's and Leach's Petrels are to the western waters of the Atlantic, the Storm Petrel is to the eastern, and there is strong resemblance between the appearance and habits of the three birds. The Storm Petrel appears only occasionally off or near the American coast, and then doubtless in most cases accidentally.

Similar in its relation to the western coast is the Least Petrel, a Pacific Ocean form, seen occasionally off the coast of California, but essentially a bird of the islands far from either shore of that vast sea. This bird's habits are also distinctly Petrel-like and need no separate description.

ORDER OF TOTIPALMATE SWIMMERS

Order *Steganopodes*

IX families are gathered in this order. All the members are large birds, two feet or more in length, but they differ greatly in appearance and habits. However, they agree in having all four toes joined with webs — hence the name " Totipalmate " has been applied to this group. Their bills are horny and are usually hooked and hard at the tip. Their mouths can be opened very wide; their tongues are small and knoblike. Each bird is equipped with a gular or throat pouch. The nostrils are very small or rudimentary.

Nests are built on the ground, on rocky ledges, or in brushy trees near the water. The eggs are single or few, usually plain-colored, but covered with a chalky incrustation. The young are hatched helpless and naked, but are soon covered with down. All of the Totipalmate Swimmers are carnivorous in diet, their food consisting almost entirely of fish.

TROPIC-BIRDS

Order *Steganopodes;* family *Phaëthontidæ*

HE Tropic-bird's habit of prolonged soaring, often at a great height, and, as it were, in the very path of the sun, suggested to Linnæus its family name *Phaëthontidæ*, which is in reference to the Greek mythological tale of Phaëton, the son of Helios, the sun god, who induced his father to let him attempt to drive the chariot of the sun across the skies, but lost control of the horses and scorched the earth by driving too near it, wherefore he was killed by a thunderbolt of Zeus.

The Tropic-bird family includes six species, two of which breed as far north as the tropic of Cancer, and are often found about the West Indies, while individuals occasionally wander along the eastern coast of North America even as far north as Newfoundland. All have white plumage of satiny appearance, often with a pinkish tinge, and a black patch or bar in the eye region. The bill may be red, yellow, or orange in color, is pointed and somewhat curved, and the edges are toothed. The wings are long and rather slim; the tail is composed of from twelve to sixteen feathers, of which the central pair are much elongated and are slenderer than the others. Excepting the last-named peculiarity, the Tropic-birds resemble in their contour large Terns. They differ from the Man-o'-war-birds in general color, and in the shape of the bill, as well as in the absence of the throat sac, and the naked area about the eyes, and by the long central tail-feathers. The plumage of the sexes in the adults is alike, but the immature birds lack the long tail-feathers and show more irregularity in their marking.

The flight of the Tropic-bird differs from that of the Albatross in that it is accomplished by uniform, rather rapid, and entirely apparent wing-strokes, whereas the movement of the Albatross's wings usually is so slight as to be almost imperceptible. Nevertheless the Tropic-bird's flight performances are often very spectacular, and include frequent and thrilling dives from great heights into the ocean. Moreover, its power of sustained flight for enormous distances is fully established, though it frequently shows signs of exhaustion by dropping into the rigging of a ship in mid-ocean, an evidence of weariness which is seldom, if ever displayed by the great bird of the Ancient Mariner. It often follows ships for long distances, and is called by seamen the "Boatswain" or "Boatswain-bird," terms which sailors apply also to the Jaegers. Like many birds of great flight power, the Tropic-bird has a clumsy, shuffling gait on shore.

The food of the Tropic-bird consists chiefly of fish, squids, and the like, which are taken by diving from the wing. Its only note is a harsh croak or chatter. It breeds in colonies, and no nest is built. The single reddish-brown or buffy egg, more or less speckled with brown, purple, or gray, is laid in a hole or a crevice, or sometimes in a tree cavity, and incubation is shared by the pair. The bird engaged in this operation is not easily dislodged, but resists the intruder by pecking, snapping, and screaming. This spirit is taken advantage of by plumage collectors, who seize the sitting bird and pull out its tail-feathers to be used in "decorating" women's hats.

YELLOW-BILLED TROPIC-BIRD

Phaëthon americanus *Grant*

A. O. U. Number 112

Other Names.— Boatswain; Boatswain-bird; Bosen-bird; Longtail.

General Description.— Length, 32 inches. Prevailing color, white.

Color.— ADULT: General plumage, pure *white;* in breeding season tinged with rosy on under parts and long tail-feathers; lores, a stripe over and behind eye, and on side of head, black; a band on wing from inner coverts to inner secondaries, outer primaries, and shafts of tail-feathers, black; bill and feet, yellow; toes, black; iris, dark brown. YOUNG: Plumage, similar, but extensively marked with black bars or crescents on most of upper parts and with spots on tail.

Nest and Eggs.— The single egg, chalky-white heavily spotted with brown, is laid in crevices or crannies of rocks on isolated sea islands.

Distribution.— Florida and Bermuda south to the West Indies and the Atlantic coast of Central America; accidental in western New York, Nova Scotia, and Arizona.

Imagine to yourself a beautiful Dove with two central tail-feathers sweeping out behind to a distance of a foot and a half, and you will have a fairly correct mental picture of the Tropic-bird. As I have watched this creature from the deck of a steamer in the Caribbean Sea, or in the Pacific Ocean, and observed its exquisite form and grace, I have more than once vowed to myself that here indeed is the most appealing, if not the most graceful, of all birds on the sea. The plumage is silky white, with just enough black on the wings and head to emphasize the dazzling glory of the whole effect. They fly rapidly, and while feeding wing their way along over the water at an altitude of forty or fifty feet. "Long-tails" is one of the names by which sailors know them.

The Yellow-billed Tropic-bird is an inhabitant of the coasts of tropical America and the nearby islands. The northernmost breeding grounds appear to be the rocky cliffs of the Bermuda Islands. Here up to a few years ago they came in spring by thousands to rear their young and would remain in the neighboring waters until the approach of cold weather would drive them again to the southward. They are not particularly popular with fishermen here, who complain that they eat many squids which should be left for men who want to use such bait when they desire to go angling. The nest is placed in holes and cracks of the rocky faces of the islands and sometimes among the low scrubby trees and bushes higher on shore.

As only a single egg appears to be laid in a season it will easily be seen that no great amount of persistent killing of the birds is necessary to reduce their numbers. Unless a sentiment is rapidly developed for their protection on these islands, the "Bosen-birds," as they are often called, will probably cease to grace these waters and one of the islands' natural beauties will be gone forever.

Writing in *Bird-Lore* in 1913, Karl Plath tells of the movements of the Tropic-birds on land as he watched them in the Bermuda Islands:

"One of the noticeable features of the Tropic-bird is its inability to walk upright or to stand on its legs; a fact which is not generally understood by taxidermists, who usually mount the bird standing on its feet like a Gull. The usual gait is an awkward waddle, or it proceeds in a series of hops. I have also seen them push themselves along by means of their feet. Before launching in the air, they creep awkwardly, with much flapping of wings, to a suitable height, and then drop, sometimes in the water before regaining their equilibrium, when they are among the most graceful of sea-birds." T. GILBERT PEARSON.

GANNETS

Order *Steganopodes;* family *Sulidæ*

THE Gannets constitute the family *Sulidæ*, and comprise the birds of that name (also called "Solan" Geese, "solan" being apparently from a Scandinavian term meaning "sea") and the Boobies. "Gannet" is thought to be derived from the Old English *gan*, meaning "gander" or "goose-like." There are eleven species in the family, and of these one is essentially a northern bird and migratory, while the others range along the tropical and subtropical coasts of the world. All are strictly sea birds, but they prefer the coastal waters and are not found at any considerable distance from land except when they are migrating. On the wing they move rapidly, alternating vigorous wing work with periods of sailing. They feed almost exclusively on fish, which they capture by diving from the wing, often from a height of forty feet or more, and with such force that they disappear entirely beneath the surface, their impact being sufficient sometimes to send the spray ten feet into the air. This constitutes one of the most picturesque and vigorous feats performed by any sea bird. Fish of considerable size are swallowed practically whole (which is made possible by a throat which can be greatly distended), and are disgorged for the young. All members of the family are highly gregarious, and nest in large colonies on uninhabited coasts or isolated islands. The bird builds a rude nest composed of seaweeds and grass and lays one or two eggs, chalky-white or dull white in hue.

The Gannets are comparatively large birds, their length being from about two to three feet. Their wings are relatively long, and acutely pointed, while the tail is wedge-shaped and consists of from twelve to eighteen feathers. Their legs are short and stout and placed nearly at the center of the body. The feet are completely webbed. The neck is rather long, and the head large. The bill is strong, cylindrical, and tapers to a point where it is slightly curved, though never actually bent into hook form. The plumage is compact and its characteristic coloration is white on the body with black or dusky wings and tail, though some species are sooty-brown or dusky.

BOOBY

Sula leucogastra *(Boddaert)*

A. O. U. Number 115

Other Names.— Brown Booby; Yellow-footed Booby; Catesby's Booby; Booby Gannet.

General Description.— Length, 30 inches. Color above, dark brown; below, white.

Color.— ADULTS: Plumage, dark brown, *abruptly white from neck on under parts;* bill and bare parts of head, variably colored, mostly dull greenish or yellowish; feet, similar; iris, white. YOUNG: Plumage, grayish-brown, paler below variegated with white on under parts from neck; bill and feet, obscured.

Nest and Eggs.— NEST: On low bushes of tropical keys; constructed of sticks and weeds; in some localities eggs deposited on bare sand or rocks, without any attempt at nest building. EGGS: 1 or 2, dull chalky white.

Distribution.— Atlantic coasts of tropical America and Pacific and Indian oceans; rare on south Atlantic and Gulf coasts of the United States from South Carolina to Louisiana; accidental on Long Island, N. Y., and in Massachusetts.

COMMON CORMORANT *Phalacrocorax carbo* (Linnaeus)
ADULT IN BREEDING PLUMAGE   IMMATURE
DOUBLE-CRESTED CORMORANT *Phalacrocorax auritus auritus* (Lesson)
ADULT IN BREEDING PLUMAGE   IMMATURE
GANNET *Sula bassana* (Linnaeus)
ADULT   IMMATURE
All ⅙ nat. size

The Booby is a common bird in the West Indies and on the coasts of tropical lands to the south. While on ship-board in the Pacific Ocean off the coast of Panama and Nicaragua I observed these birds in sight at all hours of the day. Their flight is strong and easy, and the flapping is alternated with brief intervals of sailing. At times they would wheel on set wings and plunge headlong into the sea. Their food consists of marine animal life, fish evidently constituting the bulk of their menu, as the birds were usually more numerous in the neighborhood of schools of porpoises. On three occasions I saw Boobies standing on the backs of basking sea-turtles, one of which seemed not at all disturbed by the weight of two birds that were taking a rest on his broad carapace.

Boobies collect in numbers to nest on lonely isles. In *Camps and Cruises of an Ornithologist,* Doctor Chapman has written of the habits of a colony of fifteen hundred pairs of Boobies which he visited and studied in the spring of 1907. The place was a small island known as Cay Verde, lying on the outer fringe of the Bahama Islands. The nests were simple affairs placed on the ground. Two eggs are laid about a week apart, but for some reason rarely more than one young bird is reared. Of their domestic habits he writes:

"In spite of the apparent sociability expressed by their communal habits, the Boobies immediately resented the trespass on their home site by one of their own kind. Where the nature of the ground permitted, their nests were placed with more or less regularity six or eight feet from one another. As long as a bird remained within its own domain having a diameter of approximately six or eight feet, it was not molested, but let it or its young advance beyond these limits and they were promptly attacked.

"So closely, however, are the birds confined to their own little areas that difficulties of this kind are rare and under normal conditions peace reigns in the rookery. But when we walked through the rookery, the birds in escaping from the larger evil forgot the lesser one and inadvertently backed on to a neighbor's territory, the unusual cause of the trespass was not accepted as an excuse and they found the 'frying pan' was worse than the 'fire,' as the enraged owner, with bustling feathers, furiously assailed them with open bill, sometimes taking hold. At these times, and whenever the birds were alarmed, they gave utterance to hoarse, rancorous screams or screeches, though, as a rule, they were comparatively silent."

In summer Boobies occasionally range up the Atlantic coast as far as Georgia, but such visits are rare, for they are distinctly birds of tropical and subtropical seas. Unlike the Albatross and Petrel, they are seldom seen far from land.

T. GILBERT PEARSON.

GANNET

Sula bassana (*Linnæus*)

A. O. U. Number 117   See Color Plate 9

Other Names.— Common Gannet; White Gannet; Soland Goose; Solan Goose; Solon Goose; Jan van Gent; Grand Fou.

General Description.— Length, 3 feet. Prevailing color, white. *Goose-shaped.*

Color.— ADULTS: Plumage, *white;* primaries and their coverts, black; head with a pale wash of amber-yellow; bill, grayish tinged with greenish or bluish; lores and throat sac, black; feet, black with greenish or bluish scales; iris, white or pale yellow. YOUNG: Plumage, dark brown with a tinge of olive, spotted or streaked everywhere with white; on head and neck the spots tending to form streaks, on back and wing-coverts, triangular, usually one on end of each feather; primaries and tail, dusky. Intermediates between these two plumages are common, as it requires three years to reach perfect plumage.

Nest and Eggs.— NEST: On precipitous cliffs overlooking the sea; constructed principally of seaweed. EGGS: Single, pale greenish-blue, flaked with chalky-white.

Distribution.— Coasts of North Atlantic; breeds on Bird Rock and Bonaventure Island in the Gulf of St. Lawrence and on islands off British Isles; winters from North Carolina coast south to Gulf of Mexico, and on coasts of north Africa, Madeira, and the Canaries; occurs off eastern United States in migration; casual north to Greenland; accidental in Indiana and Ontario.

The Gannet is the largest bird of our north Atlantic coast. It is about three feet from tip of bill to end of tail. It is four feet and more between the tips of its outstretched wings, and its heavy body and muscular neck would make it a formidable antagonist, if it were pugilistic in its disposition. It is a white bird with black-tipped wings and its color renders it a conspicuous object as it flies about over the dark waters of the winter sea. The Gannet likes the association of others of its kind, hence if you find one you are pretty sure to see others in the immediate neighborhood. They range all down the Atlantic coast to Florida, and it is not an uncommon sight to see small flocks almost anywhere off the shores of the eastern United States, disporting themselves in the water just outside the breakers, or wheeling about in quest of fish.

They fly usually at a height of from sixty to a hundred feet above the water. Dr. F. A. Lucas says: "The height at which the Gannet flies

catch, and then rises in pursuit of other game."

Gannets breed north of the United States. Bird Rock in the Gulf of St. Lawrence and Bass Rock at the Firth of Forth contain well-known breeding colonies of enormous numbers. The nests are usually built on ledges overlooking the sea. Where these are broad, the entire area is covered with nests, just enough space being left between them for the birds to come and go with comfort. Where the ledges are narrow and there is room only for a single row of nests, one will find nearly every brooding bird sitting with its tail pointed outward and its head in close

Drawing by R. I. Brasher

GANNET (¼ nat. size)

Like an animated spear it plunges into the ocean after its prey of fish

above the water is proportionate to the depth at which the fish are swimming beneath, and Captain Collins tells me that when fish are swimming near the surface the Gannet flies very low and darts obliquely instead of vertically upon its prey. Should any finny game be seen within range, down goes the Gannet headlong, the nearly closed wings being used to guide the living arrow in its downward flight. Just above the surface the wings are firmly closed, and a small splash or spray shows where the winged fisher cleaves the water to transfix its prey. Disappearing for a few seconds, the bird reappears, rests for a moment on the water, long enough to swallow his

proximity to the rocks. One egg is laid. It is covered with a calcareous deposit that can readily be scratched off. The young are hatched naked. The down, which appears in a few days, is of a yellowish hue. Immature birds have a peculiarly spotted appearance, as the brown feathers with which they are covered are each centered with a wedge-shaped dot of white.

It is extremely rare that the Gannet is found inland, the ones which have been occasionally reported doubtless being individuals that had lost their way, or had been driven by storms from the ocean, on whose bosom they are so much at home.   T. GILBERT PEARSON.

DARTERS

Order *Steganopodes;* family *Anhingidæ*

THE Darters (also called Anhingas and Snake-birds) comprise the family *Anhingidæ*, include four species, and are generally distributed throughout the tropic and semi-tropic regions of both hemispheres. They have an elongated body, covered with small feathers and soft down; a very long, slender, and snake-like neck; small, compressed head; and a slender, nearly straight, and very acutely pointed bill, nearly twice as long as the head, and like that of the Herons. In these respects (excepting the greater length and sinuosity of the neck, and the fact that the bill is not hooked, though it is somewhat serrated) they bear a general external resemblance to their nearest relatives, the Cormorants. The structure of the neck, however, is peculiar in that it is bent at the eighth or ninth vertebra, and is equipped with a singular muscular mechanism by means of which the bird may throw its bill forward with a rapier-like thrust, and impale its prey.

Darters' wings are long and pointed, while the tail is somewhat long, and is rigid, broad and fan-shaped; it is composed of twelve feathers which widen toward the ends; the outer pair are ribbed in a singular manner. The feet are short, and the legs are placed rather far back on the bodies, but the birds perch readily and with apparent ease. They are not marine in their habits, and are not likely to be found near the seacoasts, their favorite habitats being dense swamps. Their flight is swift, and they dive with astonishing ease and quickness. By nature they are timid and watchful; when frightened they drop from their perch into the water, and vanish not only noiselessly, but without causing more than very slight ripples. Once under water they swim very swiftly. When they are alarmed while swimming on the surface, they disappear by sinking gently backward, after the manner of the Grebes. Frequently they swim with the body submerged but with the head and neck protruding in a manner which strongly suggests a water snake.

These singular birds feed chiefly on fish, which they capture, not by diving, but mainly by a pursuit which is like that of the Loons and Grebes. They are gregarious and build, in brush near the water, rough nests in which they lay usually three or four eggs, of a pale bluish color and having a white chalk-like incrustation.

WATER-TURKEY

Anhinga anhinga (*Linnæus*)

A. O. U. Number 118

Other Names.— Anhinga; Darter; American Darter; Black Darter; Black-bellied Darter; White-bellied Darter (young); Snake-bird.

General Description.— Length, 3 feet. Color, black.

Color.— ADULT MALE: *Head, neck, and body, glossy greenish-black;* wings and tail, plain black, latter tipped with white; wings with a broad silvery gray band formed by greater and middle coverts; lesser wing-coverts, spotted, and shoulders, striped with silvery-gray; in breeding plumage, back of neck with a mane of long black feathers and a lateral series of hair-like brownish-white plumes; bill, yellow, dusky-green on ridge and tip; bare space around eye, livid-green; sac, orange; feet, dusky-olive and yellow; webs, yellow; iris, from carmine to pink. ADULT FEMALE: Throat and breast, light brown bordered behind with rich chestnut; feathers of back with brown edges and white centers; *head and neck, glazed brown* varied with rufous, buff, and whitish.

Nest and Eggs.— NEST: In swamps or bayous, on small trees or bushes over water; constructed of sticks, leaves, dry grass, roots, and moss. EGGS: 2 to 5, bluish or dark greenish-white overlaid with white chalky incrustation.

Distribution.— Tropical America north to western Mexico, Texas, Florida, southern Illinois and North Carolina; casual in Kansas; accidental in New Mexico and Arizona.

The Water-Turkey is no more a "Turkey" than the Nighthawk is a "Hawk," yet this is the name by which the American Darter is almost universally known to the people of the southern States where it is found. Of late years ornithologists have adopted the name, dropping the word "Anhinga," which was formerly used. This species haunts the shores of tree-fringed lakes and rivers, as well as the wider stretches of lakes and sloughs, if bushes or trees are here convenient upon which it can perch. It is a long-necked, long-tailed, and short-legged bird about three feet in length. The general color of the male is a glossy black. The female has the entire head, neck, and breast grayish-brown. They are silent birds and live mainly in the

out with only its slender head and beak exposed. Often it swims with body out of sight and with its long neck protruding in a most eerie and snake-like fashion.

Photo by T. H. Jackson   Courtesy of Nat. Asso. Aud. Soc.

NEST OF WATER-TURKEY

Orange Lake rookery, Florida

The Water-Turkey's food consists mainly of fish which it captures as it swims beneath the surface. When emerging from the water it often ascends some sloping log or bush with low

Drawing by R. I. Brasher

WATER-TURKEY (⅛ nat. size)

A bird of haunting mystery

silent places of the wilderness. Their whole life seems to be pervaded with a haunting mystery. It is undoubtedly the bird to which the rural preacher referred when he said, "Where the Whangdoodle mourneth for its first-born."

When you come upon one sitting on some limb deep in the swamp it will at times fly swiftly out of sight, only to return again and again, each time higher in the air until, having attained an altitude of several hundred feet, it will circle about apparently on motionless wings like a Hawk. Again, and especially if it does not suspect itself seen, it will drop from the perch into the water beneath with only the faintest splash, and after swimming to a safe distance will cautiously peer

Courtesy of Nat. Asso. Aud. Soc.

FEMALE WATER-TURKEY

At Orange Lake rookery, Florida

hanging limbs. The toes of its stout webbed feet terminate in sharp claws which enable it to climb with ease. Here, with wings spread, it will remain for a time drying its feathers in the sunshine.

They assemble in numbers, sometimes several dozen pairs together, for the business of nest building. Often they breed in colonies with Herons and Ibises, but not always; for I have found as many as twenty-five nests at a time, all clustered about in a dozen trees, and no other water birds near. The nest is a bulky affair of sticks and often some of the long gray Spanish moss is used. All the nests I have ever examined also contained freshly plucked leaves, which appeared to have been placed as a finishing touch just before the eggs were laid.

They inhabit the low countries, breeding in the coastal regions as far north as North Carolina and up the Mississippi valley to southern Illinois. They are fresh-water birds and rarely appear where the sea-water runs.

T. GILBERT PEARSON.

CORMORANTS

Order *Steganopodes;* family *Phalacrocoracidæ*

THE Cormorants comprise two genera, the *Phalacrocorax*, embracing the true Cormorants, or "Shags" as they are frequently called, and including about thirty species, and the monotypic *Nannopterum*, with Harris's Cormorant, the flightless and rare bird of the Galapagos Islands, as its single representative. This bird is very large and uses its wings only as fins in swimming.

Of the true Cormorants, about ten species occur in North America. They are chiefly maritime in their habitats, though some species are often found in fresh water far inland. They are disposed to be decidedly gregarious at all seasons, and during the breeding period they assemble in large colonies on ledges or rocky islands along the seacoast. When migrating they fly at a considerable altitude, but ordinarily they do not rise far above the water. They dive readily in pursuit of fish, but always from the surface or a low perch, and not from the air.

The superficial physical peculiarities of the Cormorants include a bare, expansible membrane under the lower mandible; a compressed bill of which the upper half is strongly hooked; nostrils which apparently in the adult do not admit air, the birds breathing through the mouth; and the claw of the middle toe armed with a comb-like process used in preening the plumage. The stiff and rounded tail of twelve to fourteen feathers is employed to assist the bird in walking and climbing. The birds are usually from two to three feet long, and the body is elongated and powerfully muscled. The neck is rather long and the legs are short and stout, and set far back. The wings are comparatively short, extending but slightly beyond the base of the tail. The plumage is very dense, and is generally dark in color, with greenish and bluish sheens. Frequently the head is crested, and during the breeding season may be further ornamented by plumes of slight feathers of hair-like structure.

That Cormorants can dive to a great depth is indicated by the record of one caught off the coast of England in a crab-pot 120 feet below the surface. They feed entirely on fishes, which they pursue and capture under water where they use both their feet and wings in swimming. If the fish captured has been seized in a position which makes swallowing it inconvenient, it is tossed into the air and caught again in a way which simplifies the swallowing operation. This diet gives the Cormorants' flesh a strongly fishy flavor, though this is less pronounced in the young birds and these are sometimes eaten.

Cormorants build rough nests, composed mostly of seaweeds, and placed usually on the ground, though sometimes in low bushes. The eggs are from three to five, of a greenish blue tinge, and covered with a crust of lime-like matter. The young are hatched naked but are soon covered with a black down. They feed by thrusting their heads down the throats of the parents and extracting the partly digested fish therefrom.

CORMORANT

Phalacrocorax carbo (*Linnæus*)

A. O. U. Number 119   See Color Plate 9

Other Names.— Common Cormorant; Shag.

General Description.— Length, 3 feet. Prevailing color, black. Throat sac, heart-shaped behind.

Color.— ADULTS IN BREEDING PLUMAGE: General color, *glossy olive-black;* feathers of back and wing-coverts, bronze-gray, sharply edged with black; primaries, secondaries, and tail, more grayish-black; a conspicuous white patch on flank; numerous long white plumes on head and neck; a black crown crest about 1 inch long; bill, dusky; bare skin around eyes, livid greenish; throat sac, yellow, bordered behind by a band of white feathers; feet, black; iris, green. ADULTS IN WINTER: No crest or white feathers on head and rump. YOUNG: Top of head and hindneck, brownish-black; back and wing-coverts, grayish-brown, the feathers with dark margins, some edged with white; throat, brownish-white; *under parts, whitish,* dusky on sides and across lower abdomen; bill, grayish-brown, black on ridge and tip; bare skin of face and sac, yellow.

Nest and Eggs.— NEST: On the ground, among rocks; constructed of sticks, moss, seaweed, and kelp. EGGS: 3 to 4, bluish-green coated with a white chalky substance.

Distribution.— Northern hemisphere; breeds from central Greenland south to Nova Scotia, and east through Europe and Asia to Kamchatka; winters from southern Greenland to Long Island, N. Y., rarely to Lake Ontario and South Carolina, and from the Mediterranean south to southern Africa, Australia, and Malay Peninsula.

Courtesy Nat. Asso. Aud. Soc.

NEST AND EGGS OF CORMORANT

Drawing by R. I. Brasher

CORMORANT (½ nat. size)

A bird of strange appearance and interesting habits

The Cormorant is found generally throughout almost all of the northern hemisphere. From its breeding grounds in Labrador and Greenland it strays southward in summer, and occurs on the Atlantic coast in winter. It is seen occasionally on inland waters, but such visits probably are purely accidental, as its normal habitats are the seacoast and the mouths of large rivers.

It lives almost entirely upon fish, which it captures under water by swimming with both wings and feet, sometimes at a considerable depth. In these operations it is very skillful and swift, while its powerful hooked bill forms an effective weapon for seizing and devouring its prey. The young are fed by regurgitation, during which the infant thrusts its bill far down the throat of the parent.

Courtesy of Nat. Asso. Aud. Soc.

YOUNG CORMORANTS

They are naked when hatched, and do not leave the nest for about a month

DOUBLE-CRESTED CORMORANT

Phalacrocorax auritus auritus (*Lesson*)

A. O. U. Number 120   See Color Plate 9

Other Names.— Crow Duck; Shag; Water-Turkey; Lawyer; Nigger Goose.

General Description.— Length, 33 inches. Prevailing color, greenish-black. *Throat sac, convex behind.*

Color.— ADULTS IN SUMMER: Glossy greenish-black; feathers of back and wings, coppery-gray with narrow distinct black edges and black-shafted; two curly black crests on head; *no white flank patches or white feathers behind throat sac;* throat sac and lores, orange; bill, dusky; feet, black; iris, green; eyelids, blue. ADULTS IN WINTER: No crests; eyelids, not blue; bill, yellow, dusky on ridge; gular sac, red in front, yellow ocher behind. YOUNG: Plain dark brown; grayish or whitish below.

Nest and Eggs.— NEST: On the ground; constructed of twigs and weeds; sometimes on ledges of sea islands where built of fresh seaweed and kelp. EGGS: 2 to 4, bluish-green with white chalky incrustation.

Distribution.— Eastern North America; breeds from central Saskatchewan, southern Keewatin, northeastern Quebec and Newfoundland south to northern Utah, South Dakota, southern Minnesota, and Penobscot Bay, Maine. Winters from North Carolina (casually Massachusetts) south to the Gulf coast; casual in Bermuda.

Cormorants are found in suitable places all over North America. They are wonderful divers and secure their prey while on their submarine excursions. They are very common on the coast and may easily be seen at many places, as, for example, on the Seal Rocks near the Cliff House at San Francisco, on Black Horse Island off the coast of Maine, and on almost every buoy and channel-stake about the harbors of Florida. On rocky coasts their nests are built on cliffs overlooking the sea, as on the Farallon Islands, California, and the Three Arch Rock Islands of Oregon. In the interior the nests are often built on the ground or on the rushes in the islands of lakes. In the swamps of the South, cypress trees are used, and along the Gulf coast of Florida large numbers breed on the low mangrove trees that cover the Keys.

Some years ago I visited a typical colony of these birds in Big Lake, in eastern North Carolina. Low-spreading cypress trees, their tops reaching, as a rule, not more than fifteen feet above the water, were the sites chosen for the nests. Eighteen trees scattered along the swampy shore for a mile and a half were thus occupied. A few trees contained but a single nest. Some were occupied by two, while in others six, eight, ten, and even twelve nests were noted. One tree contained thirty-eight, all of which contained either eggs or young. The number of occupants of a nest was in all cases either two or three.

One hundred and fifty inhabited nests were counted in the community.

The eggs were pale bluish-white overlaid with a chalky coating and were about two and one-half inches long. When first hatched the young are naked and look like little, animated, greasy rubber bags. In a few days they assume a thick growth of black down.

The food of these birds must have consisted largely of eels, for in nearly every nest signs of eels were found, and the young upon becoming excited disgorged fragments of eels which showered down upon us as we attempted to climb the trees.

The Cormorants have many local names, such as " Shag," " Lawyer," and " Nigger Goose."

There are several subspecies of the Double-crested Cormorant. These are: the Florida Cormorant (*Phalacrocorax auritus floridanus*) of North Carolina, Florida, and the Gulf coast; the White-crested Cormorant (*Phalacrocorax auritus cincinatus*) of Alaska; and the Farallon Cormorant (*Phalacrocorax auritus albociliatus*) of the coast and inland lakes of the Pacific slope.

Market fishermen everywhere complain of the inroads these birds make on the food fishes of the sea, but a recent investigation carried out by the Canadian Government proved beyond doubt that the destruction wrought by Cormorants in the Gulf of St. Lawrence has been overrated greatly.   T. GILBERT PEARSON.

Photograph by H. K. Job

YOUNG DOUBLE-CRESTED CORMORANTS
In rookery, Waterhen Island, Manitoba

[98]

BRANDT'S CORMORANT

Phalacrocorax penicillatus (*Brandt*)

A. O. U. Number 122

Other Names.— Penciled Cormorant; Tufted Cormorant; Townsend's Cormorant; Shag; Brown Cormorant.

General Description.— Length, 33 inches. Prevailing color, blackish. *Throat sac, heart-shaped behind; head, not crested;* bill, slender and nearly straight; tail, short.

Color.— ADULTS IN BREEDING PLUMAGE: General color, deep glossy greenish-black with violet or steel-blue reflections on neck and head; feathers of middle of back, plain, those of shoulders and wing-coverts with narrow black edgings; a series of yellow straight filamentous plumes two inches or more in length along each side of neck; many others longer and somewhat webbed on shoulders; *throat sac, dark blue;* a border of mouse-brown feathers behind gular sac; bill, dusky; feet, black; iris, green. ADULTS IN WINTER: Plumes, absent. YOUNG: Plain blackish-brown, more rusty below; abdomen grayish; shoulders and wing-coverts, paler-edged.

Nest and Eggs.— NEST: On ledges of rock islands; a compact structure of eel grass or seaweed, cemented with guano. EGGS: 3 to 5, light greenish-blue, with the usual chalky deposit.

Distribution.— Pacific coast, from Vancouver Island to Cape San Lucas.

Brandt's Cormorant is abundant on the Pacific coast. Its general demeanor, as it perches on rocks or snags, suggests that it is a rather dull and sluggish bird, but in reality it is very suspicious and wary, and this state of mind is shown plainly by its manner when it is in the water. Then its long neck is stretched to its fullest length, and its head is constantly turning from side to side, as if it feared the approach of an enemy from any direction.

The Cormorant dives readily and skillfully, and uses both its wings and its feet in making headway under water. In fact it seems quite as much at home in the water as a Duck, and yet, for some altogether mysterious reason, it has the very unducklike habit of perching in the sunshine, with wings spread, and evidently waiting for its plumage to dry. The Northern Raven and the Western Gull seem to have a special weakness for the eggs of the Cormorant, of which fact apparently it is very well aware; for, when the Ravens or Gulls are about, the Cormorant that is incubating will not leave the eggs until its mate is at hand to take its place immediately.

Photo by W. L. Finley and H. T. Bohlman

BRANDT'S CORMORANT AT NEST

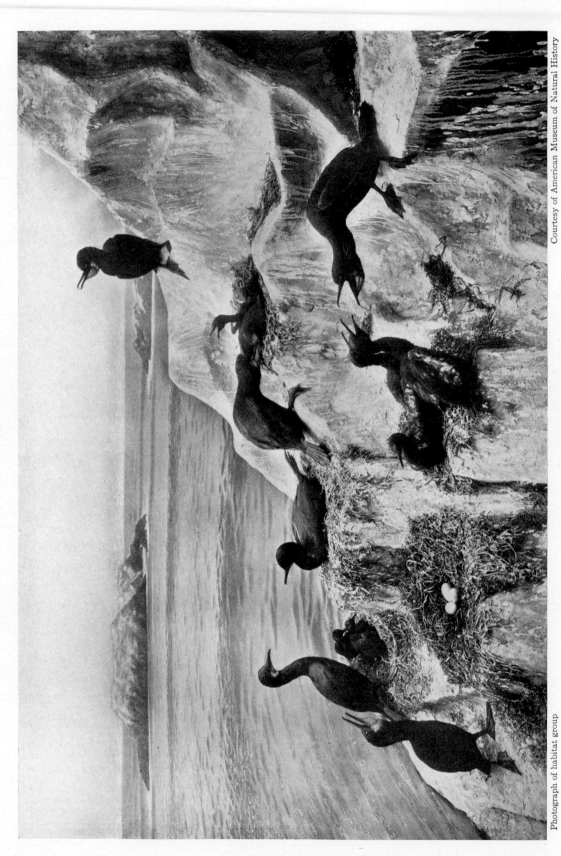

Photograph of habitat group

BRANDT'S CORMORANTS AT MONTEREY, CALIFORNIA

PELICANS

Order Steganopodes; family Pelecanidæ

WELVE species of these singularly grotesque but interesting birds are recognized, and they occur generally throughout the temperate and tropical regions of both hemispheres, three of them being North American. They are birds of considerable size, their bodies varying in length from fifty to seventy inches, while some have a wing expanse of nearly ten feet.

The distinctive feature of the Pelican is the great pouch which depends from its lower bill. As the bird's bill may be eighteen inches long, it will be realized that the capacity of this pouch, six inches or more in depth, is very considerable. Some of the species use this pouch very much as a scoop net is employed, and all of them store in it fish which they take to their young. Most of the bird's prey is captured in this manner, though some is taken by diving. Another physical peculiarity is the excrescence which develops at about the middle of the upper mandible during the breeding season. What, if any, purpose it serves is not known. It is shed coincidently with the fall molt.

The Pelican on land is very ungainly, its uncouth appearance being due in part to the awkward kink in its neck, which produces the impression of great discomfort. In point of fact, however, this position is due to the singular articulation of the eighth or ninth vertebra with the one on either side, so that it is really impossible for the bird to straighten its neck. The Pelican's flight is a combination of flapping and sailing, and though not rapid is steady and confident. A long line of these birds, flapping and sailing alternately, and often in nearly perfect unison, is an interesting spectacle.

These birds are decidedly gregarious and often breed in very large colonies. They build on the ground large nests composed of sticks. The eggs are from two to five in number and are bluish-white in color.

WHITE PELICAN

Pelecanus erythrorhynchos *Gmelin*

A. O. U. Number 125

Other Names.— American White Pelican; Common Pelican (of the North).

General Description.— Length, 5 feet; spread of wings, 9 feet. General color, white. Bill with pouch hanging from under side.

Color.— ADULTS: *Plumage, white with black primaries;* lengthened feathers of back of head, breast, and some of the lesser wing-coverts, pale straw-yellow; bill and feet, yellow tinged with reddish; lower part of bill, brighter than upper, which has the ridge whitish; pouch shading from whitish in front through yellow and orange to red at base; bare skin around eye, orange; eyelids, red; iris, pearly-white. YOUNG: Lesser wing-coverts and some feathers on head, grayish;

bill and feet, dull yellowish; otherwise as in adults.

Nest and Eggs.— NEST: On the ground; constructed by the bird scraping the sandy soil into a heap about half a foot high and erecting a shallow platform of sticks and weeds on this base. EGGS: 2, dull chalky-white with a chalky incrustation.

Distribution.— Temperate North America; breeds from southern British Columbia, Great Slave Lake, and southwestern Keewatin to Manitoba, North Dakota (formerly southern Minnesota and South Dakota), Utah, and southern California; winters from southern California to Gulf States, Florida, and Cuba south to western Mexico and Costa Rica; casual in migration east to Atlantic coast, north to New Brunswick.

The American White Pelican was formerly found in the East as well as in the West, but the range of the bird has contracted until it is rarely seen on the Atlantic coast. The bird formerly nested in Minnesota, but the most eastern nesting site to-day within the United States is in North Dakota. A bird so conspicuous in size and color, and one that nests on the ground, can never rear its young free from the disturbances of predacious animals and man unless it can find a remote island upon which to breed. The natural home of the bird is on some sandy or tule island, where a large number of them nest together. This showy bird would soon have been extinct had it not been for the efforts of the National Association of Audubon Societies in seeking out the ancestral breeding places and having them set aside as Federal wild-bird reservations. The largest colonies of White Pelicans in the United States are found on Malheur Lake, Klamath Lake, and Clear Lake reservations in southern Oregon and northern California.

Through the western part of the United States, the Pelican season begins in April after the snow and ice have melted and lasts till August or September, when the young are able to care for themselves. Sometimes one will find eggs just hatching from May up to July. The Pelican generally lays two or three eggs and incubates about four weeks before they hatch.

The Pelican has a large skinny bag that hangs from the lower part of his bill. This, when distended, holds several quarts of water. When not in use, this sack is contracted so it occupies very little space. The White Pelican uses this as a dip-net by swimming along and scooping up the young fry. It was formerly thought that this pouch served to convey live fish swimming in water to the little Pelicans at home, but, as Audubon remarked long ago, it is doubtful whether a Pelican could fly at all with his burden so out of trim.

The first time I ever saw a motley crowd of half-grown Pelicans, I thought Nature had surely done her best to make something ugly and ridiculous. It was a warm day and the birds stood around with their mouths open, panting like a lot of dogs after a chase, their pouches shaking at every breath. When I went near, the youngsters went tottering off on their big webbed feet with wings dragging on this side and that, like poorly handled crutches. The youngsters huddled together by hundreds in a small place. Those on the outside pushed and climbed to get near the center, till it looked worse than any football scrimmage I ever saw.

One might wonder how such a huge-billed bird as a Pelican could feed helpless chicks just out of the egg. It was done with apparent ease. The old bird regurgitated a fishy soup into the front end of his pouch and the baby Pelican pitched right in and helped himself out of this family dish.

As the young bird grew older and larger, at each meal he kept reaching farther into the big pouch of his parent until finally, when he was half-grown, it was a most remarkable sight. The mother opened her mouth and the whole head and neck of her nestling disappeared down the capacious maw, while he hunted for his dinner in the internal regions.

WILLIAM L. FINLEY.

Photo by W. L. Stevens   Courtesy of *Field and Stream*

YOUNG PELICANS

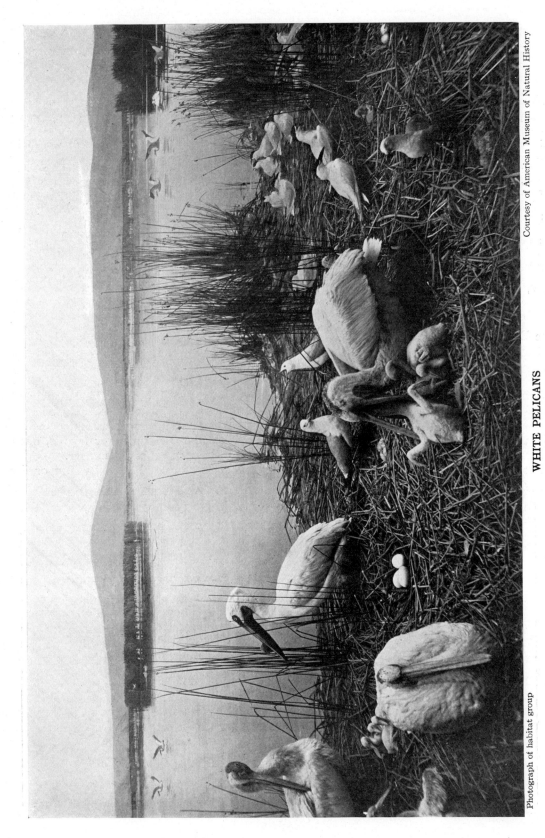

WHITE PELICANS

Well might one wonder how such a huge-billed bird could feed helpless chicks just out of the shell

BROWN PELICAN

Pelecanus occidentalis *Linnæus*

A. O. U. Number 126

Other Name.— Common Pelican (of Florida).

General Description.— Length, 4½ feet; spread of wings, 6½ feet. General color, brown, darker above. Bill with pouch hanging from under side.

Color.— ADULTS: Head, white tinged with yellow on crown, the white extending down neck in a narrow border on side of pouch; rest of neck, dark chestnut; *upper parts, dusky brown,* each feather whitish-centered; wing-coverts, pale gray with white streaks; primaries, black; secondaries, dark brown with pale edges; tail-feathers, gray; under parts, grayish-brown striped with white on sides and flanks; lower fore-neck, variegated with ocher, chestnut, and black; bill, mottled with light gray and dusky, tinged in spots with carmine; bare space around eyes, blue; iris, white; eyelids, red; pouch, blackish; feet, black. In winter most of the neck is white. YOUNG: Neck, plain brownish; other plumage similar but less intense than in adults.

Nest and Eggs.— NEST: In rookeries, on shores or marshy islands, usually on the ground or sometimes in low mangrove bushes; constructed of sticks, coarse grass, and weed stalks and lined with finer grasses. EGGS: 2 or 3, chalky-white.

Distribution.— Gulf coast of United States and Atlantic coast of Central and South America; breeds from Florida and Louisiana south to Brazil; rare in North Carolina; accidental in Wyoming, Nebraska, Iowa, Illinois, Indiana, Massachusetts, and Nova Scotia.

The Brown Pelican is an interesting southern and tropical bird, great of bulk, powerful in flight, and withal a mightly fisher. It is numerous on our Atlantic coast from South Carolina to Texas, where it breeds on various isolated islands. Fishermen dislike it because the pouch-net which it carries under its great beak is large, and its appetite for fish in proportion. But, considering that man's nets are so much vaster, and that two or three men kill more fish in one day than can thousands of Pelicans, surely there are fish enough in the ocean that we should not begrudge the lives of these interesting and spectacular birds. It is not Pelicans that will ever exterminate any species of fish, but only avaricious man, who all too often petrifies his soul and artistic sense through inordinate greed of hoarding. The poor Pelican never hoards, but only satisfies the stern behest of hunger.

The sight of the advancing wedge or line of

Photograph by H. K. Job   Courtesy of National Association of Audubon Societies

BROWN PELICANS

On East Timbalier Reservation, Louisiana

Photograph of habitat group

BROWN PELICANS

Interesting birds, great of bulk, powerful in flight, and mighty fishers great Pelicans, with their heavy flappings and intervals of soaring, is impressive, as is the amazing headlong plunge into the sea after fish. Mirth-provoking is the sequel sometimes witnessed. The smaller Laughing Gull follows the great Pelican and hovers above the spot where it plunges. The Pelican soon emerges, holding the fish, which it has seized, in its bill. The fish, perchance, must be turned, and the mouthful of sea-water ejected. While the Pelican is arranging matters, the Gull alights on the great beak, leaning over to watch. No sooner is the bill opened than the sly Gull reaches in, seizes the fish, and flies away, we may well imagine laughing. The solemn old Pelican sits there blinking, too much astonished at first to move. Finally the dread truth seems to dawn on the dull mind. With a few disgusted flaps, away it goes in pursuit of another fish.

On some islands the Brown Pelican breeds on the mangrove trees, constructing quite a bulky nest of sticks. On others, which often are mere low sand-bars, the nest is a mere hollow in the sand, only slightly lined. Two or three large coarse-shelled white eggs are laid. On the trees they are comparatively safe, but on the ground storms and floods often wash them away and break up the nesting. The birds do not attempt to rescue eggs, when these are drifted together in windrows at high-water marks, but sit off on the water and solemnly ponder. Usually, in time, they will lay again.

Pelican Island, in Indian River, Fla., is the best-known breeding colony, the first such to be made a government reservation. Formerly there were mangrove trees, but these have died off, and the thousands of Pelicans nest on the ground. Now and then a storm floods the island and destroys all eggs and young. It is remarkable that in this protected colony the birds each year have nested earlier and earlier, until now laying is begun in November, though on the west coast of Florida the eggs are not laid until April and May.

On June 21, 1915, I visited a great colony of ten or twelve thousand breeding on East Timbalier Island, on the west coast of Louisiana, this also being a government reservation. Though it was so late in the season, the Pelicans had just laid their eggs; not one had yet hatched. The nests were all on the sand of the low island. Their lateness may have been due to robbery or disaster elsewhere earlier in the season. At any rate, it made them too late to mature the young before a terrible tropical hurricane visited the coast in August, and every one of the thousands of young birds on the islands perished.

Surely the birds have enough to contend with without having man as an enemy!

HERBERT K. JOB.

MAN-O'-WAR-BIRDS

Order *Steganopodes*; family *Fregatidæ*

THE Man-o'-war-birds, or Frigate Birds, as they are often called, include two species constituting the family *Fregatidæ*. The larger (*Fregata aquila*) occurs in subtropical and tropical seas of both hemispheres, mainly north of the equator, and visits more or less regularly the coasts of California, Texas, and Florida, wandering northward occasionally as far as Nova Scotia. The other forms appear in the central Pacific and Indian oceans, and further south.

In general the Man-o'-war-birds' plumage is uniformly blackish in the adult males, while the females have the upper parts blackish and the sides and lower parts white. Other characteristic physical peculiarities are the unusually long and stoutly hooked bill, the very short shank, the serrated claw of the middle toe, the narrow web between the toes, and the pneumatic structure of the bones of the skeleton, which makes the body lighter than that of any other bird in proportion to the length of the wings, which are greatly elongated. The tail also is long and deeply forked like that of the Barn Swallow.

Their most curious physical feature, however, is the pouch or air sac of the male, which lies along the throat and, when fully distended, extends forward as far as the end of the bill, and downward so as to obscure the breast. When completely inflated (which is accomplished by means of tubes connected with the bronchi) it presents the appearance of a large, scarlet balloon. Doubtless this is a sexual manifestation, and plays a part in the courtship demonstration analogous to the Peacock's display of his upper tail-coverts, the strutting of the Grouse, and so on. When the pouch is deflated it is invisible beneath the plumage of the neck.

Like the Skuas and Jaegers, the Man-o'-war-birds are predatory in their habits, and get a large part of their food by robbing the Gulls and Terns, pursuing them and forcing them to drop or disgorge their food, which the pursuer catches as it falls. In their flight they are probably the most graceful and dashing of all birds. They soar for hours at a time with no apparent effort, and frequently make astonishing aërial dives from very great heights. They build their nests, sometimes on the ground and sometimes in stunted bushes, of small, dead twigs, and lay usually one, sometimes two, white eggs about the size of those of a domestic hen. In their breeding habits they are decidedly gregarious, and groups of nests are often placed very close to one another, even when there is no necessity for such proximity.

MAN-O'-WAR-BIRD

Fregata aquila (*Linnæus*)

A. O. U. Number 128

Other Names.— Hurricane Bird; Frigate Bird; Rabihorcado.

General Description.— Length, about 40 inches. Plumage, brownish-black.

Color.— ADULT MALE: *Plumage, brownish-black* with green or purplish reflections on head and shoulders, where the feathers are long and lance-shaped; below, plain; bill, various shades of whitish, flesh color, bluish, or blackish; bare space around eye, livid; sac, carmine to orange; iris, brown; feet, dusky. ADULT FEMALE: Less iridescent than male; feathers of back, less elon-gated; back of neck, brown; wing-coverts, mostly brown with darker centers and paler edges; *foreneck, breast, and sides, pure white.*

Nest and Eggs.— NEST: Usually on low trees or bushes, sometimes on rocks; extraordinarily small for the size of the bird, and flimsily constructed of a few dry twigs. EGGS: 1 to 3, plain white.

Distribution.— Tropical and subtropical coasts; in America north to southern California, Texas, Louisi-ana, and Florida; accidental in Kansas, Wisconsin, Iowa, Ohio, and Nova Scotia.

The Man-o'-war-bird is a genuine feathered aëroplane, if any bird is deserving of that distinction. Without moving its wings, seemingly for hours at a time, it calmly floats high in air, ascending in spirals, or drifting lazily along, directing its easy flight by changes of the angle of its "planes" so slight that any such effort is not apparent. In this respect, and perhaps in certain others, there is a resemblance to the Buzzards, which, in flight and lack of industry, manifest the soporific influences of the tropics. It is distinctly a tropical bird, seldom being seen further north than along the coasts of Florida, the Gulf States, and southern California.

Breeding is conducted mostly on tropical or subtropical islands, where crude nests of sticks are built on mangroves or low trees or bushes, in each of which one plain-white egg is laid. In the Bahamas large colonies of the birds nest, and eggs are usually seen in February. By late spring the period of nesting is over, and they forthwith appear in large numbers on our Flor-ida and Gulf coasts. They are not definitely known to breed in the United States, though I think it probable that they do so occasionally, as there are reports of this on islands off the coast of Louisiana, and on an island near this group in June a member of our party picked up an egg, dropped on the sand, which clearly belonged to this species.

This bird is very impressive by reason of its size and the enormous stretch of its long, narrow wings, measuring some seven and one-half feet across. When a great flock of thousands soar on motionless pinions, they appear like an aërial army of invasion. Yet after all they are sluggish, lazy creatures. I have watched them go to roost at sundown in bushes or mangrove trees by the shore, and seen them sleeping, with head under wings, when the sun was some hours aclimb. Of course, they eat, but somehow I have seldom seen them actually securing food. Occasionally I have watched one snatch a fish or other marine creature from the surface of the ocean, but usually they are seen lazily floating in space, or else on their roosts or flocking on the beach.

On Bird Key, Dry Tortugas, off Florida, some hundreds of them stay in the Tern colony during the nesting season. While I was there they committed no depredations, but the warden says they attack the Terns as these are bringing fish for their young, compel them, through vicious swoops, to disgorge, and deftly catch the delicacy, usually before it reaches the water. Thousands of them, likewise, stay on Indian Key Reservation, Fla., near St. Petersburg, and wonderful soaring flights may be seen poised over the island. At close range their great hooked bills give them a rather fierce appearance, though of talons they have little to boast, their feet being weak and clumsy, fit only for perching. But their wings might well be the envy and despair of many another bird. HERBERT K. JOB.

Drawing by R. I. Brasher

MAN-O'-WAR-BIRD (⅛ nat. size)

A genuine feathered aëroplane

Plate 10

Louis Agassiz Fuertes

RED-BREASTED MERGANSER *Mergus serrator* Linnaeus
FEMALE MALE
AMERICAN MERGANSER *Mergus americanus* (Cassin)
FEMALE MALE

RUDDY DUCK *Erismatura jamaicensis* (Gmelin)
FEMALE MALE
BUFFLE-HEAD *Charitonetta albeola* (Linnaeus)
MALE FEMALE

All ⅕ nat. size

ORDER OF LAMELLIROSTRAL SWIMMERS

Order *Anseres*

BUT one family is included in this order; this, however, is divided into five subfamilies: Mergansers, River Ducks, Sea Ducks, Geese, and Swans. The general appearance and habits of this group are well known through their familiar representatives in barnyards and parks. There are about two hundred species scattered throughout all parts of the world; about fifty occur in North America. Economically they are among the most important of all birds.

The name given to the order is descriptive of the bill which is characteristic of all the members of the order except the Mergansers. This subfamily have round bills with saw-toothed edges, but the Ducks, Geese, and Swans have the bill flat and lamellate, or fitted along the edges with a series of flutings, with a membranous covering, and with a nail, or hard spot at the tip. Other characteristics of the Lamellirostral Swimmers are: tail generally short; wings moderately long; legs short and placed far apart, not so near the center of the body as in the Gulls and not so far back as in the Grebes; the knee joint buried in the general body covering and the thighs feathered nearly to the heel joint; toes four in number, hind toe free and elevated, front toes webbed; a peculiar waddling gait; neck usually long; plumage soft and dense, especially on the breast, with a copious covering of down.

The nest is placed on the ground, or among rocks, or in the hollow of a tree or stump. The eggs are usually numerous, of an oval shape, and plain in color. The young are covered with down when hatched, and as soon as this natal down is dry they are able to leave the nest and follow the mother.

There is a great variety of coloration among the birds of this order. With some species the female is the brighter, in others her dress is as plain as that of any Sparrow while the male is gaudily clad, and in other species there is no difference in coloration between the sexes. In some species the postnuptial molt of the male is not complete — an unusual proceeding in the bird world. This incomplete change is called the "eclipse plumage"; at this period these birds also lose their power of flight, because all the flight-feathers are shed at one and the same time. The eclipse plumage is worn only until the wing-feathers are regained, when it is shed and the distinctive male plumage again acquired.

MERGANSERS

Order *Anseres;* family *Anatidæ;* subfamily *Merginæ*

THE Mergansers constitute a small group (*Merginæ*) of fish-eating Ducks often called Fishing Ducks, Sheldrakes, or Sawbills. They are characterized by comparatively long, narrow, cylindrical bills, whose saw-toothed edges enable the birds to seize and devour fish of considerable size. This diet imparts a rank favor to the flesh of the various species, except that of the Hooded Merganser which evidently takes food enough of other kinds to counteract the effect of the fish eaten. This species and the common Merganser are also peculiar in that they nest in hollow trees or on a ledge of a cliff. All of the species have more or less striking and beautiful plumage and both sexes are usually crested. There are nine recognized species of Mergansers, three of which range throughout North America and as far south as Cuba.

MERGANSER

Mergus americanus *Cassin*

A. O. U. Number 129   See Color Plate 10

Other Names.— American Goosander; American Sheldrake; American Merganser; Greater Merganser; Pond Sheldrake; Big Sheldrake; Fresh-water Sheldrake; Winter Sheldrake; Buff-breasted Sheldrake; Buff-breasted Merganser; Fishing Duck; Fish Duck; Saw-bill; Big Saw-bill; Break Horn; Dun Diver (female); Morocco-head (female).

General Description.— Length, 25 inches. Adult males have the head and upper parts greenish-black; while the females and immature have the head red and the upper parts gray; all have the under parts white. Bill, cylindrical.

Color.— ADULT MALE: Head and upper part of neck, dark lustrous green; upper parts, glossy black shading to ashy-gray on rump and tail, this color running up back of neck acutely *but not reaching the green of head;* outer edge of shoulder and most of wing, pure white, crossed by one black bar formed by bases of greater coverts; primaries and outer secondaries, black, the latter shading to white and black inwardly; under parts, pure white, shaded along sides with pale pinkish where marbled with dusky; bill and feet, vermilion; hook of bill, black with some of the same color

on ridge; iris, red. ADULT FEMALE: Head and neck, reddish-brown; the slight crest more brownish; chin, throat, and under parts, white; upper parts, ashy-gray, the feathers slightly darker centrally; white of wing restricted to a patch formed by secondaries and greater coverts; primaries, dusky; bill, reddish, paler at base with dusky ridge; feet, orange with dusky webs; iris, yellowish-red. IMMATURE: Similar to adult female.

Nest and Eggs.— NEST: In hollow tree, on ground, or in crevices of rocks; constructed of moss, leaves, and grass, and warmly lined with down. EGGS: 6 to 10, pale buffy.

Distribution.— North America; breeds from southern Alaska across British America to southern Ungava and Newfoundland, south to Oregon, South Dakota, Minnesota, Michigan, Vermont, New Hampshire, Maine, and northern New York, and in mountains south to northern California, central Arizona, northern New Mexico, and Pennsylvania (formerly); winters throughout the greater part of its range south to northern Lower California, northern Mexico, Texas, Louisiana, Florida, and Bermuda.

In the dead of winter when the " white death " covers the land and even the ice-bound waters, we may find here and there in the courses of the larger New England rivers an open stretch where

the floods foam over the rocks of a broken rapid. Here we may see a pair of large wild Ducks breasting the torrent, swimming and diving as composedly in the turmoil of waters as if they

Drawing by R. I. Brasher

MERGANSER (¼ nat. size)

A fresh-water bird, rarely seen on salt water.

were taking their exercise in a placid lake. Their marking, the dark green glossy head of the male, its glistening light under parts, and the crested head of the female at once identify them as Mergansers, for this is the only American Duck the female of which is crested while the adult male is not. The feathers on the head of the male are elongated somewhat but he has no such crest as that of the female. The young of both sexes are more or less crested.

The birds are silent and if undisturbed they diligently dive and chase their finny prey beneath the surface. If disturbed they rise and fly to some other rapid, for only in such places can they find food in winter. Sometimes when suddenly alarmed they croak solemnly but this is rare. Ordinarily they fly at a speed of perhaps forty miles an hour but if startled they can distance a railroad train going at that speed.

This is a fresh-water bird, rarely seen on salt water except when driven there by very severe freezing weather. As soon as the ice breaks up in spring numbers of these sheldrakes may be seen in the ponds and rivers of the North following retreating winter to his lair.

The Merganser nests normally in hollow trees and is said to carry the young to the water in its bill. It feeds mainly on fish that are not much valued by man, such as minnows, chubs, and suckers, and in the salt water it devours also crustaceans and mollusks.

Its flesh as ordinarily cooked is so rank and strong that its flavor is not much superior to that of an old kerosene lamp-wick but some of the hardy gunners of the Atlantic coast know how to prepare it for the table in a way to make it quite palatable.

EDWARD HOWE FORBUSH.

RED-BREASTED MERGANSER

Mergus serrator *Linnæus*

A. O. U. Number 130   See Color Plate 10

Other Names.— Shelduck; Shell-bird; Long Island Sheldrake; Spring Sheldrake; Salt-water Sheldrake; Saw-bill; Common Saw-bill; Fishing Duck; Fish Duck; Red-breasted Sheldrake; Red-breasted Goosander; Sea Robin.

General Description.— Length, 24 inches. Adult males have the head and upper parts greenish-black, while the females and immature have the head red and the upper parts ashy-gray; all have the under parts white, but the males have a band of brownish-red on the breast. Both sexes have *a long crest of thin pointed feathers.*

Color.— ADULT MALE: Head and upper neck all around, dark mallard green; under parts, white, usually with pale pinkish shading; *fore-breast, brownish-red streaked with dusky; sides, finely waved with the same color;* fore-back, shoulders, and long inner secondaries, black; middle and lower back, gray waved with whitish and dusky; rump and tail, grayish; *a narrow black line extending up back of neck, reaching color of head;* wings, mostly white; inner secondaries, edged on outer web with black; lesser coverts, encircled by black; two black bars across wing behind greater coverts; pri-

maries, dusky; bill, carmine, dusky on top and tip; feet, bright red; eyes, carmine. ADULT FEMALE: Crest, double; head, chestnut, more brown on crown and crest; throat, paler but not white; beneath, white, shaded on sides with ashy-gray; above, plain ashy-gray, the feathers dark centrally; white of wing restricted to a patch formed by ends of greater coverts and outer secondaries; the base and ends of greater coverts, dusky; primaries, plain dusky; bill, red, paler at base, with dusky ridge and tip; feet, dull reddish, webs darker; iris, red.

Nest and Eggs.— NEST: On the ground, in brush or crevices of rocks, near water; made of leaves, grass, and mosses, and lined with feathers and down from the parents. EGGS: 6 to 12, usually 9 or 10, olive buff.

Distribution.— Northern part of northern hemisphere; breeds in North America from Alaska along Arctic coast to Greenland (latitude 73°) south to British Columbia, Alberta, Minnesota, Wisconsin, northern New York, Maine, and Sable Island; winters throughout most of its range south to Lower California, Louisiana, and Florida; occurs casually in the Bermudas, Cuba, and Hawaii.

The Red-breasted Merganser is a swift and rather silent flyer, and an exceedingly expert diver. While swimming on the surface it sometimes raises and lowers its crest. This is more of a marine species than the American Merganser, but is nevertheless not uncommon in the interior of the country, particularly in the lake regions, during migration.

In the winter, most of the birds of this species which are seen in Massachusetts appear to be full-plumaged males, while in summer the few which remain with us appear to be females. Some of them, however, may be males in the "eclipse" plumage. I have noticed that practically all the birds seen in winter in Florida are females or young. This, together with the fact that most of those seen in Massachusetts in winter are males, seems to indicate that the hardy males do not go so far south in winter as do the females and young.

The Red-breasted Mergansers feed largely on fish, diving and charging through the schools of small fish, which they seize and hold fast with their saw-toothed bills. Thoreau notes that he saw Sheldrakes (presumably of this species) chasing fish by both swimming and flying along the surface. A few shell-fish are eaten at times.

EDWARD HOWE FORBUSH, in *Game Birds, Wild-Fowl and Shore Birds.*

Courtesy of S. A. Lottridge

RED-BREASTED MERGANSER

A swift and rather silent flyer, and an exceedingly expert diver

HOODED MERGANSER

Lophodytes cucullatus (*Linnæus*)

A. O. U. Number 131   See Color Plate 11

Other Names.— Hooded Sheldrake; Little, Wood, Swamp, Pond, Mud, Pickax, or Summer, Sheldrake; Little Fishing, or Fish, Duck; Little Saw-bill Duck; Saw-bill Diver; Round-crested Duck; Fan-crested Duck; Tree Duck; Wood Duck; Spike-bill; Hairy-crown; Hairy-head; Moss-head; Tow-head; Tadpole; Water Pheasant.

General Description.— Length, 17½ inches. Males are black above and white below; females are grayish-brown above and whitish below. Bill, narrow and thin. The adult male has a thin semi-circular crest capable of being opened or shut like a fan.

Color.— ADULT MALE: Head, neck, and upper parts, black shading to brown on lower back; *crest, mostly white with narrow black border behind and wider black space in front;* the white extending a little below level of eyes; breast and under parts, white, invading the black area just in front of wings by two broad streaks; a white speculum with two black bars formed by the outer webs of secondaries and greater coverts; inner secondaries, black with white center stripes; sides below, regularly and finely waved with rufous and black; under tail-coverts, waved with dusky; bill, black; feet, yellowish; iris, yellow. ADULT FEMALE: Crest bushy; head and neck, grayish-chestnut, browner on crown; back and sides, dusky-brown, the feathers with paler edges not waved; speculum of wing, smaller and crossed by only *one* dark bar; throat and under parts in general, whitish; bill, dusky, orange at base below; feet, brownish.

Plate 11

Louis Agassiz Fuertes.

MALE   HOODED MERGANSER *Lophodytes cucullatus* (Linnaeus)   FEMALE

¼ nat. size

Nest and Eggs.— NEST: In hollow trees, lined with grass, leaves, feathers, and down. EGGS: 6 to 10, ivory white.

Distribution.— North America at large; breeds from central British Columbia, Great Slave Lake, across British America to Newfoundland south to southern Oregon, northern New Mexico, southern Louisiana, and central Florida; winters in southern British Columbia, across the United States on about latitude 41° south to Lower California, Mexico, the Gulf States, and Cuba; rare in northeastern part of range; recorded from Alaska, and from Europe and Bermuda.

The Hooded Merganser is a distinctively American bird and is the most beautiful of its family. Vivacious, active, elegant in form, graceful in carriage, its presence adds a peculiar charm to the little ponds and streams on which it delights to disport. It frequents clear streams and muddy pools alike, and its white and black plumage strongly contrasted against the shining water and the surrounding foliage makes a picture not soon forgotten. One who has seen a small flock of this species playing on the dark waters of a tiny shaded pool with two or three beautiful males darting about among the others, opening and closing their fan-like crests and throwing the sparkling drops in showers over their glistening plumage, will rarely find anywhere a finer and more animated picture of bird life.

It is well known that this bird nests in hollow trees and that the young are either carried to the water by the mother soon after they are hatched, or are pushed out of the nest and, falling unhurt to the ground, are led to the water by the parent. She seems to be rather a silent bird, but has a hoarse croak at times and probably has vocal means of communication with her little ones. This Duck is exceedingly swift on the wing, a proficient diver, and a fast swimmer both on and under the surface. Its toothed bill places it with the fish-eating Ducks, but it feeds on vegetable matter also, and Col. John E. Thayer says that "it readily eats corn." No doubt it could be domesticated, and if so it would make a great addition to the ornamental waterfowl on parks and large estates. Notwithstanding its unpalatable fishy flavor it is shot by gunners at every opportunity and has decreased greatly in numbers where formerly it was common.

EDWARD HOWE FORBUSH.

DUCKS

Order *Anseres;* family *Anatidæ;* subfamilies *Anatinæ* and *Fuligulinæ*

UNDER the general term "Duck" are included a very large variety of forms, some of which do not measure up to the popular notion of what a real Duck is. From the scientific point of view, the Ducks include a large group of birds constituting the subfamilies River Ducks and Sea Ducks of the order *Anseres* or Waterfowl. Most of them have the body longer than the neck, and a broad, flattened bill, while the front of the tarsus is fitted with overlapping scales. The sexes are unlike in color. The characteristic "waddle" of the Duck on land is due to the fact that its legs are placed far back on its body, an arrangement which, however, increases its skill in swimming and diving. The wings are rigid, strong, and usually pointed, and capable of driving the bird's body at great speed; the plumage is exceptionally dense and soft.

Wild Ducks fall naturally into the two groups known as River or Pond Ducks and Sea or Bay or Diving Ducks. The Sea Ducks (which are found virtually all over the world) differ from the River Ducks in having the hind toe broadly lobed or webbed, and include species mainly of large size. The terms "Sea" and "River" should not be taken too literally, for certain species of each group may be found on the ocean, on rivers, or on bodies of fresh water well inland. The Sea Ducks, of which about seventy species are recognized, feed mainly on mollusks, shellfish, and the roots and seeds of aquatic plants, which they get by diving, often to a considerable depth, as is proved by the fact that in Lake Erie Old-squaw Ducks have been caught in fishermen's nets at depths of from eighty to one hundred feet

Most of their feeding is done in daytime, and at evening they go out to sea where they pass the night often several miles from shore.

The River Ducks, of which there are about seventy species, get most of their food by searching the bottom in water so shallow that diving is not necessary. With a few exceptions — notably the Canvas-back — their flesh is more palatable than is that of the Sea Ducks. Again, the Sea Ducks often go in enormous flocks, while the River Duck flocks are comparatively small, rarely exceeding forty or fifty individuals. The range of the River Ducks, like that of the Sea Ducks, is very wide, representatives of the group occurring in both hemispheres. The plumage of both groups displays a very great variety of colors, from the plain hues of the Black Duck to the remarkably gaudy and variegated Wood Duck. Usually the secondary quills of the wings show patches of varied or iridescent color and this patch is called the speculum.

Excepting the Wood Duck, all of the American River Ducks build their nests, which are composed of grasses, leaves, moss, and the like, on the ground, sometimes on dry land at a distance from water, but more frequently in swampy land, where the grass is high enough for concealment. Their eggs usually show shades of green, buff, or cream colors. The Sea Ducks also build ground nests of leaves, grasses, twigs, seaweed, and the like, which are lined with down from the breast of the sitting bird. The eggs number from four or five to a dozen or more, and are buffy, greenish, bluish, or cream in color.

MALLARD

Anas platyrhynchos *Linnæus*

A. O. U. Number 132   See Color Plate 12

Other Names.— Common Wild Duck; Stock Duck; English Duck; French Duck; Green-head (male); Gray Duck (female); Gray Mallard (female).

General Description.— Length, 22 to 24 inches. Color of male: head, green; back, grayish-brown; under parts, gray with purplish-chestnut breast. Color of female: dusky-brown and tawny, variegated and lighter below than above.

Description.— ADULT MALE IN WINTER AND BREEDING PLUMAGE: Frequently several of the upper tail-coverts curl upward. *Head and upper neck, glossy green,* with shadings of purple and deep Prussian blue; *around neck, a white ring;* back, grayish-brown, more brown in center and on shoulders; lower back, rump, and tail-coverts, glossy black; tail, mostly whitish with center feathers long and recurved; *speculum, violet, purplish, and greenish, framed in black and white tips of greater coverts and secondaries,* forming all together two black and two white bars; lesser wing coverts, plain grayish; breast, rich purplish-chestnut; rest of under parts, silvery-gray finely zigzagged with dusky; bill,

olive; feet, orange-red; iris, brown. ADULT MALE IN SUMMER: Similar to female. ADULT FEMALE: Entire body, variegated with dusky-brown and tawny, with yellowish-brown edges to most of feathers, lighter in color below than on back; head and neck, quite buffy with streaks of brownish; *wing as in male;* feet, dull yellow; bill, dusky spotted with orange; iris, brown. IMMATURE: Similar to adult female.

Nest and Eggs.— NEST: On the ground in a tussock of grass or weeds; built of fine reeds, grass, or leaves; well lined with down. EGGS: 6 to 10, pale olive or buffy-green.

Distribution.— Northern hemisphere; in North America breeds from Pribilof Islands and northwestern Alaska across British America to Greenland, south to Lower California and across the United States on about the parallel of 37°; winters from Aleutian Islands, Montana, Wyoming, Nebraska, southern Wisconsin, Ohio, Maryland, and Nova Scotia (rarely) south to Mexico, the Lesser Antilles, and Panama; casual in Bermuda and Hawaii.

Asked to name the one duck most important to the human race, the economist would reply at once — "The Mallard." Other ducks are numerous in certain lands but the Mallard occupies most of the northern hemisphere and is

abundant wherever it has not been destroyed or reduced in numbers by man. Wild Mallards have furnished mankind with countless tons of food from time immemorial and domesticated Mallards have provided our race with vast quantities of eggs, flesh, and feathers for thousands of years. The Mallard, bred while in domestication, forms an important part of the food supply of China, the most populous country on the globe, and now the Pekin Duck is the staple stock of many a huge poultry plant in America. The Mallard is the chief waterfowl of most game preserves, on some of which 10,000 birds are reared annually. It has gained its ascendancy among the waterfowl of the world by taking advantage of every opportunity to increase and multiply. It never overlooks a chance. One spring day Dr. William T. Hornaday, director of the New York Zoological Park, found in Montana a little water hole hardly ten feet across; all about in every direction for miles and miles stretched a desert of sage-brush shim-

young are hatched. Then she leads them to water, watches over them, driving away their weaker enemies and decoying away the stronger, while the little ones skulk, dive, or hide among the water plants. Inherited experience has taught them the way of life; but many are seized by great fish, frogs and turtles, and no doubt the Hawks capture some. The brood is large, however, and the survivors are many.

When advancing winter seals the waters of their northern home and warns them to be gone, then there is a great flight from northwest to southeast, for few Mallards breed in the East, but many winter there. They reach the Atlantic from Maine to the Carolinas and, moving south, spend the winter largely in the southern States.

EDWARD HOWE FORBUSH.

Drawing by R. I. Brasher

MALLARD (¼ nat. size)

The chief waterfowl of most game preserves

mering in the sun. As he dismounted to drink, a female Mallard sprang from her nest in the sage-brush by the side of the little pool. One can understand from this episode how the Mallard has been able to spread over the northern hemisphere.

The Mallard is wary, wise, handsome, and strong. When in security it is one of the noisiest of all Ducks and its loud quack has become typical of the Duck the world around, but when in danger it can steal away as silently as the shades of night. It is a hardy bird, remaining in the North even in winter wherever open fresh water and food may be found. The female nests very early in the season, lines the nest and covers the eggs with down, and rarely leaves them until the

"The Mallard is quite omnivorous in regard to its food. The animal food consists of small frogs, tadpoles, toads, lizards, newts, small fish, fish fry, snails, mussels, leeches, earthworms, mice, and similar small game that it finds about the pond and in the edges of the woods. Its vegetable food includes grass, many species of seeds and aquatic plants, grain, nuts, acorns, fruits, etc. It is particularly fond of wild rice. In the South the Mallard is one of the friends of the rice farmer, as it destroys the scattered rice or volunteer rice of the field, which, if left to grow, would greatly reduce the value of the crop. It is serviceable to the southern people in another way, as it feeds very largely upon crayfish, which burrow into and undermine the levees and dikes.

Examinations of one hundred and twenty-six stomachs of Mallards, made at the Biological Survey, revealed 17 per cent. animal food and 83 per cent. vegetable. The most important items

Photo by Edward Fleischer
FEMALE MALLARD

of the animal food were dragon-fly nymphs, fly larvæ, grasshoppers, beetles, and bugs. Mollusks, earthworms, and crustaceans were found. The principal elements of the vegetable food, as found by the experts of the Biological Survey, were the seeds of the smartweeds, seeds and tubers of pondweed and of sedges. Other items of importance were the seeds of wild rice and other grasses, of burr reed, hornwort, water shield and widgeon grass. A great many vegetable substances of less importance were included in the Mallard's diet, of which the following are worthy of note; wild celery, algæ, roots of arrowhead; fruits, such as grapes, dogwood, sour gum, and bayberries; and the seeds of such small aquatic plants as millweed, horned pondweed, and mermaid weed." (Forbush, in *Game Birds, Wild-Fowl and Shore Birds.*)

BLACK DUCK

Anas rubripes *Brewster*

A. O. U. Number 133   See Color Plate 12

Other Names.— Dusky Duck; Black Mallard; Dusky Mallard; Red-legged Duck; Summer Black Duck; Spring Black Duck.

General Description.— Length, 22 to 24 inches. Color, dusky-brown. Darker than female Mallard and not so much white in the wing.

Color.— *General plumage, dusky-brown,* paler below; crown, darker than sides and throat, being quite blackish with pale brown streaks; ground color of neck, grayish-brown with dark streaking; wing-coverts, dusky-gray, the lesser ones varied with light edges; greater coverts, tipped with black and edging *purplish-blue speculum;* below, the lighter edgings of feathers in excess of

darker centers; above, the reverse; bill, olive; feet, orange-red with dusky webs; iris, brown.

Nest and Eggs.— NEST: On the ground; a rather large well-made structure of weeds and grass with a deep cup; lined with down and feathers. EGGS: 6 to 12, very pale buff or pale greenish-buff.

Distribution.— Eastern North America; breeds from central Keewatin and northern Ungava south to northern Wisconsin, northern Indiana and southern Maryland; winters from Nova Scotia south to southern Louisiana and Colorado; in migration west to Nebraska and central Kansas; casual in Bermuda; accidental in Jamaica.

The Black Duck and the Mallard are in certain ways supplementary each of the other. The former is the common Wild Duck of the eastern half of North America; the latter, of the western half, though they overlap considerably. They are enough alike in form, size, and habits to be called popularly " Black " Mallard and " Gray " Mallard. There is, nevertheless, a decided difference in temperament. Though the wild Mallard is a very shy bird, it soon loses this fear in captivity, as is seen in the fact that it is the progenitor of the domesticated Mallard. The Black Duck, under restraint, remains the same shy, timid skulker it always was. In fact I know of no Duck more implacably wild.

In the eastern half of the United States it breeds, in suitable localities, in the Middle States and as far north as well up into Labrador. The locations chosen for its nesting are thick, bushy swamps, reedy bogs, the higher edges of meadows, tracts of weeds or low brush on small islands, and the like. As with all Wild Ducks, the nest is hard to discover, except by accidentally flushing the female from the eggs. My first experience was in plodding through the thick of an alder swamp, when a big bird suddenly shot from the ground almost into my face, revealing a dozen large yellowish-white eggs under the vegetation.

Nesting is quite early in Connecticut, sometimes

as soon as the first days of April, but more generally from about April 20 to the first week in May. The broods keep very close in the thick swamps, and seldom show themselves on open water, unless it be close to thick aquatic reeds or grass. During August they take to wing, and the number of them reared in the vicinity can be judged somewhat by their evening flights. They are crepuscular and considerably nocturnal, flying and feeding during the night and at dawn and dusk.

The planting of wild-duck foods has become a real art. Captured birds are induced to breed in marshy enclosures. The eggs are given to domestic poultry, which raise the young somewhat tamer. These hand-reared birds breed much more readily than the wild parents. Many of the young are allowed to go wild, and these, through " the homing instinct," return in spring to breed in the locality. HERBERT K. JOB.

" In the interior the food of this species is largely vegetable, particularly in the fall. In

Photograph by H. K. Job

BLACK DUCKS

Just after alighting

The Black Duck is notably hardy, and can endure almost anything in the line of cold, so long as it can find open water in warm springs or small streams, where its food of aquatic animals or plants is accessible. I have seen it in wooded swamps in mid-winter, where there was open the merest little channel of a small stream. At times, in regions along the sea-coast, it flies out on the bays, or the open sea in daytime, to take refuge from disturbance.

Important practical projects have been carried out by private enterprise to establish the breeding of this and other species of Wild Ducks in large tracts of swampy land, where there are ponds.

the spring more animal food is taken. The vegetable food includes grass roots taken from meadows, roots, and shoots of aquatic plants, wild rice, grains, weed seeds, hazel nuts, acorns and berries. The animal food includes small frogs and toads, tadpoles, small minnows, newts, earthworms, leeches, and small shell-fish. The food of the Black Duck has the same practical interest for the game preserver as has that of the Mallard, for the Black Duck is closely related to the Mallard, thrives almost equally well on grain, and when grain fed, becomes a very excellent bird for the table." (Forbush, in *Game Birds, Wild-Fowl and Shore Birds.*)

FLORIDA DUCK

Anas fulvigula fulvigula *Ridgway*

A. O. U. Number 134

Length.— *22* inches.
Color.— Lighter colored than the Black Duck, the buff markings in excess of the dark ones, giving a lighter general tone; cheeks, chin, and throat, *plain* pale buffy; bill, olive; nail, black and dark spot at base; feet, orange-red; iris, brown.
Nest and Eggs.— Similar to the Black Duck.
Distribution.— Northwestern to southern Florida.

The Florida Duck is one of our little-known species of water-fowl because its range is very limited and nowhere does it seem to be abundant. It closely resembles the common Black Duck of the northern States, practically the only difference being the absence of streaks on the neck and also the fact that it is of smaller size. So far as known at the present time it is confined to Florida and the coast country of Louisiana. On the palmetto prairies of Hillsboro County, Florida, I discovered some one summer swimming about with their young in the small sloughs and grassy ponds of the region. When pursued the female would flutter away with a great splashing and giving every evidence of a highly nervous state of mind. The young meantime scampered for cover, with bodies raised high out of the water, propelling themselves forward at a most astonishing rate. The male bird was in no case seen in company with his family. Another time I came upon several of them at Lake Flint and again at Lake Hicpochee in the Okechobee country. Here they were feeding in the shallow water in company with numerous Coots which abound in the region. They are great birds to dabble and seem thoroughly to enjoy the sensation of muddying the waters. Frequently they quacked to each other, but their notes seemed to me to be indistinguishable from the call of the Black Duck.

Along the Louisiana coast there exist extensive salt and brackish water marshes through which wide creeks or bayous wind their serpentine way to the open sea. This is a haven for the myriads of Ducks and Geese that repair here to spend the winter. Upon the approach of spring, however, they depart for their northern breeding grounds and the deserted marshes are left to the mosquitoes, the snakes, and the alligators. And yet a few scattered birds tarry and brave the discomforts of the sweltering summer days. Should you at this season quietly paddle a pirogue along the smaller bayous, there would be a chance of coming upon the rare, elusive Florida Duck and her brood, and you might get a glimpse, or even a quick photograph, of them before they hurry into the marsh and disappear.

T. GILBERT PEARSON.

The Mottled Duck (*Anas fulvigula maculosa*) is a geographical variation of the Florida Duck and is resident in southern Texas and southern Louisiana. The two forms differ but little.

GADWALL

Chaulelasmus streperus (*Linnæus*)

A. O. U. Number 135   See Color Plate 12

Other Names.— Gray Duck; Gray Widgeon; Creek Duck; Bleating Duck; Speckle-belly; Blarting Duck; Red-wing.
General Description.— Length, 22 inches. Males are brownish-gray above and gray below; females are like female Mallards, but smaller and wing-patch is like that of the male. The only River Duck with a pure white, black-bordered wing-patch. Wings, long and pointed; tail with 16 feathers.
Description.— ADULT MALE: Wide low crest on top of head. Head and neck, grayish-brown, darker on crown and nape; sides of head, throat, and neck, speckled with dusky; lower neck, breast, sides of body, and foreback, dusky with crescentic bars of whitish on breast and waved with lighter along sides; lower back, dusky shading into black on rump and upper tail-coverts; shoulders, tinged with brown; lesser wing-coverts, gray; *middle coverts, chestnut; speculum, white,* formed by outer webs of secondaries, framed in velvet-black of greater coverts and bordered behind with black and ash; abdomen, white minutely zig-zagged with gray; under tail-coverts, velvet-black. ADULT FEMALE: No crest. Above, variegated with dusky and tawny-brown, very similar to female Mallard, without any crescentic or wavy marks of male; breast and abdomen, white with dusky spotting; wing as in male, without chestnut coverts.
Nest and Eggs.— NEST: A slight hollow in a bunch of grass or reeds, usually near water; constructed of dry grass; lined with down and feathers. EGGS: 8 to 12, creamy or buffy-white.
Distribution.— Nearly cosmopolitan; in North Amer-

Plate 12

Louis Agassiz Fuertes

GADWALL
Chaulelasmus streperus (Linnaeus)
MALE   FEMALE

MALLARD
Anas platyrhynchos Linnaeus
MALE   FEMALE

All ⅓ nat. size

BLACK DUCK
Anas rubripes Brewster
MALE

ica breeds from southern British Columbia, central Alberta and central Keewatin south to southern California, southern Colorado, northern Nebraska and southern Wisconsin; winters from southern British Columbia, Arizona, Arkansas, southern Illinois, and North Carolina south to Lower California, central Mexico, and Florida; accidental in Bermuda, Cuba, and Jamaica; rare in migration on the Atlantic coast of the Middle and New England States north to Newfoundland.

In North America this almost cosmopolitan species, the Gadwall, breeds mainly, if not entirely, in the western provinces. There is reason

Photo by H. K. Job   Courtesy of Outing Pub. Co.

GADWALL DUCKLINGS

to believe that the Gadwall was once not uncommon in New England; but within the last half century not many specimens are known to have been taken. Wilson believed it to be rare in the "northern parts of the United States," and it was probably always less common in the New England States than in the West and South; but I am convinced, by the statements of the older ornithologists and by descriptions given me by some of the older gunners, that the Gadwall was more often seen in the early part of the last century than it now is, and that some of the so-called Gray Ducks which were then killed here were of this species.

The Gadwall is a swift flier, resembling the Baldpate or Widgeon when in the air. It is quite distinctly a fresh-water fowl, and gets much of its living along the shores of lakes and rivers, concealed by the reeds, grasses, and bushes that grow near the shore or overhang it. It is a good diver at need, and is seen usually in pairs or small " bunches," often in company with other Ducks.

When approached from the land they usually make no attempt at concealment, but swim toward open water and take wing, making a whistling sound with their wings, that is not so loud as that made by the Baldpate. This is an excellent bird for the table, which accounts largely for its present rarity. It is fond of grain and is easily domesticated. It breeds naturally in the latitude of Massachusetts, and it might prove a great acquisition to the game preserve or to the farm-yard if it could be propagated in sufficient numbers. It seems a promising species with which to experiment with this end in view.

The food of this bird consists of the tender shoots of grasses, blades and roots of aquatic

Photo by H. K. Job   Courtesy of Outing Pub. Co.

NEST OF GADWALL

plants, seeds, nuts, acorns, insects, mollusks and other small forms of aquatic life, including small fish.

Edward Howe Forbush, in *Game Birds, Wild Fowl and Shore Birds.*

EUROPEAN WIDGEON

Mareca penelope (*Linnæus*)

A. O. U. Number 136   See Color Plate 13

Other Names.— Widgeon; Whistler; Whewer; Whew; Whim.

Length.— 18 to 21 inches.

Color.— Adult Male: Differs from the Baldpate in having head and neck uniform cinnamon-red; top of head, creamy or white; rest of plumage similar. Adult Female: Differs in having entire plumage more suffused with yellowish-brown.

Nest and Eggs.— Similar to those of the Baldpate.

Distribution.— Northern part of the eastern hemis-
phere; occurs in winter and in migrations rarely in
Wisconsin, Michigan, New York, Nova Scotia, New-
foundland, and Greenland south to Nebraska, Missouri,
Indiana, Ohio, North Carolina and Florida, and in
Alaska, British Columbia, and California.

The European Widgeon is an Old World
species which occasionally appears in the western
hemisphere. Normally it breeds among the
grassy swamps and lakes of Norway and Sweden
and is accounted the most abundant of the Ducks
in Lapland. Sometimes it breeds on the lakes of
northern Scotland but it is always an abundant
winter visitor to southern Scotland and throughout England. In size and general character it
closely resembles the Baldpate.

BALDPATE

Mareca americana (*Gmelin*)

A. O. U. Number 137   See Color Plate 13

Other Names.— American Widgeon; Bald Widgeon;
Green-headed Widgeon; Southern Widgeon; California
Widgeon; White-belly; Bald-head; Bald-crown; Ball-
face; Smoking Duck; Wheat Duck; Poacher.

General Description.— Length, 18 to 21 inches.

Males are brownish-gray above, and brownish-red and
white below. Females are yellowish-brown above, and
brownish and white below. Bill, small, widest near the
base; tail with 14 feathers.

Description.— ADULT MALE: Head with short crest.

Drawn by R. I. Brasher

BALDPATE (¼ nat. size)

A shy, wary, and garrulous Duck

Forehead, crown and back of head, white; a broad patch of glossy green on side of head extending around and down back of neck where it meets its fellow; cheeks and rest of neck, whitish with dusky spots; throat, dusky; back, shoulders, and rump, pale brownish-gray finely waved with dusky; breast, light brownish-red with pale gray edgings on feathers; sides of body, the same color waved with dusky; rest of lower parts, pure white except under tail-coverts which are black; lesser wing-coverts, plain gray; middle and greater coverts, pure white forming a large area, edged behind by black tips of the greater coverts; *speculum, glossy green bordered behind by black;* long inner secondaries, black with sharp white edges; rump and upper tail-coverts, white; the outside feathers of latter, dusky; primaries and their coverts, and tail, pale brownish-gray; this perfect plumage seen only in old drakes; bill, grayish-blue, black at tip and base below; feet, the same with dusky webs; iris, brown; usually the whole head and neck are pale brownish-yellow speckled with greenish and dusky. Adult Female: Head and neck all around, pale grayish; crown and back of neck, more brown with dusky spots; upper parts, yellowish-brown barred on back with dusky; shoulders spotted with the same; rump and upper tail-coverts, mixed brownish and white; tail, grayish-brown, the feathers white edged; wing, as in male but white area mottled with grayish; breast, brownish; rest of under parts, white; bill, feet, and eye, as in male.

Nest and Eggs.— Nest: On the ground in marshes; a neat well-built structure (for a Duck) of grass and weeds; lined with feathers and down from the breast of the bird. Eggs: 8 to 18, pale buffy.

Distribution.— North America in general; breeds from northwestern Alaska, northern Mackenzie, and central Keewatin south to Oregon, Nevada, Utah, Colorado, Kansas, southern Wisconsin, and northern Indiana; winters from southern British Columbia, southern Illinois, Maryland, and Delaware (casually Massachusetts and Rhode Island) south to southern Lower California, the West Indies, and Costa Rica; rare in migration to northern Ontario, northern Quebec, and Newfoundland; accidental in Hawaii, Bermuda, and Europe.

In the East the Baldpate or American Widgeon is a shy and wary bird and a great tell-tale. Quick to take the alarm itself, it is not slow to communicate it to others; and whenever a few Baldpates mix with a flock of other Ducks the sportsman must "mind his eye," or all his stratagems, disguises, and concealments will fail. In the Far West it is less wary.

Wild isolated lakes and rivers not much frequented by other Ducks often are chosen by the Baldpate as favorite nesting spots. Here they nest, usually among bushes or trees amid the dead leaves, often on high ground and not always near the water, but the eggs are well concealed and covered with their blanket of down. While the females are incubating, the males gather and, like the males of other River Ducks, go into the "eclipse" plumage, which closely resembles that of the female and leaves them inconspicuous in color during the summer while they molt and grow new wing quills.

As the season of migration approaches the Baldpates begin to move southward and many are shot in the northwestern States while flying from pond to pond; but they soon become shy, flying high over marshes and keeping well out of range of suspicious points, and by the last of October when they appear on the Atlantic coast they are difficult to kill.

The usual note of this bird is a soft whistle which is repeated often when the flock is on the wing. The flight is either in a line nearly abreast or in a group much like a flock of pigeons. Whenever anything alarms one of the flock a louder whistle warns all the others to shy off or climb the air.

The species is very fond of wild celery, but is a poor diver and depends somewhat upon the flocks of Redheads, Canvas-backs, Scaups, and

Courtesy of Nat. Asso. Aud. Soc.

NEST AND EGGS OF BALDPATE

The largest families are found among Ducks, Grouse, and Quails, the young of which are able to leave the nest as soon as the natal covering is dry

Coot to dive for its food which it steals from their bills the moment they appear above water. The male may be recognized by the conspicuous white of the forehead and wing-coverts.

Edward Howe Forbush.

GREEN-WINGED TEAL

Nettion carolinense (*Gmelin*)

A. O. U. Number 139   See Color Plate 13

Other Names.— Green-wing; Red-headed Teal; Winter Teal; Mud Teal.

General Description.— Length, 14 inches. Males are gray and red above, and whitish and red below; females are brown above, and whitish below.

Description.— ADULT MALE: Head, slightly crested. *Head and upper neck, rich chestnut with a glossy green patch behind eye,* blackening on lower border and on back where it meets its fellow, bordered below by a whitish streak; upper parts, grayish, very finely waved with dusky; *speculum, velvet-black on outer half, rich glossy green on inner;* primaries and wing-coverts, grayish; greater coverts with chestnut tips margining the speculum in front; breast, warm brownish; rest of lower parts, whitish speckled with round dusky spots on breast; sides, grayish, finely waved with dusky; a white crescent in front of wing; bill, dusky lead color, darker below; feet, bluish-gray; iris, brown. ADULT FEMALE: Head (no crest) and neck, light warm brown, whitening on throat and darkening on crown,

spotted with dark brown; upper parts, dark brown, each feather with distinct tawny edgings; sides of body, the same; rest of lower parts, whitish; wing as in male but speculum duller. YOUNG OF THE YEAR: Resemble adult female.

Nest and Eggs.— NEST: On the ground, usually in a thick growth of grass or among willows; constructed of dry grass; lined with feathers and down. EGGS: 8 to 11, sometimes 12, pale buff.

Distribution.— North America at large; breeds from the Aleutian Islands across British America to Newfoundland, south to central California, northern New Mexico, northern Nebraska, northern Illinois, southern Ontario, Quebec, and New Brunswick; winters from Aleutian Islands, British Columbia, Nevada, southern Nebraska, northern Indiana, western New York, and Rhode Island (casually Nova Scotia) south to southern Lower California, the West Indies, and Honduras; accidental in Hawaii, Bermuda, Greenland, and Great Britain.

Teals might be called the bantams of the duck tribe, as regards size. Their swiftness of flight is in inverse ratio to mere bigness, and probably there is nothing more rapid that flies. The celerity with which a Teal can vault into the air

Photo by H. K. Job   Courtesy of Outing Pub. Co.
NEST OF GREEN-WINGED TEAL

when alarmed is astonishing. In all its movements it evinces a real grace, a peculiar charm. From the culinary standpoint, surely there is nothing more luscious in the realm of waterfowl, no, not even the vaunted Canvas-back.

The Green-wing and the Blue-wing are the

two Teals of North America which are well known and widely distributed. Of the two the Green-wing is the hardier, lingering in the northern States late in the fall and even at times well into the winter, as long as there is any open water at all to be found in the ponds or at warm spring-holes. It is also, on the whole, the more northerly of the two, both in its winter range and in its breeding.

Of late years both species have been growing regrettably scarce in the eastern districts of the country. When found at all it is usually only a single bird or a pair. But in parts of the central and western districts there are still good flocks to be seen.

The nesting of the Green-wing is mostly in the Northwest, not so commonly on the sloughs of the open prairies of the Dakotas and southern Manitoba as in the more brush-grown regions further west and north. It grows more numerous as one penetrates into northern Manitoba and western Saskatchewan. In the latter it likes the alkaline ponds, and in the former the poplar forest lakes. The nest has seemed to me one of the most difficult of Ducks' nests to discover, in that it is usually located well back from water, sometimes near the edge of meadow and forest. These Teals frequent the open marshy pools, but my search for their nests in the grass nearby was usually in vain. They were generally discovered by accident. One was found near the cabin of an Indian half-breed by the edge of a cattle-pasture, amid grass, weeds, and low brush.

Plate 13

Louis Agassi Fuertes.

BALDPATE
Mareca americana (Gmelin)
MALE   FEMALE

EUROPEAN WIDGEON
Mareca penelope (Linnaeus)
MALE   FEMALE

GREEN-WINGED TEAL
Nettion carolinense (Gmelin)
MALE   FEMALE

All ⅓ nat. size

Others were under low bushes at the drier edges of meadows, back from the lake almost to the forest.

On a large island of a big alkaline lake in Saskatchewan it was my good fortune to discover my first nest of this species, which made the twentieth kind of Duck whose nesting I had discovered. The island was high and dry, open, overgrown with prairie grass and tracts of low brush. Many kinds of Ducks were nesting here and they kept flushing from their eggs close in front of me as I tramped about — Pintails, Gadwalls, Shovellers, Mallards, both Scaups, Blue-winged Teals, and others. Suddenly up fluttered a small duck with green on the wings. In the thick of the grass was a nest lined with soft down, containing a complement of eggs.

I have hatched and reared the young and find them hardy and easy to manage.

HERBERT K. JOB.

" The Green-winged Teal is fond of wild oats and rice, and takes seeds of various grasses and weeds, also chestnuts, acorns, wild grapes, berries, insects, crustaceans, worms, and small snails. Audubon states that he never found water lizards, fish, or even tadpoles in stomachs of this Teal. He regarded it, when fed upon soaked rice or wild oats, as far superior to the Canvasback, and considered it the most luscious food of any American Duck. Possibly it might be domesticated to advantage, as it has been bred in captivity in a small way." (Forbush, in *Game Birds, Wild-Fowl and Shore Birds.*)

BLUE-WINGED TEAL

Querquedula discors (*Linnæus*)

A. O. U. Number 140   See Color Plate 14

Other Names.— Blue-wing; White-faced Teal; Summer Teal.

General Description.— Length, 16 inches. Males are variegated dark and light brown above, and purplish-gray and yellowish-gray below with spots of black.

Females are dark brown above, variegated with lighter, and whitish below, mottled with brown.

Color.— ADULT MALE: Crown, grayish-black; *a large white black-edged crescent in front of eye;* rest of head, purplish-gray; lower hind-neck and fore-back,

Photo by H. K. Job

Courtesy of Nat. Asso. Aud. Soc.

FLIGHT OF BLUE-WINGED TEALS

Louisiana

variegated with brownish-black and yellowish-brown; lower back and rump, dark brown with a greenish tinge; *wing-coverts and outer webs of some of the shoulder feathers, dull cobalt blue; speculum, rich mallard green* enclosed by white tips of greater coverts and secondaries; some inner secondaries, greenish-black on outer web, greenish-brown on inner, striped lengthwise with reddish-buff; breast, very pale purplish-gray; rest of under parts, yellowish-gray with innumerable round black spots on breast, sides, and below, changing to bars on flanks behind; under tail-coverts, black; a patch on each side of rump, pure white; bill, ashy, darkening on ridge and tip; feet, yellow, webs duller; iris, brown. ADULT FEMALE: Head and neck, dull buff; crown, brownish-dusky streaked with brownish-black; cheeks and chin, whitish, markings small or obsolete; upper parts, dark brown with pale yellowish-brown edgings to all feathers; below, grayish-white, slightly more brown on breast, mottled on breast with dusky spotting and on sides and flanks with V-shaped brownish marks; wings as in male but speculum duller; bill, greenish-dusky; feet, paler yellow. YOUNG OF THE YEAR: Resemble adult female.

Nest and Eggs.— NEST: In marshes or on dry ground; constructed of grass and weed stems and lined with feathers and down. EGGS: 8 to 12, pale buffy.

Distribution.— Western hemisphere; breeds from central British Columbia, across British America to Newfoundland, south to Oregon, Nevada, New Mexico, Missouri, Indiana, northern Ohio, western New York (occasionally Rhode Island), and Maine; winters from about the parallel 36° south to the West Indies and South America as far as Brazil and Chile; accidental in Bermuda and Europe.

The Blue-winged Teal is quite similar to the Green-winged in many of its ways. One difference is that it is less able to endure cold. Before the heavy frosts of late autumn arrive, it is well to the southward. I have been told by hunters in Louisiana that in late October and November large columns of them pour along the Gulf coast and pass on into Texas and Mexico. However, a good many remain in Louisiana on the great reservations for the winter. In the winter of 1915–16 I saw there considerable numbers of this species, associating with the Green-wing, sometimes in flocks of several hundreds. Both kinds became quite gentle under protection, and would swim up within a few feet of blinds and of our cabin window and feast on rice which was scattered for them.

Quite a number of the Blue-wings remain each summer to breed in Louisiana. The general impression seemed to be that this is a rather new

Photo by H. K. Job   Courtesy of Outing Pub. Co.

BLUE-WINGED TEALS

About one month old

thing, and that they are breeding further south than usual because of protection. For the same reason, since the abolition of spring shooting, they are said to be nesting more and more in the central-western States. The Green-wing, however, still elects to go well to the north.

The Blue-wing is the common summer Teal of the open prairie regions of the northwest. In selecting its nesting-site it does not retire as far from the water as the Green-wing, but generally chooses the thick growth of prairie grass of the preceding year's growth, only a few rods back from the shallow marshy sloughs. Sometimes, however, it is placed on the dry prairie, half a mile from water.

The mother Blue-wing always approaches her nest with great caution, not flying directly to it, but, alighting at a distance, she sneaks through the grass and weeds. In leaving the nest she

Drawing by R. I. Brasher

BLUE-WINGED TEAL (⅛ nat. size)

It becomes quite gentle and tame under protection

pulls over it the blanket of gray down which she has plucked from her breast as a lining, entirely concealing the eggs, and making the nest practically invisible. After returning she sits very close, allowing herself almost to be stepped on before she will leave. Confident of her powers of concealment, she seems more apt than most other Ducks, except perhaps the other Teals, the Pintail, and the Shoveller, to nest carelessly near the haunts of man, in the prairie regions of her choice. The nests of these confiding Duck mothers may be placed beside a path or road, in a cattle-yard, or near a house. One summer I was at a hunter's camp just back from Lake Manitoba, and many times a day we followed a little path to the water. One day a boy walked a little off the trail, and came tearing back to camp to report having flushed a Duck from her eggs. It was a nest of this species, only a dozen feet from the path, in the prairie grass.

The Blue-wing prefers little shallow marshy pools, or meadows and bogs, to the larger open waters. Its food in the ponds includes much vegetable matter, seeds, grasses, pondweeds, etc.

It also at times devours snails, tadpoles, and many insects.

Photo by H. K. Job   Courtesy of Outing Pub. Co.

NEST OF BLUE-WINGED TEAL

Formerly in North Dakota I used to see it, often with the Shoveller or the Pintail, almost wherever there was the merest puddle by the roadside, in spring and early summer. Let us hope that it may continue abundant and intimate on the western farm.   HERBERT K. JOB.

CINNAMON TEAL

Querquedula cyanoptera (*Vieillot*)

A. O. U. Number 141

Other Names.— South American Teal; Red-breasted Teal.

General Description.— Length, 17 inches. Males have the head and under parts chestnut, and the upper parts brown. Females are dark brown above, variegated with lighter, and whitish below, mottled with brown.

Color.— ADULT MALE: *Head, neck, and entire under parts, rich purplish chestnut,* browner on crown and chin, blackening on center of abdomen; under tail-coverts, dark brown; fore-back, a lighter shade of same color crossed by brown curved bars; lower back and rump, greenish-brown, the feathers edged with paler; wing-coverts, cobalt-blue; some of the shoulder feathers, blue on outer web with a yellow center stripe; others, dark green, also with center stripe; *speculum, bright green* framed between white tips of greater coverts and white ends of secondaries; bill, dusky; feet, orange,

webs, darker; iris, brown. ADULT FEMALE: Quite similar to female Blue-winged Teal, but larger with longer bill and under parts with some tinges of the chestnut color of the male; bill, dusky, paler below and along edges; feet dull yellowish; iris, brown.

Nest and Eggs.— NEST: In tall grass, usually near water; very well constructed of woven grass and lined with feathers and down. EGGS: 9 to 13, creamy-white.

Distribution.— North and South America; breeds in North America from southern British Columbia, southwestern Alberta, Wyoming, and Western Kansas south to northern Lower California, southern New Mexico and southwestern Texas; winters from southern California, central New Mexico and southern Texas south to southern Lower California and central Mexico; rare east of the 100th meridan; occurs in South America from Peru and Brazil south to the Falkland Islands.

There are several curious facts concerning the Cinnamon Teal. It seems to have been first described from a specimen taken in the far-away Straits of Magellan early in the 19th century. Its first recorded appearance in the

United States apparently was in Louisiana near the town of Opelousas in 1849, but strangely enough it is now seldom seen in that State. At about that time, indeed, it appeared frequently in the lower valley of the Mississippi, but its normal range now appears to be much further to the west and south, for reasons which are not apparent. It is now essentially a bird of the West.

A flock of Cinnamon Teals in the water are likely to present an enlivening spectacle, as the males often engage in some sort of play not unlike the boy's game of leap-frog.

"The Cinnamon Teal nests very commonly in the lake region of southern Oregon. I have seen it nesting all through this section from Klamath Lake to Malheur Lake. In some places in southern Oregon it is more abundant than the Mallard or the Pintail. I think sportsmen often mistake the female for the Blue-winged Teal, because of the blue wing-markings." (W. L. Finley, MS.)

SHOVELLER

Spatula clypeata (*Linnæus*)

A. O. U. Number 142   See Color Plate 14

Other Names.— Spoonbill; Spoonbill Duck; Spoonbill Teal; Broady; Blue-winged Shoveller; Red-breasted Shoveller; Shovel-bill; Swaddle-bill; Butter Duck; Cow-frog.

General Description.— Length, 17 to 21 inches. Males have the colors green, white, blue, black, grayish-brown, and red in patches, while the females are pale brownish-yellow with spots and streaks of dusky. Both sexes have the bill long and clumsy and broadened at the tip.

Color.— ADULT MALE: Head and neck, dark glossy green; lower neck and *fore-breast, pure white,* extending almost around body; a narrow line from green of head down back of neck and back, dark grayish-brown shading into black on rump and upper tail-coverts; shoulders, broadly white; *wing-coverts and some outer feathers of shoulders, dull cobalt;* speculum, rich green set between white tips of greater coverts and black and white tips of secondaries; the long inner secondaries, greenish-black with white stripe; *lower breast, abdomen, and sides, purplish-chestnut,* lightening behind, followed by a white space; center tail-feathers, dusky; outer ones, white; under tail-coverts, black; bill, purplish dusky; feet, vermilion or orange; iris, orange or yellow. ADULT FEMALE: Ground color all over, pale brownish-yellow closely and narrowly streaked on crown, finely spotted on sides of head and neck all around with dusky; feathers of back and sides, broadly brownish-black, leaving only narrow edges of the lighter color; wing as in male but coloration duller; bill, yellowish shading to dull greenish at tip with some orange below and at base; iris, yellow; feet, dull orange.

Nest and Eggs.— NEST: Located in the marshes or in dry grass or under bushes; constructed of grass and leaves, and lined with feathers and down. EGGS: 8 to 14, olive-greenish or buffy.

Distribution.— Northern hemisphere; in North America breeds from Alaska, Mackenzie and southern Keewatin south to southern California, central New Mexico, northern Texas, northern Missouri and northern Indiana; winters from southern British Columbia across the United States on about the parallel 35° south to the West Indies, Colombia, and Hawaii; in migration occasional in Bermuda, and north to Nova Scotia and Newfoundland.

Drawing by R. Bruce Horsfall

SHOVELLER (¼ nat. size)

A quaint Duck, always carrying with it a prodigious spoon

Plate 14

Lou Agassiz Fuertes.

SHOVELLER
Spatula clypeata (Linnaeus)
FEMALE   MALE

WOOD DUCK
Aix sponsa (Linnaeus)
FEMALE   MALE

BLUE-WINGED TEAL
Querquedula discors (Linnaeus)
FEMALE
MALE

All ¼ nat. size

Though it is the wise practice to try to establish only one vernacular name for each species, I think that this Duck is better known as "Spoonbill" by the average hunter and out-door person. Nor is this name absurd, as is sometimes the case with popular names. The bird certainly carries quite a prodigious spoon with it upon all occasions, and is never at a loss to use it deftly in its natural haunts. A popular name for it might well have been "mud-sucker." The great bill is edged with a long fringe of bristles, and the quaint little Duck, almost top-heavy in appearance, paddles through the slough, constantly dabbling in water and ooze, which it takes into its bill, and, ejecting the refuse through its "sieve," retains whatever nutritious matter there may be.

This is another fresh-water Duck which is scarce in eastern districts but common in the West. There it frequents the shallow sloughs and bogs. It seems to be more strictly insectivorous than some of the other Ducks. Though they were abundant in Louisiana in winter, and were associated with the many Pintails and Teals which ate the rice put out for them, the Shovellers seldom touched it, not that they were particularly shy, but apparently because they preferred the natural fare of bugs and aquatic growths.

I have watched the Shovellers a good deal, as they nested in the prairie sloughs of the Northwest. In spring the male is a very gaudy creature, far outshining his plain little wife as they swim in the slough. They are then quite tame and easy to observe, and I have seen them in roadside pools, and even in swampy barnyards, where it seemed that they must be domesticated Ducks, until suddenly they flew away.

Nesting is usually in rather thick grass, frequently only a short distance back from the edge of the slough, or even in a tussock on quite moist ground. Yet, on the other hand, it is often far back on the dry prairie, quite a distance from water. Really there is no accounting for the tastes of individual Ducks.

Speaking of taste, in another sense, many people have the idea that the Shoveller is a lean, scrawny sort of bird, always thin and poor eating. My experience has been that, on its winter grounds in the South, it is fat and luscious, quite as good as one of those delicious little morsels, the Teals.

It is a rather delicate bird, and does not stand

the cold as well as many other Ducks. Hence it migrates fairly early and goes well to the South. If kept in captivity over winter in the North, both it and Teals should have some shelter from the worst of the winter weather. I have known them, in very bitter cold, to have their bills accumulate balls of ice as the water trickled down the bristles and froze. Probably no better plan could be employed for wintering these delicate Ducks than the model aquatic house which we have adopted for this purpose at the experiment station of the National Audubon Society at Amston, Conn. It is a small house built out in

Photo by H. K. Job   Courtesy of Outing Pub. Co.

YOUNG SHOVELLERS

the water on posts, the inside being a swimming-pool and a float, with large frame windows to the south and west, to utilize all possible sunshine. There the Ducks thrive in comfort all winter, without having the water freeze, even when 15 degrees below zero outside, and in spring they are not reduced in vitality, and are in fine condition to breed.   HERBERT K. JOB.

"Audubon states that repeated inspections of stomachs of these species disclosed leeches, small fish, earthworms, and snails. It feeds also on aquatic plants, grasses, grass seeds, and bulbs, which it procures along the shores of small ponds which it frequents. It often feeds by wading and dabbling in the mud, straining mud and water through its peculiarly constructed bill. Dr. James P. Hatch states that it feeds on aquatic insects, larvæ, tadpoles, worms, etc., which it finds in shallow, muddy waters; also crustaceans, small mollusks and snails." (Forbush, in *Game Birds, Wild Fowl and Shore Birds*.)

PINTAIL

Dafila acuta (*Linnæus*)

A. O. U. Number 143   See Color Plate 15

Other Names.— MALE: Sprig-tail; Split-tail; Spike-tail; Picket-tail; Peak-tail; Sharp-tail; Sprit-tail; Spring-tail; Spindle-tail; Kite-tail; Pigeon-tail; Pheasant-dock; Sea-pheasant. FEMALE: Gray Duck; Pied Gray Duck; Pied Widgeon. EITHER SEX: Winter Duck; Lady-bird; Long-necked Cracker; Harlan; Smee.

General Description.— Length, 24 to 30 inches. Males are gray above and whitish below; females are brown, varied on body with ocher and dusky. Both sexes have the head small and not crested, the neck long, and the tail long and pointed with 16 feathers; in the male *the two central tail-feathers are from 5 to 9 inches in length.*

Color.— ADULT MALE: Head and neck above, dark brown glossed with green and purple; back of neck with a stripe shading into the gray color of back; back, finely waved with dusky and white; shoulder-feathers and long inner secondaries, striped lengthwise with velvety-black and silvery-gray; lesser wing-coverts, plain gray; *greater coverts, tipped with rufous or cinnamon,* edging front of speculum; speculum, greenish in front, bronzy with violet reflections behind where edged with the white tips of secondaries; *two long central tail-feathers, black;* the remaining fourteen tail-feathers, gray; throat, white running up behind back of head in a narrow stripe; breast, abdomen and sides, whitish, finely waved with black on sides; under tail-coverts, black; bill and feet, grayish-blue; iris, brown. ADULT FEMALE: Head and neck all around, warm yellowish-brown with indistinct streaking; rest of plumage, varied with ocher, plain brown, and dusky; tail without long central feathers; wing, as in male but much smaller; bill, dusky bluish; feet, dull grayish-blue; iris, brown.

Nest and Eggs.— NEST: On the ground, usually in tall bunches of prairie grass, near water; made of dry grass, snugly and warmly lined with down. EGGS: 7 to 10, pale greenish to olive-buff.

Distribution.— Northern hemisphere; in North America breeds on Arctic coast from Alaska to Keewatin and south to southern California, southern Colorado, northern Nebraska, northern Iowa, and northern Illinois; winters from southern British Columbia, Nevada, Arizona, southern Missouri; southern Wisconsin, southern Ohio, Pennsylvania (rarely), and Delaware south to Porto Rico and Panama, and in Hawaii; in migration occasional on the Atlantic coast to northern Ungava, Greenland, and Newfoundland, and in Bermuda.

In other writings I have characterized the Pintail as the greyhound among waterfowl. It is an interesting, agile, swift-flying, hardy species, the male being wonderfully garbed in a most effective blending of gray, white, and brown, surpassing many other birds of more gaudy hues.

Though shy enough ordinarily, it becomes readily accustomed to man. The young are easy to rear and grow up very tame. I predict that the time is not far distant when the domesticated Pintails will be almost as familiar as tame Mallards, and will be raised on preserves and estates

Photograph by H. K. Job   Courtesy of Outing Publishing Co.

PINTAILS

Flying past blind and decoys, Little Vermilion Bay, Louisiana

Plate 15

PINTAIL *Dafila acuta* (Linnaeus)
MALE

FEMALE

⅓ nat. size

for sporting purposes, for food, or for ornament.

Though Pintails breed in the northerly parts of the continent, they also do so in our northwestern States. They are hardy and early, arriving in spring often before all the ice is out of the lakes. In northern Manitoba I have seen young on June 25 that were fully fledged except that the primaries were not quite long enough for flight. The eggs must have been laid in late March or April when conditions there are decidedly wintry. The nest is usually in dry grass or in a clump of weeds. Small dry islands are favorite locations. Otherwise it seems to be placed quite regardless of proximity to water. Frequently I have found it far back on the dry prairie, probably a mile from the nearest slough. It is perhaps more flimsily built than with most other Ducks, and often has rather less down than the average. The number of eggs in a clutch has seemed to me, in my experience, to run slightly less than with other species, seven or eight being most common, and seldom over nine or ten.

In migration it is not at all common in eastern waters, but in the Mississippi valley and west it is probably next to the Mallard in abundance. It prefers shallow ponds and marshy areas where grass and sedge grow from the water. In the sloughs where it breeds, the mated pairs swimming about make a beautiful sight. Even in autumn when the male has lost for the time his distinctive plumage, the birds are quite distinct, owing to their slender forms and long necks, and their movements always have the air of grace and good breeding. In fact the Pintail is one of my special favorites. Though I prefer it alive, I must admit that it is very fine on the table, and that I had just as soon eat it as any other Duck. On one of my winter jaunts in Louisiana, the hunters of the party provided many a Pintail, and it was considered that one Duck at a meal for each man was just the right amount.

By November the Pintails are abundant on the marshes of Louisiana where, in some localities, they winter by thousands. In the winter of 1915 I found it the general testimony that this species had increased wonderfully in abundance during the last few seasons, which result was attributed directly to the stopping of spring shooting — that outrage against reason and conservation, now made an offense by Federal Law and by our International Treaty. They were fond of grain, and, on putting this out, various Ducks, but chiefly Pintails, would assemble in large numbers to feast upon it, becoming so bold that I was able to film and to photograph large numbers of them from blinds, and even from the windows of our cabin on the marsh.

HERBERT K. JOB.

WOOD DUCK

Aix sponsa (*Linnæus*)

A. O. U. Number 144   See Color Plate 14

Other Names.— Summer Duck; The Bride; Bridal Duck; Wood Widgeon; Acorn Duck; Tree Duck.

General Description.— Length, 20 inches. Males are green, blue, and purple above with white streaks, and red, yellow, and white below. Females are brown above, and yellowish-brown and whitish below. Both sexes have long, full crests; the bill narrow, higher at base than wide; the tail long with soft, broad feathers.

Color.— ADULT MALE: Head, including crest, iridescent green and purple; a narrow white line from bill over eye to rear of crest; another commencing behind eye and running to nape; a broad white patch on throat forking behind, one streak curving upward behind eye, the other curving on side of neck; above, lustrous violet and bronzy green; shoulders and long inner secondaries, velvet-black glossed with purple and green; a greenish-blue speculum bounded by white tips of secondaries behind; primaries, white-edged and frosted on webs near end; upper tail-coverts and tail, deep dusky black; *sides and front of lower neck and breast, rich purplish-chestnut evenly marked with small V-shaped white spots;* a large black crescent in front of wing preceded by a white one; sides, yellowish-gray waved with fine black bars; rest of *under parts, white;* lengthened flank feathers falling in a tuft of rich purplish-red below wing; bill, white in center, black on ridge, tip, and below, with a square patch at base of lake-red; feet, yellowish-orange; iris and lids, crimson. ADULT FEMALE: Crest small; head and neck, grayish-brown, darker on crown; feathers at base of bill narrowly all around, chin, upper throat, and *a broad circle around eye running into a streak behind, pure white;* upper parts, brown with some gloss; fore-neck and sides of body, yellowish-brown streaked with darker; breast spotted indistinctly with brown; abdomen, white; bill, grayish with a white spot in center, reddish at base; feet, dusky yellow; iris, brownish red.

Nest and Eggs.— NEST: In a hollow tree from 20 to 40 feet from ground, lined with feathers and down. EGGS: 8 to 14, creamy-white.

Distribution.— Temperate North America; breeds from southern British Columbia eastward on about the parallel 46° to New Brunswick and Nova Scotia, south to central California, Texas and Florida; winters chiefly in United States from about 37° southward; accidental in Bermuda, Mexico, Jamaica, and Europe.

The Wood Duck is one of the most richly and beautifully colored birds of the United States, and, for a migratory bird, is peculiarly

MALE WOOD DUCK

ours, in that it breeds nearly all over our national domain, from north to south, and in winter it mostly remains within our borders. More than any other Duck it is a woodland bird. It frequents ponds and streams which are bordered by woods, and makes excursions, a-wing or a-foot, or both, back from water into the real woods, where it devours nuts, as well as whatever insect or other small life it encounters. I have examined specimens, taken in the fall, which had their crops completely filled with whole acorns. Such a meal, surely, should " stand by " for a long time!

The regular natural nesting site is in a hollow tree, preferably in the woods, and it is often quite a distance back from water. Owing to the increasing scarcity of large hollow trees, these Ducks seem at times hard pressed to find suitable locations. On a farm in Connecticut back from a pond, an old apple tree growing in a pig-pen by the barn was cut down, and, in chopping open a hollow branch, eleven eggs of the Wood Duck were discovered, though never had a Duck been seen about the premises. About a mile from this place another farmer showed me a nest with ten eggs at the top of the hay in his barn, up near the roof. The mother Duck came through a broken clapboard up near the peak of the roof, dug a hollow in the hay, and lined it with down from her breast. Still another nest, on this same farm, was in an apple tree of the orchard. A couple of miles away another was in a large maple beside the highway, so low down than one could just peer in from the ground. It is surprising through what a small hole a Duck can pass to enter and leave a nest.

In one case which I witnessed, a Golden-eye, emerging from quite a narrow slit, had fairly to wriggle from side to side to force its way out.

After the nesting season the Wood Ducks are seen in small flocks, probably family parties. They frequent the wooded swamps, and fly out to the more open ponds and streams about dusk. Where dead trees or branches have fallen into water, a typical sight, to be witnessed by creeping very silently through the bushes, is a row of these beautiful Ducks standing on the fallen timber enjoying the sunshine, some asleep, with bills under the wing-coverts, others preening their feathers, but all appearing very well contented with their lot in life.

This bird was classed by the Government as one of our vanishing species. This aroused widespread concern, and caused a number of States to prohibit shooting for terms of years;

NEST AND EGGS OF WOOD DUCK

The regular nesting site is in a hollow tree, preferably in the woods, and is often a distance from water

the same action was adopted also by Federal regulations. There seems now to be a marked change for the better, in which result artificial propagation is playing an important part. It had been found that this Duck, through somewhat peculiar but perfectly practicable methods, can be bred and reared in captivity, birds thus raised bringing high prices. Quite an industry arose in breeding American Wood Ducks in Holland and selling them in America. Now we have learned the process ourselves, and anyone who desires can breed these beautiful birds in almost any small fenced pool or pond. To those who desire it, the National Association of Audubon Societies, through its Department of Applied Ornithology, imparts detailed information and furnishes literature. HERBERT K. JOB.

REDHEAD

Marila americana (*Eyton*)

A. O. U. Number 146   See Color Plate 16

Other Names.— American Pochard or Poachard; Red-headed Broadbill; Raft Duck; Red-headed Raft Duck.

General Description.— Length, 23 inches. Males have the head red, the neck and fore part of the body blackish, and the remainder of the body silver-gray above and on the sides with a center line below of white; females have the head duller and paler and the back browner. Both sexes have the *bill short, the skull rounded and high-arched, the feathers on the head presenting a puffy appearance,* and the hind toe with a web or lobe.

Color.— ADULT MALE: The entire head and the *neck all around, rich pure chestnut* with bronzy reflections; back, white crossed with fine black wavy lines, the colors about *equal* in amount, producing a distinct silvery-gray shade; sides of body, the same; lower neck and fore-parts of body with rump and tail-coverts above and below, blackish; wing-coverts, gray finely dotted with white; speculum, ash, bordered inside with black; center line of body below, whitish; bill, dull blue with a black band on end; feet, grayish-blue with dusky webs; *iris, yellowish-orange.* ADULT FEMALE: Head and upper neck, dull brownish-red, fading to whiter on cheeks, chin, and a space behind eye; upper parts, brownish, the feathers with paler edges; breast and sides, brownish, remainder of lower parts, white; bill, dull grayish-blue with brown belt near end; feet and iris, as in male.

Nest and Eggs.— NEST: On ground near water or in a clump of dead reeds over the water; bulky but well-constructed and lined with down. EGGS: 7 to 10, pale olive or light buff.

Distribution.— North America; breeds from southern British Columbia, central Alberta, central Saskatchewan, and southwestern Keewatin south to southern California, Utah, southern South Dakota, southern Minnesota, and southern Wisconsin; winters from southern British Columbia, Utah, New Mexico, Kansas, Illinois, Maryland, Delaware, and Massachusetts south to Lower California, central Mexico, and Florida; accidental in Jamaica; in migration casual in Alaska and regularly on the Atlantic coast north to southern Labrador.

In the Redhead we have the counterpart of the Canvas-back. The young of either can hardly be distinguished save by the shape of the bill, especially in the downy stage. Later they grow more apart, yet they retain many resemblances. Many a person who thinks he has eaten Canvas-back has very likely dined instead on Redhead.

It is usual to find the Redhead the more numerous of the two, though along the Gulf coast of Louisiana, where Audubon found Redheads in plenty, I have found them now to be rare, even in sections where the Canvas-back is abundant. Like the latter, it is found mostly on the sea-coast or on the larger bodies of water inland. It feeds much by diving, catching small fish and other aquatic life. Also it is partial to roots and shoots of aquatic plants. I have

Photo by H. K. Job   Courtesy of Outing Pub. Co.

YOUNG REDHEADS

Eighteen days of age

watched both species together diving, and both exhibit the same skill and celerity in this pursuit, with no noticeable difference.

This species, like the others, breeds in the sloughs and marshes of the Northwest, in about the same localities, but is generally the more common. Wherever I have found the Canvas-back breeding, the Redhead has been there too, whereas the converse is not true; there are many sloughs in which Redheads breed where there are no Canvas-backs. If there is any distinction in the choice of nesting-sites, I should say that the Redhead is even more apt than the other to build out in reeds or canes growing in quite deep water. In northern Manitoba, on Lake Winni-pegosis, in places where the Canvas-back was nesting in meadows in the sedge, with water not knee-deep, I found Redhead nests among the outer reeds on the margins of boggy ponds, where one needed a canoe to reach them.

Perhaps the Redhead is not more prolific than any other Duck, but I have found larger numbers of eggs in some of their nests than is at all usual with others, the maximum number being twenty-two, the most I ever found in a wild Duck's

Photo by H. K. Job   Courtesy of Outing Pub. Co.

NEST OF REDHEAD

Built over water on edge of channel in a clump of flags and rushes

nest, and all fertile and advanced in incubation. The eggs are quite different from those of the Canvas-back, being yellowish-white in color, and with a very smooth glossy surface, almost like billiard balls, and easy to recognize.

In the Northwest where wild Ducks nest in abundance, it is not uncommon for individual

Photo by H. K. Job   Courtesy of Outing Pub. Co.

HARDY AND DOCILE

Some more young Redheads

Ducks to lay in each other's nests. The Redhead and the Ruddy Duck seemed to me to be especially addicted to the practice. They laid rather freely in each other's nests, and frequently palmed off their offspring thus on the unsuspecting Canvas-back.

Both kinds have been kept and studied in captivity. I have reared both from the egg to maturity, and under my direction have had both kinds breed. Though the young of both were quite easily reared, the Redhead presents fewer difficulties than the Canvas-back. It breeds more readily under favorable conditions, and the young are especially hardy and docile, though the young Canvas-backs, too, are quite manageable. Most experimenters, in time past, have had much less difficulty in keeping Redheads than Canvas-backs under artificial conditions.

As a result of this line of experimental research, I am confident that in the not distant future both kinds will regularly be propagated on estates where there are suitable ponds.

HERBERT K. JOB.

CANVAS-BACK

Marila valisineria (*Wilson*)

A. O. U. Number 147   See Color Plate 16

Other Names.— White-back; Bull-neck; Can.

General Description.— Length, 24 inches. Males have the head red, the lower part of the neck and the fore part of the body blackish, and the remainder of the body grayish-white above with a center line below of white; females have the head and neck yellowish-brown and the body grayish-brown. Both sexes have *the profile long and sloping (lines of head and bill nearly one)*, bill three times as long as wide, and hind toe with web or lobe.

Color.— ADULT MALE: Feathers of entire head and upper neck (all around) dark reddish-brown, obscured on the crown and in front of eye and throat by dusky; upper parts, white very finely waved with narrow black zigzag bars, the general effect much lighter than in the Redhead; rest of plumage substantially as in that bird but upper tail-coverts and rear parts in general, grayer; *bill, plain dusky bluish, not banded;* feet, grayish-blue; *iris, red.* ADULT FEMALE: Very similar to the female

Redhead; head and neck, more brownish without rufous shade but easily distinguished from that bird *by the much longer and differently shaped bill;* iris, reddish-brown; bill and feet, as in the male Canvas-back.

Nest and Eggs.— NEST: Usually in tall rushes or reeds near water; bulky; constructed of dry grass and reeds; lined with down. EGGS: 6 to 10, pale olive green.

Distribution.— Whole of North America, breeding from Oregon, Nevada, Nebraska and southern Minnesota northward to southwestern Keewatin, Great Slave Lake, Fort Yukon, and central British Columbia; winters from southern British Columbia, Nevada, Colorado, Illinois, Pennsylvania, and western New York south to central Mexico and Gulf coast; in winter formerly abundant in Maryland, Virginia, and North Carolina, now rare; occasional south to Florida, and casual in the West Indies, Bermuda, and Guatemala; in migration north rarely to New Brunswick and Nova Scotia.

CANVAS-BACK (¼ nat. size)

The king of waterfowl, famous for the flavor of its flesh

Drawing by R. I. Brasher

Though the Canvas-back has acquired a great reputation for the flavor of its flesh, it is probable that this characteristic taste depends upon

Photo by H. K. Job   Courtesy of Doubleday, Page & Co.
TYPICAL NEST OF CANVAS-BACK

the local food supply. Various water-plants besides the spicy wild celery please His Majesty, the assumed king of waterfowl, so he is not always spiced up. At various times when I have eaten Canvas-back, I really could not distinguish it from other good-meated wild Ducks. In northern Manitoba the local hunters, I was told, when shooting, usually single out Mallards first, finding them meatier and fully as tasty.

None the less is the Canvas-back a most fascinating waterfowl. Swifter than the proverbial arrow, the flocks fairly sing like bullets, as they pass down wind. Wonderfully agile and graceful are their movements in the water, especially when they leap headlong for the dive, leaving one to guess where they may reappear. I once watched two Indians in the Northwest, each in a canoe, out on a large lake, try to catch a large young Canvas-back not yet quite able to fly. It took them about an hour of the liveliest sort of work before the bird rose, winded, to the surface and let one of them pick it up.

Its breeding-grounds are the marshes and sloughs of the interior Northwest — North Dakota, Manitoba, Saskatchewan, and on up into the trackless wilds. There I have often found

its nest, a semi-floating pile of dead stems, usually amid a clump of reeds or rushes, or else in long sedge, but always in vegetation growing from water usually at least knee deep. The nest is a sort of deep wicker-basket, lined with dark gray down, in contrast with the white down of the Redhead. The eggs usually number eight to eleven, and are of a peculiar lead-bluish color, with some olive tinge, differing from that of any other Duck. The ducklings are of a decided yellow-olive color. From the first they may be distinguished from others by the straight profile of the upper mandible, always characteristic of the Canvas-back.

A most hardy species, it is driven southward only by the actual freezing of the lakes. Numbers of them stay in Lake Cayuga, New York, and other similar bodies of water, till they sometimes freeze in and perish. One of their principal lines of migration is southeast across country from the breeding-grounds of the Northwest out to the Atlantic coast at Chesapeake Bay — a noted winter resort of the species.

Photo by H. K. Job   Courtesy of Outing Pub. Co.
CANVAS-BACK
About six weeks old

Despite incessant persecution, I think that the Canvas-back is on the increase, owing to the stopping of the suicidal practice of spring shoot-

REDHEAD
Marila americana (Eyton)
MALES
CANVAS-BACK
Marila valisineria (Wilson)
FEMALE
MALES
All ¼ nat. size

ing. Recently, I was studying waterfowl in the Mississippi Delta country, and was anchored off the exit of Pass, in a dense fog. This suddenly lifted, and we saw, stretched out before us, a solid "bed" of Ducks, surely half a mile long and one hundred yards wide. The guide and I estimated that there were thirty-five thousand, over one-half of which were Canvasbacks. And this was but one of many such hordes along that coast. Cheer up, friends of wild birds, the "King" still lives!

HERBERT K. JOB.

SCAUP DUCK

Marila marila (*Linnæus*)

A. O. U. Number 148   See Color Plate 17

Other Names.— Mussel Duck; Green-head; Black-neck; Gray-back; Blue-bill; Greater Blue-bill; Blue-billed Widgeon; Broad-bill; Raft Duck; Flock Duck; Shuffler; Black-head; Big Black-head; Floating Fowl; American Scaup Duck; Greater Scaup Duck; Troop-fowl.

General Description.— Length, 20 inches. Males have the fore parts black, and the rest of the body white marked with black; females are dusky-brownish above and yellowish-brown below. Both sexes have the bill short and wide, and the hind toe with web or lobe.

Color.— ADULT MALE: *Entire head, neck, and fore parts of body, black with green and bluish reflections;* middle of back, shoulders, and most of under parts, white, everywhere except on flanks and abdomen marked with fine transverse zigzag lines of black; wing-coverts similar but more obscurely waved; greater coverts, tipped with black; *speculum, white framed in black* of greater coverts and ends of secondaries;

primaries, brownish-black; *bill, dull bluish-gray* with black nail; feet, bluish-gray; webs, dusky; iris, yellow. ADULT FEMALE: *A belt of pure white around face at base of bill;* black parts of male replaced by dusky-brown; upper parts in general, dusky-brownish without black marking; wing, as in male; below yellowish-brown, duskier on breast and along sides; center line of body, whitish; bill, legs, and eyes as in male.

Nest and Eggs.— NEST: In marshy ground, made of weeds, grass and lined with down. EGGS: 9 to 12, pale buffy-olive or olive-gray.

Distribution.— Northern part of northern hemisphere; in North America breeds from about the parallel 48° northward, rarely on Magdalen Islands, in Ontario, and Michigan; winters from Maine to Florida and the Bahamas, and from Alaska, Nevada, Colorado and Lake Ontario south to southern California, southern New Mexico, and southern Texas; in migration rare in central Ungava, Newfoundland, and Nova Scotia.

Photograph by A. A. Allen

SCAUP DUCKS

Flying over Cayuga Lake

Scaup is the European name of this bird but it will hardly be recognized under that title by American gunners. Here it is known as the Broad-bill, Blue-bill, Blue-billed Widgeon, Widgeon, etc. It seems more inclined to migrate to salt water than does the Lesser Scaup, but this may be because its winter habitat is more northern and it is more likely to be driven to the open sea by the freezing of the fresh water. It is common in winter in the unfrozen marshes and lakes of central New York, but if these freeze it must go to the sea or starve. Therefore, the species is often more numerous in the late winter and early spring on the coastal waters than it is in the autumn and early winter while the lakes remain open.

These birds breed mainly in the Northwest in marshes and about numerous small ponds. Those that migrate to the Atlantic coast winter chiefly from Massachusetts to Chesapeake Bay, while farther south their place is taken mainly by the Lesser Scaup. They are swift flyers, showing a stripe of white on the wing as they pass in a characteristic waving line. The male may be distinguished from the male Lesser Scaup, which he closely resembles, by the color of the head which has a greenish luster in contrast with the purplish cast common on that of the lesser bird. At a distance both appear black; therefore, they are called Black-heads, indiscriminately. The white faces of the females of both species are very conspicuous.

The Scaup is an excellent diver and when it has been feeding in the interior on the roots of the wild celery (*vallisneria*) and other water plants, its flesh is fit for the epicure, and even when it feeds on the eel grass and other vegetation on salt marshes and flats it is fairly well flavored, but after it has fed for a time in salt water on crustaceans and mollusks it grows fishy and is not highly prized for the table.

EDWARD HOWE FORBUSH.

LESSER SCAUP DUCK

Marila affinis (*Eyton*)

A. O. U. Number 149   See Color Plate 17

Other Names.— Black Jack; River Broad-bill; Creek Broad-bill; and names of the Scaup Duck with or without qualifying terms.

Length.— 17 inches.

Description.— ADULT MALE: Varies principally from the Scaup Duck in size; *iridescence of head chiefly purple;* flank feathers finely marked with black in a zigzag pattern; otherwise similar. ADULT FEMALE: Very similar to the female Scaup Duck but smaller and with breast and sides more inclined to rufous-brown.

Nest and Eggs.— Similar to Scaup, eggs averaging smaller.

Distribution.— North America at large; breeds from the northern borders of the United States northward; more rarely to southern Montana, Colorado, northern Iowa, northern Indiana, and western Lake Erie; winters from southern British Columbia, Nevada, Colorado, Lake Erie, and New Jersey south to the Bahamas, Lesser Antilles, and Panama; rare in migration in Newfoundland, New Brunswick, and Nova Scotia.

The species of marine Duck which is probably under more general observation than any other is the Lesser Scaup. These are the Ducks which are seen in great "rafts" or "beds" just offshore in harbors or bays in winter and early spring nearly all along the Atlantic coast, from Long Island Sound to Florida. They feed, by diving, largely on mollusks or other sluggish marine life.

A flock settles on the water over some mussel-bed or clam-flat, and the members are soon diving actively. Another passing flock sees and joins it, and so on, until there may be several thousands. These usually stretch out into a long column, and keep swimming to windward, after satisfying their hunger, the white-penciled backs of the males glistening brilliantly in the sunshine.

In some localities, where they are not persecuted, these flocks become quite tame. At Tampa, Florida, they swim up right among the vessels lying at the wharves. The greatest sight is at Palm Beach, Florida, in Lake Worth. There flocks of them swim close up to the boat-landings back of the hotels. Guests throw out bread and are wonderfully amused to see wild Ducks fight for food within six to ten feet of their benefactors. Sometimes they even take food from

Plate 17

RING-NECKED DUCK
Marila collaris (Donovan)

MALE   FEMALE

LESSER SCAUP DUCK
Marila affinis (Eyton)

MALE   FEMALE

All ¼ nat. size

SCAUP DUCK
Marila marila (Linnaeus)

MALE   FEMALE

the outstretched hand. The strangest part of this is that when they fly outside the protected area they become as shy as ever.

Hardy, like all the marine Ducks, they are especially late in arriving in autumn along the Atlantic coast of the United States. Little is seen of them till November. At first they seem inclined to keep out on the open sea, and the gunners get little chance at them before severe cold drives them in.

One reason for this tardiness is that, next to the White-winged Scoter, the Scaup is ordinarily the last Duck to breed. They nest in the same

of July. As it is ten or eleven weeks before they can fly, the young are not a-wing before late September or early October.

The nests are not usually built out over the water like those of the Canvas-back and Redhead, but either in weeds or grass on a dry shore, a little back from the water's edge, or else in a firm tussock of meadow grass, right at the margin of a boggy slough, where the female can slip into the water from the nest.

I have raised the young by hand, and find them especially interesting. At first they are rather wild, great on jumping, but soon they become

Photograph by H. K. Job   Courtesy of Houghton Mifflin Co.

LESSER SCAUP DUCKS

At Palm Beach, Florida, in March

prairie marshes of the Northwest as do the Canvas-back and Redhead. There I have found that their layings are not complete until about the middle of June. The first young broods are generally seen in the sloughs toward the middle

very docile. Their soft downy suits are of rich dark olive-brown color, and they erect their crown-feathers somewhat under excitement, which gives them quite a striking appearance.

HERBERT K. JOB.

RING-NECKED DUCK

Marila collaris (*Donovan*)

A. O. U. Number 150   See Color Plate 17

Other Names.— Ring-bill; Moon-bill; Marsh Blue-bill; Black Jack; Bunty; Ring-billed Blackhead; Bastard Broad-bill; Ring-necked Scaup Duck; Ring-necked Scaup; Ring-neck; Ring-billed Duck.

General Description.— Length, 18 inches. Males have head, upper parts, and breast black, and remaining

lower parts white; females have upper parts brown, and lower parts yellowish-brown and white.

Color.— ADULT MALE: Head and neck all around lustrous black with purple reflections; extreme chin, white; *chestnut ring around lower neck;* fore-breast and upper parts, black; speculum, bluish-gray; under parts from breast, white; lower abdomen and sides, finely marked with black; tail and under tail-coverts, black; wings, dark brown; *bill, black with bluish-gray base and a band of same color near tip;* feet, grayish blue with dusky webs; iris, yellow. ADULT FEMALE: Forehead, narrowly, sides of face more broadly, pure white; rest of head, umber-brown, lightening on cheek and throat; *a white eye-ring;* upper parts, dusky-brown; breast, sides of body, brown, variegated with lighter; abdomen, white; wing as in male; speculum, duller, bill, legs, similar to male; iris, brownish–yellow.

Nest and Eggs.— NEST: On the ground in marshes; made of dry grass and leaves and lined with down. EGGS: 6 to 12, usually 9 or 10, rarely 15, grayish-white to buff.

Distribution.— North America in general; breeds from northern California, North Dakota, northern Iowa and southern Wisconsin northward; winters from southern British Columbia, New Mexico, northern Texas, southern Illinois and New Jersey south to Porto Rico and Guatemala; occurs in migration north to Newfoundland, Nova Scotia, and Quebec.

Distinctive peculiarities about the Ring-necked Duck are that it is almost never seen in large flocks, and seldom in open water. It swims buoyantly, and is much given to raising its head with a swan-like movement of its neck, and to erecting the feathers on the back of its head. It rises readily, from water or land, its wings whistling faintly; its flight is swift and direct.

It is expert at diving and in that way captures many minnows, crawfish, snails, tadpoles, and frogs, though a considerable portion of its food consists of the roots of aquatic plants and seeds.

Nowhere is this Duck recorded as very common. It resembles the Lesser Scaup in appearance, size, and habits, and the two species mingle together.

GOLDEN-EYE

Clangula clangula americana *Bonaparte*

A. O. U. Number 151   See Color Plate 18

Other Names.—Golden-eyed Duck; American Golden-eye; Garrot; Whistler; Whistle-Duck; Whistle-wing; Brass-eyed Whistler; Whiffler; Jingler; Merry-wing; Great-head; Bull-head; Iron-head; Cub-head; Copper-head; Cur; Spirit Duck.

General Description.— Length, 20 inches. Males have the head greenish-black, the fore part and sides of the body white, and the back and tail black; females have the head and back brown and the under parts grayish. Both sexes have fluffy crests, and bills that are short, high at the base, and narrowed near the tip.

Color.— ADULT MALE: *Head and neck, glossy greenish-black; a large oval spot in front and below eye, white;* lower neck, under parts, middle and greater wing-coverts, most secondaries, and some shoulder-feathers, white; long inner secondaries, edge of wing, primary coverts, primaries and back, black; tail, ashy; some flank feathers with narrow dusky streaks on top edge; bill, dusky with *yellow tip;* feet, orange, dusky webs; *iris, yellow.* ADULT FEMALE: Chin, upper throat and head all around, brown; neck and entire lower parts, dull whitish, shaded on breast and sides with ashy; upper parts, brownish; some feathers of upper back with lighter edges; upper tail-coverts, tipped with pale brown; bill, feet, and eye as in male; white wing spaces much more restricted.

Nest and Eggs.— NEST: In hollow tree, made of grass, leaves, and moss and lined with down. EGGS: 9 to 12, light greenish.

Distribution.— North America; breeds from central Alaska, across British America to Newfoundland, south to southern British Columbia, southern Montana, northern North Dakota, northern Michigan, northern New York, and northern New England; winters from about the parallel 43° south to southern California, central Mexico and Florida.

The Golden-eye is commonly known as the Whistler because of the peculiar penetrating whistle made by its wings in flight. There are times when these cutting strokes can be heard even before the bird itself can be clearly made out. The Whistler breeds from just above the latitude of Massachusetts northward to the limit of trees, making its nest in a hollow tree near some fresh-water pond or river. It breeds in

the interior of Alaska, but is very rarely seen on the coast. It is found almost throughout the interior of North America, and is distinctively a fresh-water bird until the frosts of winter begin to close the ponds and rivers, when most of the Whistlers in New England go to the salt water. Some, however, still remain in the unfrozen fresh waters of the North, South, and West.

The Whistler is a remarkably active bird,

AMERICAN GOLDEN-EYE *Clangula clangula americana* Bonaparte
MALE   FEMALE
⅓ nat. size

dives like a flash, and rarely comes well to decoys. It has learned to be extremely wary and cautious, but in stormy weather it often keeps close to shore, which gives the shore gunner his chance. It does not always dive for its food, but sometimes dabbles in the mud along the shore with Blue-bills or other Ducks. Offshore it feeds largely on mussels, which it dislodges and brings up from the bottom. Audubon found it feeding on crawfish on the Ohio River. Wayne says that in South Carolina a small mussel of salt or brackish water is its favorite food. Knight has observed it feeding on these and also on some vegetable substances. He states that it eats small fish and fry also, and along the coast it feeds on mussels and other mollusks; but Elliot believes that in the interior the Whistler feeds on vegetable matter, such as grasses and roots.

When feeding there and when it first comes to the salt water, in autumn, the young are fairly tender and well-flavored, being about on a par with the Blue-bill as a table delicacy. Some of the residents of Cape Cod consider it superior to the Scoters. Nuttall says that it eats fresh-water vegetation, such as the roots of Equisetums and the seeds of some species of Polygonums.

EDWARD HOWE FORBUSH, in *Game Birds, Wild-Fowl and Shore Birds.*

BARROW'S GOLDEN-EYE

Clangula islandica (*Gmelin*)

A. O. U. Number 152

Other Names.— Rocky Mountain Garrot; Rocky Mountain Golden-eye.

Description.—ADULT MALE: Coloration exactly as in Golden-eye except that the *white spot in front of eye is triangle-shaped* and white of wing is divided by a dark bar formed by bases of greater coverts; averages larger than the Golden-eye; bill, differently shaped, being shorter and deeper at base. ADULT FEMALE: Indistinguishable from the female Golden-eye in color but separable by shape of bill.

Nest and Eggs.— NEST: In hollow trees; made of grass, leaves, and weed stems and lined with feathers and down. EGGS: 6 to 10, dull greenish.

Distribution.— Northern North America; breeds from south-central Alaska and northwestern Mackenzie to southern Oregon and southern Colorado, and from northern Ungava to central Quebec; winters from southeastern Alaska, central Montana, the Great Lakes, and Gulf of St. Lawrence south to central California, southern Colorado, Nebraska, and New England; accidental in Europe; breeds commonly in Iceland, and is a rare visitor to Greenland.

Drawing by R. I. Brasher

BARROW'S GOLDEN-EYE (¼ nat. size)

An active bird, diving like a flash, and rarely coming well to a decoy

Barrow's Golden-eye closely resembles the American Golden-eye. It is not easy to distinguish between the males at a distance and it is impossible to tell with certainty to which species the females and young belong. Their habits are also similar but the Barrow's breeds farther south and winters farther north. Its note is a low croaking sound.

BUFFLE-HEAD

Charitonetta albeola (*Linnæus*)

A. O. U. Number 153   See Color Plate 10

Other Names.— Buffle-headed Duck; Buffalo-headed Duck; Bumblebee Duck; Butter Duck; Butter-ball; Butter-box; Butter-back; Spirit Duck; Wool-head; Hell-diver; Conjuring Duck; Marionette; Dipper; Dipper Duck; Dapper; Dopper; Robin Dipper; Little Black and White Duck (male); Little Brown Duck (female).

General Description.— Length, 15 inches. Males are black above, and white below; females are grayish-brown above, and whitish below.

Color.—ADULT MALE: Head, puffy and crested, and iridescent, purple, and green; *a large white patch on each side behind eye, running some distance below eye and joining its fellow over top of head;* neck all around, under parts, shoulders, nearly all wing-coverts, and most secondaries, pure white; some shoulder feathers edged with black, forming a narrow length-wise line; back and upper parts, black; tail, grayish; bill, dull bluish-gray with black tip and base; feet, pale flesh color; iris, brown. ADULT FEMALE: Head, thinly crested, dusky-gray with a *lighter patch on side;* upper parts, grayish-brown; *wings the same with small white areas;* below, whitish shaded on sides of neck and body with ashy; bill, feet, and iris, as in male.

Nest and Eggs.— NEST: In hollow trees or stumps near water; lined with down and feathers. EGGS: 9 to 14; from creamy-white to buff or dull olive.

Distribution.— North America; breeds from Maine, Ontario, Iowa, northern Montana, and British Columbia north to Alaska; winters from British Columbia, Aleutian Islands, Idaho, Colorado, Missouri, southern Michigan, western New York, and New Brunswick south to northern Lower California, central Mexico, and Florida.

This little Duck is widely known on fresh waters, for it is by nature a fresh-water bird, which in autumn and winter frequents the seashore. It was named Buffle-head (or Buffalo-head) because of its large fluffy head, which looks particularly big when its feathers are erected. The Buffle-head was not much sought by gunners until within recent years. Its great weakness is a fondness for decoys.

The male is a handsome bird; its bright contrasting tints are highly ornamental, but, as is usual among Ducks, the female is dull and inconspicuous in color and much smaller. My youthful experience with the Dipper Duck convinced me at the time that it could dive quickly enough to dodge a charge of shot; but its immunity from danger probably was due more to my inexperience and to the inferior quality of the gun and ammunition used than to the quickness of the bird. However, it dives like a flash, and is very likely to escape unless the gunner, warned by experience, uses a close shooting gun, judges well his distance and holds exactly right. When a few are together one usually keeps watch when the others are under water and warns them of danger by its short quack.

In flight it hurls itself through the air with tremendous speed, its rapidly moving wings almost forming a haze about its glancing form, which buzzes straight away as if bound for the other end of the world. It alights on the water with a tumultuous splash, sliding along for a little distance over the surface. When it has once alighted it seems to prefer the water to the air, and will often dive, rather than fly, to escape danger. It is sometimes so fat that in the Middle States it is known as the Butter-box or Butter-ball, but the flesh is not usually of a very good quality. As with all Ducks the quality of its flesh depends largely on the character of the food it has recently eaten, and this species, like others, is much more palatable when killed in the interior than when taken on the sea-coast.

In February the males begin their mating antics, when they have a habit of stretching forth the neck and erecting the glossy feathers of the head as it is moved back and forth, so as to display their beauties to the best advantage in the sunlight. They are quite quarrelsome in the mating season and fight furiously for the possession of favored females.

Nuttall says that the Buffle-head feeds principally upon fresh-water and submerged vegetation, and that it sometimes visits the salt marshes "in quest of the laver (*Ulva lactuca*)," as well as crustacea and small shell-fish. Audubon states that it feeds on shrimps, small fry, and bivalves in salt water, and on crawfish, leeches, snails, and grasses in fresh water. It also takes locusts, grasshoppers and many other insects.

When it is considered that the minnows on which the Buffle-head feeds to a considerable extent eat eggs of trout and other food fishes, it seems probable that it is a useful bird, and certainly it is a very interesting one. Its diminution on the Atlantic sea-board has been deplorably rapid. In 1870 Samuels regarded it as a " very common and well known bird " in New England and abundant in migration. At its present rate of decrease, another century will see its extinction as surely as the last century saw that of the Great Auk and the Labrador Duck. Its rate of decrease should be watched, and, if necessary, a close season should be declared for several years in every State and province where it breeds or which it visits in its annual migrations. It is unsafe to procrastinate in matters of this kind.

EDWARD HOWE FORBUSH, in *Game Birds, Wild-Fowl and Shore Birds.*

OLD-SQUAW

Harelda hyemalis (*Linnæus*)

A. O. U. Number 154   See Color Plate 20

Other Names.— Long-tailed Duck; Long-tail; Swallow-tailed Duck; South-southerly; Old Wife; Old Injin; Old Granny; Old Molly; Old Billy; John Connolly; Uncle Huldy; Coween or Cowheen; Calloo; Cockawee; Scoldenore; Scolder; Quandy; Squeaking Duck; Winter Duck; Hound.

General Description.— Length, male 23 inches; female 16 inches. In summer the males are black and brown above, and white below; in winter they show more white and less dark; females are grayish-brown above, and whitish shaded with dark below. Both sexes are without crests, have comparatively short necks, and short bills; males have long slender tails, the two central feathers of which are elongated.

Color.—ADULT MALE IN SUMMER PLUMAGE: Lores *broadly, space above eye, sides of head and cheeks, silvery gray; forehead, crown, and back of head, blackish-brown;* rest of neck all around, upper back, and breast, dark chocolate-brown; upper parts and long tail-feathers, blackish; shoulders, yellowish-brown striped with darker; shorter tail-feathers, whitish; wing, dusky; under parts, white; bill, flesh color with black tip and base; feet, bluish-gray with dusky web; iris, yellow, orange, or red. ADULT MALE IN WINTER: *Head, neck, fore-back, and upper breast, white; a gray patch commencing in front of eye, including cheeks and side of head, extending down side of neck* in a point, changing to rufous; upper parts, including long tail-feathers, black; shoulders, broadly white; lower breast with a large patch of deep brown rounded behind, running up and meeting black of back; rest of under parts, pure white. ADULT FEMALE IN SUMMER: Head, neck, and upper parts, dark grayish-brown, paler on throat, with a grayish-white patch around eye and another below on side of neck; under parts, white shaded across breast and on sides with ashy-brown; bill, mostly dusky with a light space in center. ADULT FEMALE IN WINTER: Crown, back of head, and back of neck, mottled grayish and brown; rest of head and neck, white with a dusky patch back of eye; upper parts, dusky-brown; shoulders, mixed with lighter brown and gray; breast shaded with grayish; rest of under parts, white; bill, dusky.

Nest and Eggs.— NEST: Placed under bushes or grass near water; constructed of grasses and dry weed stems and lined with feathers and down. EGGS: 5 to 9, from dull pea-green to light olive-buff.

Distribution.— Northern hemisphere; in North America breeds from Alaska across British America to Labrador, principally beyond the tree limit; winters from the Aleutian Islands to Washington and from the Gulf of St. Lawrence south to the Great Lakes and North Carolina and rarely to Colorado, Texas, Louisiana, and Florida.

Drawing by R. I. Brasher

OLD-SQUAW (¼ nat. size)

It has earned this name from its propensity to ceaseless chattering

We class the Old-squaws among the Sea Ducks and seemingly they do prefer to live about sea-water. They occur inland, however, on many of the larger rivers and lakes. On the Pacific side of the continent, California is their southern limit, and on the Atlantic coast they go down to North Carolina and sometimes to Florida. The summer home is in the high northern latitudes. Their food consists mainly of shellfish and crustaceans. Wayne reports finding them in company with Surf Ducks feeding on mussels along the South Carolina coast.

As they are not regarded as good for the table, market-hunters seldom kill them, and only the less experienced sportsmen shoot them if other Ducks are within reach. Their habits, including their manner of flying, feeding, and diving, are very similar to those of the Scoters, with which birds they much associate.

Along the North Carolina coast the Old-squaws assemble in large flocks, especially in the spring. At this time they are often very noisy; in fact no wild Duck in North America has so much to say to his fellows as this handsome species. This propensity for ceaseless chattering is given as the reason for naming the bird "Old-squaw." Many hunters call it "Old South-southerly," through some fancied resemblance between those words and the notes of the bird. Another local name is "Longtail," the extended tail-feathers of the male, especially in the spring plumage, giving point to this name.

Old-squaws are said to indulge in a variety of interesting aërial evolutions during the mating season. At great speed they chase one another through the air and often dart down to the water and disappear, as they carry on the chase for a brief time beneath the surface.

T. GILBERT PEARSON.

HARLEQUIN DUCK

Histrionicus histrionicus (*Linnæus*)

A. O. U. Number 155   See Color Plate 19

Other Names.— Painted Duck; Mountain Duck; Rock Duck; Lord-and-Lady; Squealer; Sea Mouse.

General Description.— Length, 17 inches. Males are deep bluish-slate; females are brown above, and grayish-brown below. Both sexes have small crests, short bills, and long, sharp tails.

Color.—ADULT MALE IN FULL PLUMAGE: General color deep bluish-slate with a purplish tinge blackening on top of head, lower back, rump, and tail, a darker shade on head and neck than on breast and back; a white patch between bill and eye curving upward and backward, changing to chestnut along nape; a round white spot on side of head, a long white streak on side of upper neck, a white collar around neck, complete or not — all these marks with black borders; a white crescentic bar in front of wings; two white streaks on back; outer webs of inner secondaries and a bar across end of greater coverts and some of the secondaries, also white; speculum, dull purplish; sides and flanks, broadly chestnut with a small white spot at root of tail; bill, dull olive, lightening on sides; feet, grayish-blue with dusky webs; iris, brown. Three years required to reach this perfect plumage; male usually seen intermediate between this and plumage of female. ADULT FEMALE: Head, neck, and upper parts, dull dark brown, deepest on head and rump; lower parts grayish-brown whitening on abdomen; a lighter spot in front of eye, another larger one below it and still another one further back on side of head, all obscure whitish; bill, dusky; feet, dull leaden-gray; iris, brown. YOUNG: Similar to adult female in summer.

Nest and Eggs.— NEST: In hollow tree or stump, under driftwood or in crevices of rock, usually near swiftly running streams; constructed of weeds, grass, and leaves and lined with down and feathers. EGGS: 6 to 8, pale cream or buffy.

Distribution.— Northern North America and eastern Asia; breeds from Alaska, on the Arctic coast, to Greenland, south to British Columbia, central Mackenzie, northern Ungava, and Newfoundland and in the mountains to central California and southwestern Colorado, northeastern Asia, and Iceland; winters on the Pacific coast from Aleutian Islands to California, in the interior to Colorado, Missouri, Lake Michigan, and western New York, and on the Atlantic Coast from Gulf of St. Lawrence regularly to Maine, rarely to New Jersey, and accidentally to Florida; accidental in Europe and not rare in Asia south to Japan.

Harlequin, well named! fantastically decorated, but still a thing of beauty. Delightful in color, elegant in form, graceful in carriage, rightly are its little companies called the "Lords and Ladies" of the waters. This is the loveliest of the Sea Ducks, but its beauty is reserved mainly for the cold and inhospitable North, and the wave-lashed rocks of isolated ledges in the wintry sea. It breeds principally in the Far North along the coasts of the Arctic Ocean. Yet, strange as it may seem, some individuals prefer the glacial streams in the mountains, and follow the higher ranges as far south as California, where they rear their young amid snow-clad peaks and disport themselves in the foaming mountain torrents until the rigors of approaching winter drive them to the sea.

Nests have been found on the ground, in holes in rocks and banks, and in hollow trees. The downy young take to the water as soon as they become strong and then they tumble about among the rocks and rushing waters perfectly at home as are their parents on the sea. In the breeding season the Harlequin is quite a solitary bird but there appear to be many unmated or infertile ones or possibly those that have finished breeding,

which may be found on the sea in May and the summer months. Such little flocks, often led by a full-plumaged male, enjoy themselves on the waters of Puget Sound among the outer islands, diving, playing about on the surface and dressing their plumage, apparently without a care in the world. On the Atlantic coast they are scarcer now in Maine and rarer still to the southward but in some severe winters flocks are seen south of Nantucket and Marthas Vineyard off the coast of Massachusetts. They are fond of swift waters, mad currents, tide rips and flowing seas; are tremendously tough and hardy, and feed largely on mussels, which they get by diving, often to considerable depths. When nesting along mountain streams they eat many insects.

EDWARD HOWE FORBUSH.

LABRADOR DUCK

Camptorhynchus labradorius (*Gmelin*)

A. O. U. Number 156

Other Names.— Pied Duck; Skunk Duck.

General Description.— Length, 29 inches. Males were black with white heads and markings; females were grayish-brown above, and grayish-white below.

Color.—ADULT MALE: Head and upper neck, white with a longitudinal black stripe on crown and nape; lower neck, ringed with black continuous with that of upper parts; below this a white half-collar continuous with that of shoulders; rest of under parts, black; wing-coverts and secondaries, white, some of the latter margined with black; some long shoulder-feathers, pearly-gray; primaries, their coverts, and tail-feathers,

brownish-black; bill, black with orange base and edges; feet, grayish-blue with dusky webs; iris, chestnut. ADULT FEMALE: Above, grayish-brown; several secondaries white, forming a speculum, but no white on wing-coverts or shoulders; below, grayish-white barred with dull brown; a spot on side of head and another in front of eye, white; bill, feet, and iris, as in male.

Nest and Eggs.— Unknown.

Distribution.— Formerly along the northern Atlantic Coasts; supposed to have bred in Labrador and to have wintered from Nova Scotia south to New Jersey; now extinct.

The most remarkable fact about the Labrador Duck, which seems to have been common on the Atlantic coast one hundred years ago, is that it is now extinct and no one knows why. If it is a fact that it bred only on rocky islands about the Gulf of St. Lawrence and the coast of Labrador, the feather hunting of the eighteenth century and the egging and shooting of the nineteenth probably resulted in its extinction, but no one, now living, knows to a certainty that it bred in Labrador. John W. Audubon was shown nests at Blanc Sablon that were said to be those of this species. Newton writes that it was common in summer on the coast of Labrador until about 1842. Major King writes (1886) that it was common on the northern shore of the Gulf of St.

Lawrence and bred there, but gives no dates. I have seen no other evidence of its breeding in Labrador. There are no definite records of its nesting, and not one of its eggs is in existence. It may have bred much farther north but so far the records show that no one has ever seen it to the northward. We must be satisfied, then, with the probable explanation that, like the Great Auk, the species bred more or less locally and was exterminated in much the same way. Probably the exact facts never will be known.

The history of the bird is brief. It was first made known to science by Gmelin in 1788, nearly thirty years after the New England feather hunters had ceased to raid the islands where it was believed to breed, the birds having become so reduced in numbers that feather hunting was no longer profitable. Audubon never saw it alive, but asserted that it remained off the coasts of Maine and Massachusetts all winter and was unknown south of Chesapeake Bay. Dekay (1844) averred that the bird was well known to gunners on the New York coasts, but Giraud, writing about the same time, regarded it as rare there. Elliot says that between 1860 and 1870 he saw a considerable number of the species in the New York markets, but that a full-plumaged male was exceedingly rare although no one imagined that the species was on the verge of extinction. The last Labrador Duck on record died by the hand of man near Long Island, New

Little is known about the habits of this Duck. It frequented sandy shoals off the New England coast and was so tame and confiding that it was not difficult to shoot.

It was said to feed largely on shellfish, and Audubon relates that a bird stuffer at Camden, New Jersey, had many fine specimens taken with hooks baited with mussels. It was a strong flyer and a good diver and, as is the case with most Sea Ducks, its flesh was rank and fishy. It was hardy and in every way well fitted for the battle of life but was not able to cope with civilized man. It is significant that its extinction occurred in the nineteenth century when marked improvements in firearms were

LABRADOR DUCKS

A group of mounted specimens in the American Museum of Natural History, New York City

York, in 1875. According to Dutcher's summary, there are only forty-two recorded specimens in existence in the museums and scientific collections of the world.

accompanied by the extermination of far more species of birds than in any other century since the dawn of history.

EDWARD HOWE FORBUSH.

SPECTACLED EIDER

Arctonetta fischeri (*Brandt*)

A. O. U. Number 158

Other Name.—Fischer's Eider.

General Description.— Length, 22 inches. Males are white above and grayish-black below; females are yellowish-brown, streaked and barred with darker. Both sexes have dense patches of velvety feathers around the eyes, outlined with black, suggesting spectacles; very fine, stiffened frontal feathers; and crown feathers lengthened into a short hanging hood in the male, slightly indicated, or not, in the female.

Color.—ADULT MALE: Most of head, neck all around, most of back, lesser and middle wing-coverts, long inner secondaries and a patch on side of rump, white; frontal feathers on head, nape, and cheeks strongly tinged with pale sea-green; spectacle area pure silvery-white framed as aforesaid, with black; rest of plumage, including wings, grayish-black; bill, orange; feet, yellowish; iris, white surrounded with a light blue ring. ADULT FEMALE: Varies as do all Eiders; general coloration, yellowish-brown, streaked on head and neck, and barred on body, except abdomen, with black and brown.

Nest and Eggs.— NEST: On the ground among rocks; made almost entirely of feathers and down from the bird's breast. EGGS: 5 to 8, light olive.

Distribution.— Very locally distributed on coast of Bering Sea and adjacent Arctic Ocean; breeds in Alaska from Point Barrow to mouth of the Kuskokwim and on the northern coast of Siberia west to mouth of Lena River; winters in Aleutian Islands.

The Spectacled Eider is essentially an Alaskan Duck, as far as its habitat on this continent is concerned, and is most commonly seen in and near Norton Sound, where it breeds. Its principal winter home seems to be on the islands of the Aleutian Archipelago. Like the Emperor Goose, this Duck is likely to fly near the surface of the water or the land; its normal progress on the wing is very swift and steady. Dur-

ing July and August the birds undergo a severe molt which deprives them even of the use of their wing-feathers. When they are thus helpless the Eskimos kill them wholesale with sticks and clubs. The natives also make caps of the heavily feathered skins of this Eider, and use the bright green plumage for headdresses of various kinds.

Drawing by R. I. Brasher

SPECTACLED EIDER (⅛ nat. size)

The Eskimos make caps of its skin

NORTHERN EIDER

Somateria mollissima borealis (*Brehm*)

A. O. U. Number 159

General Description.— Length, 24 inches. Males are white above, and black below; females are pale rufous-brown, variegated with darker.

Color.—ADULT MALE: Crown, glossy blue-black, including eyes, and separating behind to receive white of hind neck; *head, neck all around, fore-breast, most of back, most of wing-coverts, long inner secondaries, and sides of rump, white* tinged with creamy-pink on breast; sides of head washed with pale sea-green;

middle of rump, upper tail-coverts, tail, lower back, and under parts from breast, deep sepia black; bill, yellowish, brownish in center with white tip; legs, yellowish; iris, brown. ADULT FEMALE: Ground color of entire plumage, pale rufous-brown, darker on crown, streaked on side of head and neck and variegated elsewhere with transverse bars of black and chestnut-brown; abdomen, plain grayish-brown.

Nest and Eggs.— NEST: Between stones, on rocks

or banks, or any suitable hollow; made of seaweed and lined with down plucked from the breast of the bird; additional down is added as incubation proceeds, and the quantity is often so great as to conceal the eggs entirely. Eggs: 6 to 10, greenish-drab.

Distribution.— Northeastern North America; breeds from Ellesmere Land and Greenland south to northwestern Hudson Bay and southern Ungava; winters in southern Greenland, south rarely to Maine and Massachusetts.

The Northern Eider is a North American race of the common Eider of Europe and is almost identical with it. It nests on islands off the northern coast of Labrador.

This bird furnishes much of the eider-down that is gathered by the Greenlanders, and it is not improbable that it was one of the species sought by the feather hunters on the coast of Labrador in the eighteenth century.

EDWARD HOWE FORBUSH, in *Game Birds, Wild-Fowl and Shore Birds.*

EIDER

Somateria dresseri *Sharpe*

A. O. U. Number 160   See Color Plate 19

Other Names.— American Eider; Common Eider; Eider Duck; Dresser's Eider; Drake (male); Sea Duck (female); Black and White Coot (male); Isle of Shoals Duck; Squam Duck; Wamp; Canvas-back.

Description.— Length, 24 inches. This Eider differs from the Northern Eider in shape of bill; in latter base of bill extends along each side of forehead between the narrow pointed extension of crown feathers, this lateral extension being very narrow and ending in a point, whereas in the Eider the processes are more than twice as broad with obtuse rounded ends; the sides of head are more extensively greenish but otherwise the coloration is similar.

Nest and Eggs.— Nest: On the ground, in grass, in crevices between rocks, or in any sheltered locality; made of moss, seaweed, and lichens and lined with gray down from breast of the bird, the lining being added gradually during the month of incubation. Eggs: 6 to 10, usually 6, plain dull greenish-drab.

Distribution.— Northeastern North America; breeds from southern Ungava and Newfoundland, on the southern half of Hudson Bay to southeastern Maine; winters from Newfoundland and Gulf of St. Lawrence south on Atlantic Coast to Massachusetts, rarely to Virginia, and in interior rarely to Colorado, Iowa, Wisconsin, Ohio, and western New York.

Eiders are native to both Europe and America but the European and Northern Eiders differ from the American in the shape of the processes of the bill, which extend upward and backward toward the eyes. These maxillæ are less attenuated and more rounded at the ends in the American species than in the European and the Northern. This is one of the famous species that are responsible for the greater part of the eider-down of commerce. The female plucks from her own breast the down to line her nest and, as is the case with other species, she felts this down into a blanket or mantle which not only lines the nest but extends up so that she can cover the eggs with a flap or coverlet of the same warm substance. In Iceland, Norway, and some other parts of Europe the down is considered so valuable that the birds are conserved, tended, and protected, so that they become almost as tame as domesticated fowls. Nesting places are made for them in the turf or among the stones, and some of them even nest on the sod roofs of the houses, where sods are removed or arranged for their accommodation. In some places the nests are so numerous that it is impossible to step among them without endangering the sitting birds. Some birds become so tame while on the nest as to allow the inhabitants to stroke their feathers. When the first downy lining and the eggs are removed from the nest by the down gatherers, the female plucks her breast again, renews the lining, and lays more eggs. If her treasures are removed a second time, it is said that the male denudes his breast for a third lining. The down and eggs taken are not sufficient to interfere with the breeding of the

Plate 19

KING EIDER *Somateria spectabilis* (Linnaeus) HARLEQUIN DUCK *Histrionicus histrionicus* (Linnaeus)
FEMALE MALE MALE FEMALE
AMERICAN EIDER *Somateria dresseri* Sharpe
FEMALE MALE All ⅓ nat. size

birds, and both the birds and the inhabitants prosper in the partnership.

We do it differently in America. The coast of Labrador formerly was a great breeding ground of the Eider Duck. Before the year 1750, vessels were fitted out in New England for the Labrador coast for the express purpose of collecting feathers and eider-down. The crews landed on the coasts and islands when the young birds were still unfledged and while the parents were molting their flight quills and unable to fly. They surrounded the birds, drove them together and killed them with clubs, thus destroying " millions " for their feathers alone, as there was no market for their flesh. This was continued until not long after 1760, when the birds had become so reduced in numbers that feather hunting became unprofitable and was given up. In the meantime, and ever since, eggers, fishermen, and settlers have destroyed both birds and eggs, until the vast Eider nurseries of the Labrador coast are little more than a memory, and now we import eider-down gathered by the wiser and more humane people of the Old World.

However, the Eider is by no means extinct in this country. It still breeds in the more inaccessible regions of northern Ungava and about Hudson Bay and a few are preserved in Maine under the protecting care of the National Association of Audubon Societies. The nests are hidden away carefully under thick shrubbery on rocky islands where the waves of the Atlantic break ceaselessly on jagged rocks and the birds when not on their nests keep at sea.

The only note I have ever heard from one of these birds was a hoarse croak when the female was suddenly startled from her nest, but the male is said to have a soft note in the breeding season.

In migration they seem to be rather silent birds, flying in long undulating lines and alternately flapping and sailing. The Massachusetts gunners call them Sea Ducks for they seem to prefer the outer ledges jutting into the sea.

Numbers frequent the islands south of Cape Cod in winter where they feed largely on mussels for which they dive sometimes in at least ten fathoms of water. They are hardy and handsome. Their flesh is fishy and unattractive. If

Photo by T. G. Pearson   Courtesy of Nat. Asso. Aud. Soc.

NEST OF EIDER

At Way Ledge, near Isle au Haut, Maine

protected on their breeding grounds they might become in time a great source of revenue to the people of the northern coasts.

EDWARD HOWE FORBUSH.

KING EIDER

Somateria spectabilis (*Linnæus*)

A. O. U. Number 162   See Color Plate 19

General Description.— Length, 22 inches. Males are white above and brownish-black below; females are light brown, streaked and barred with darker. Males have the bill with immense square frontal processes bulging high above rest of bill; bills of females are less developed but retain the same general outlines.

Color.—ADULT MALE: Fore parts, most of wing-coverts, and a spot on each side of rump, white, tinged on side of head with pale sea-green, and on breast with creamy-brown; *top of head and back of neck, pearl-gray; eyelids and spot below eye, black;* rest of plumage, deep brownish-black, including the long inner secondaries; a black V-shaped mark on chin; bill, reddish-orange, the enlarged part surrounded in front, on top, and rear with a black border; tip, white; feet, yellowish-orange with dusky webs; iris, brown. ADULT FEMALE: Hardly separable from other female Eiders in coloration, but easily distinguished by the shape of bill; the bill, yellowish, dusky at end, with white tip.

Nest and Eggs.— NEST: In depressions of ground or among rocks; composed entirely of down. EGGS:

Usually 6, but sometimes more, light olive-gray to grayish-green.

Distribution.— Northern part of northern hemisphere; breeds along the whole coast of northern Siberia, Bering Sea, and Arctic coast of America from Icy Cape east to Melville Island, Wellington Channel, northern Greenland, northwestern Hudson Bay, and northern Ungava; winters on Pacific coast from Aleutian Islands to Kodiak Island, in the interior rarely to the Great Lakes, and from southern Greenland and Gulf of St. Lawrence south regularly to Long Island, rarely to Georgia; accidental in California and Iowa.

The King Eider is an arctic species and its habits resemble those of the common Eider. It is a deep-water Duck, feeding mostly on mussels. The female lines her nest with down, as do the other species, and it forms part of the eider-down of commerce, which is gathered by the natives in Greenland.

The raised frontal processes at the base of the bill, which adorn the head, develop immensely in the breeding season, bulging high above the rest of the bill. These processes are soft, and are

supported upon a mass of fatty substance. They shrink and become more depressed in winter, when the general formation of the beak is not much different from that of other Eiders. The female, however, does not resemble the male, and is not easily distinguished in the field from that of the American Eider. When in hand, the general resemblance of the bill and the head feathering to that of the male may be noted.

EDWARD HOWE FORBUSH, in *Game Birds, Wild-Fowl and Shore Birds.*

SCOTER

Oidemia americana *Swainson*

A. O. U. Number 163   See Color Plate 20

Other Names.— MALES: Black Scoter; Sea Coot; Black Coot; Black Sea Coot; Fizzy; Broad-billed Coot; Hollow-billed Coot; Pumpkin-blossom Coot; Booby; Butter-bill; Black Butter-bill; Butter-billed Coot; Butter-nose; Copper-bill; Copper-nose; Yellow-bill. FEMALES: Brown Coot; Gray Coot; Smutty Coot.

Description.— Length, male 21 inches; female 17 inches. ADULT MALE: *Entirely black,* less glossy below; bill, black, with a yellow protuberance at base; feet, dusky; iris, brown. ADULT FEMALE: Sooty-brown, paler below, lightening on abdomen, with dusky speckling; sides and flanks waved with dusky; throat and sides of head, distinctly whitish; bill, dusky and not peculiar; feet, dull olive with black webs; iris, brown.

Nest and Eggs.— NEST: On ground near water; made of coarse grass, feathers, and down. EGGS: 6 to 10, pale buff.

Distribution.— Northern North America and eastern Asia; breeds in northeastern Asia and from Kotzebue Sound to Aleutian Islands, including Near Islands; also on west shore of Hudson Bay, Ungava, and Newfoundland; winters on Asiatic coast to Japan and from islands of Bering Sea south rarely to Santa Catalina Island, California; in the interior not rare on the Great Lakes, and casual or accidental in Missouri, Louisiana, Nebraska, Colorado, and Wyoming; on the Atlantic coast abundant during migration from Newfoundland and Maine south, but rarely as far as Florida.

We have no means of knowing the early history of any one of the Scoters as they all were generally grouped together as "Coots" or "Black Ducks" by the early historians. The Scoters or "Coots," as they are called by the gunners and fishermen, are typical diving Ducks. They are very muscular and powerful in build. The bony framework is strong, the skin tough,

and the feathers strong, coarse, and very firmly attached to the skin. The whole structure seems to be formed to resist the tremendous water pressure that they encounter while diving at great depths. Fishermen, both along the Massachusetts coast and in the lake region of Wisconsin, have told me that they have taken these diving Ducks in nets set from 50 to 100 feet below the surface. This may be an exaggeration. Under water they use both legs and wings for propulsion, and are even more at home there than in the air. If threatened with danger they are as likely to dive as to fly, and sometimes, when in full flight, they have been seen to dive. The Scoters are universally known as Coots along the New England coast, a name derived probably from the French fishermen who first established the fishing industry on the banks of Newfoundland. The true Coot, however, is a lobe-footed fresh-water bird.

As food, Ducks of this genus are regarded as nourishing but not very appetizing. Some writers have gone so far as to stigmatize them as abominable; but the people of Cape Cod are able,

quite as likely to mix with flocks of the other Scoters. The flight of the Scoters is swift. I have heard it estimated at 200 miles an hour with a strong wind, but this is probably exaggerated. They may possibly fly at the rate of over 100 miles an hour under favorable conditions, but this is a high rate of speed for any bird. This bird usually flies in lines at some distance from the shore, and the flocks are often led by an old experienced male, who will lead his following high in air while passing over the boats where gunners lie in wait.

In migration this bird is often seen in flocks of 100 or more, and in smaller groups at other times, but it associates with the other two species. Little is known about its early abundance, but it

SCOTER (⅓ nat. size)

As food, this Duck is nourishing, but not very appetizing

by parboiling, etc., to make a dish of even the old birds, which, though it may "taste a little like crow" to the uninitiated, serves as an agreeable variant to a diet of salt fish.

A cultured Boston lady assures me that when she attempted to cook a Coot it drove everybody out of the house, and that she had to throw away the kettle that it was cooked in. Nevertheless, I have found the young palatable if properly prepared, though hardly equal to the celery-fed Canvas-back. Many Scoters are shot for food and sold in the markets, but large numbers are killed merely for sport, and either left to lie where they fall or to drift away on the tide.

The American Scoter, Black Coot, or Little Gray Coot, as it is commonly called, while a common bird, is the least numerous of the three Scoters. While at times it keeps by itself it is

is probable that on the Atlantic it has decreased more in proportion to its former numbers than the other two common species. It is far more numerous now on the Pacific coast than on the Atlantic. So little is known of its breeding grounds in northeastern North America that Professor Cooke is obliged to reason, by exclusion, that as we have no record of its breeding west of Hudson Bay until we reach the Yukon valley, nor in Labrador south of about latitude 52 degrees, the multitudes seen in winter on the Atlantic coast must breed east of Hudson Bay, in northern Ungava. As this is one of the least explored regions of the world, it is quite possible that vast numbers of Scoters and Mergansers breed there. It breeds mainly in fresh-water marshes and ponds in the north and also upon islands in the sea. It is a very expert diver, and is often able to get so nearly under water at the flash of a gun that the shot injures it very little if at all.

Its food consists largely of mussels, and when feeding on fresh water it prefers the fresh-water clams to most other foods. Thirteen Massachusetts specimens were found to have eaten nearly 95 per cent. of mussels; the remaining 5 per cent. of the stomach contents was composed of starfish and periwinkles. It is a common belief that all Scoters feed entirely upon animal food, but this is not a fact. Along the Atlantic coast they appear to subsist mostly on marine animals, but, in the interior, vegetable food also is taken.

EDWARD HOWE FORBUSH, in *Game Birds, Wild-Fowl and Shore Birds.*

WHITE-WINGED SCOTER

Oidemia deglandi *Bonaparte*

A. O. U. Number 165   See Color Plate 20

Other Names.— Velvet Scoter; Velvet Duck; Lake Huron Scoter; White-winged Surf Duck, or Sea Coot or Scoter; Black White-wing; Black Surf Duck; Pied-winged Coot; Uncle Sam Coot; Bell-tongue Coot; Bull Coot; Brant Coot; Sea Brant; May White-wing; Eastern White-wing; Assemblyman.

General Description.— Length, male 23 inches; female 20 inches. General color of male, black; female, brown above and gray below. Bill swollen at base over nostrils and on sides; feathers of lores come close to nostrils.

Color.—ADULT MALE: *Black,* paler below, more brownish on sides; a small white spot under and behind eye; *speculum white,* formed by tips of greater coverts and most of secondaries; bill, black at base and on knob, a white space in front of knob; sides of bill reddish shading to orange on tip; feet, orange or red with black webs and joints; Iris, pale yellow. ADULT FEMALE: Sooty-brown above; pale grayish below; a large space in front of and below eye, and another back of it on side of head, whitish; closely resembles the other two female Scoters but can always be distinguished by the

white speculum; bill smaller than in male and grayish-dusky; feet, dull flesh color with black webs; iris, dark-brown.

Nest and Eggs.— NEST: Usually concealed under overhanging bushes, small spruces, or willows; sometimes near salt water, at other times 2 or 3 miles from the sea; a depression in the ground, lined with a little grass and, after the clutch is complete, with a little down. EGGS: 5 to 14, usually 7 or 8, pale salmon-buff or flesh color.

Distribution.— North America; breeds from the coast of northeastern Siberia, northern Alaska, northern Mackenzie, and northern Ungava south to central British Columbia, Alberta, northern North Dakota, and southern Quebec; winters on the Asiatic coast to Bering Island, Japan, and China, and in North America from Unalaska Island to San Quintin Bay, Lower California, the Great Lakes (casually to Colorado, Nebraska, and Louisiana), and the Atlantic coast from the Gulf of St. Lawrence south (rarely) to Florida; non-breeding birds occur in summer as far south as Rhode Island and Monterey, California.

The White-winged Scoter, the largest of the three dark-colored marine Ducks commonly called "Sea Coots" along the Atlantic coast and readily distinguished from the other two by its white wing-bars, is very familiar to gunners. Toward the end of August flocks of adult males, flying southward, begin to be noticed along the New England coast. The lighter-colored females and young are not due till about the middle of October and later. Then there is a great procession of them past the headlands, flying swiftly and low over the water. They stream by in single files, in wedge-shaped formation, or in irregular columns, the three kinds being often intermingled.

The "coot shooters," starting out at the first glimmer of dawn, or before, anchor their boats in a line straight out from some headland, about a gunshot apart, and lie low, after anchoring out wooden decoys in front. The Scoters, coming swiftly on, may swing around the boats further out to sea, or rise higher in the air. Often, however, trusting to their swiftness, they dash through the line. Then the guns speak. On some mornings when there is a big flight it sounds like a regular battle. Scoters are thickly armored, however, with feathers, down, fat, and a tough hide, and many a time I have heard the impact of the shot on their bodies when there was not the least visible effect. They fly more especially early in the morning, but on lowery, windy days, particularly when a storm is brewing, I have watched them pass by thousands all day long.

Such big thick-set birds, floating rather high on the water, make themselves quite conspicuous, and are easily recognized. They like to gather

Plate 20

Louis Agassiz Fuertes

OLD-SQUAW
Harelda hyemalis (Linnaeus)

FEMALE } WINTER   SUMMER } FEMALE
MALE   MALE

SURF SCOTER
Oidemia perspicillata (Linnaeus)
FEMALE
MALE

AMERICAN SCOTER
Oidemia americana Swainson
MALE } FEMALE
WHITE-WINGED SCOTER
Oidemia deglandi Bonaparte
FEMALE

MALE

All ⅓ nat. size

over submerged beds of mussels and other bivalves, and feed upon them by diving. Being very hardy birds, they do not go as far south in winter as many of the Ducks. Large numbers of them remain in the winter about Nantucket and Long Island. Few get as far as the southern States.

This Scoter is the most southerly of the three in its breeding range. I have found quite a number of their nests in North Dakota and Manitoba. Though so hardy, they are the last of the water-birds to breed. Usually they finish laying from June 20 to July 1. When beginning to lay, the female swims ashore, preferably on an island, and creeps into the thickest weeds or brush she can find near by. There she scratches a hollow, lays a very big creamy-white egg, and rakes the soil over it. Next day she digs it out, adds another, and buries both. When the set is nearing completion she plucks down from her breast and lines the nest. Examining a nest of eggs before incubation begins is like digging potatoes.

She sits very close, and when almost stepped on tries to scurry through the weeds to the water. Once I caught a Scoter leaving her nest. She did not act frightened, but gazed quietly at her captor. Suddenly she gave a violent flap, slipped to the ground, and managed to get to the water first. The young are large for ducklings, clad in black

and white suits of down, and walk almost erect, reminding one of little men. HERBERT K. JOB.

The stomachs of nine White-winged Scoters from Massachusetts waters, examined by Mr. W. L. McAtee, of the Biological Survey, contained

Photo by H. K. Job   Courtesy of Doubleday, Page & Co.
NEST OF WHITE-WINGED SCOTER

of mussels, about 44 per cent.; quohogs, 22 per cent.; periwinkles, 19 per cent.; hermit crabs, 9 per cent.; the remainder was caddis larvæ and algæ and other vegetable matter. Three birds from Nantucket had eaten only the common mussel.

SURF SCOTER

Oidemia perspicillata (*Linnæus*)

A. O. U. Number 166   See Color Plate 20

Other Names.— Surf Duck; Surf Coot; Surfer; Sea Coot; Bay Coot; Gray Coot; Brown Coot; Box Coot; Spectacle Coot; Butterboat-billed Coot; Hollow-billed Coot; Speckle-billed Coot; Blossom-billed Coot; Horsehead; Horse-head Coot; Patch-head; Patch-head Coot; Patch-polled Coot; White-head; White Scop; Baldpate; Skunk-head; Skunk-head Coot; Skunk-top; Pictured-bill; Plaster-bill; Morocco-jaw; Goggle-nose; Snuff-taker.

General Description.— Length, 21 inches. Predominating color of male, black; female, sooty-brown above, gray below.

Color.—ADULT MALE: *Black, glossy above, duller below; a triangular white patch on forehead pointing forward; another one on nape pointing downward; no white on wings; basal half of bill, white with a large round spot of black, this bordered above and behind by red and yellow in a very narrow line; front half, yellowish-orange crossed by a white band; upper half, crimson and orange; feet, orange-red with dusky webs and joints; iris, white.* ADULT FEMALE: *Above, sooty-brown; below, gray; two whitish patches on side of*

head, thus scarcely different from females of other two species. Distinguished from female Scoter by larger bill, and from female White-winged Scoter by absence of white speculum.

Nest and Eggs.— NEST: On the ground in a bunch of marsh grass; more rarely in the low branches of dwarf spruces; constructed of grass and plant stems, and lined with down. EGGS: 5 to 8, cream color.

Distribution.— North America; breeds on the Pacific coast from Kotzebue Sound to Sitka, and from northwestern Mackenzie and Hudson Strait to Great Slave Lake, central Keewatin, and northern Quebec; non-breeding birds occur in summer in northeastern Siberia and south on the Pacific coast to Lower California, and in Greenland and south on the Atlantic coast to Long Island; winters on the Pacific coast from the Aleutian Islands south to San Quintin Bay, Lower California, on the Great Lakes, and south casually to Colorado, Kansas, Iowa, Illinois, and Louisiana, and on the Atlantic coast from Nova Scotia to North Carolina, rarely to Florida; casual in the Bermudas; frequent in Europe.

The Sea Coots are birds of the ocean and the larger lakes of the interior during the period of their sojourn in the United States. Now and then a few may be seen on some of the more important rivers, but one need not look for them on small ponds and in marshes where many other wild Ducks love to dwell.

From the studies which economic ornithologists have made of their feeding habits we learn that about 80 per cent. of the food of coastwise specimens consists of mussels which they procure by diving. They also eat periwinkles, algæ, and eel-grass. The flesh of few, if any, birds whose diet consists largely of fish or shell-fish is really palatable; and it would seem that this fact alone would protect the Scoter from gunners. Nevertheless they are extensively shot, particularly where the supply of other Ducks is not very great. This is partially true along the New England coast.

Here they are hunted in a communal fashion. The gunners of a locality agree on a day when they will go Coot shooting. At least fifteen or twenty boats must go, if success is to be attained. The boats are anchored in line offshore from some headland that separates two bays where the birds are accustomed to feed, and are stationed at a distance of about one hundred yards from each other. All this is done very early in the morning for by sunrise the companies of Coots will begin to pass. They fly swiftly and the man who secures many must be a good shot.

Speaking of the Scoter as an article of food, Walter H. Rich in *Feathered Game of the Northeast says:*

"They are unusually tough customers either in life or at the table. Most of our cooks believe it impossible to so prepare this bird as to make it decent food for any but a starving man. The best recipe I have seen runs somewhat as follows: First, skin your fowl and let it parboil in saleratus water at least one day, or until it can be dented with a fairly sharp ax. If your courage holds out, the game is now ready to stuff and bake as you would any other Duck, except that you must put enough onions into its inside to take away all Coot flavor. Arriving at this stage of proceeding there are two lines of retreat yet open to you; either throw your delicate morsel away or give it to someone against whom you hold an ancient grudge — on no account should you try to eat it."

The summer home of the Surf Scoter is in the Far North; none is known to rear its young in the United States. Those occasionally found within our borders in summer are either cripples, as the result of winter shooting, or are non-breeding individuals. Audubon describing a nest he found in Labrador writes that it was hidden among tall grasses and raised about four inches above the ground. It was made of weeds and lined with down of the bird in a manner similar to the nest of the Eider Duck.

T. GILBERT PEARSON.

RUDDY DUCK

Erismatura jamaicensis (*Gmelin*)

A. O. U. Number 167   See Color Plate 10

Other Names.— Dumpling Duck; Daub Duck; Deaf Duck; Fool Duck; Sleepy Duck; Butter Duck; Brown Diving Teal; Widgeon Coot; Creek Coot; Sleepy Coot; Booby Coot; Ruddy Diver; Dun Diver; Sleepy Brother; Butter-ball; Batter-scoot; Blatherskite; Bumblebee Coot; Quill-tailed Coot; Heavy-tailed Coot; Stiff-tail; Pin-tail; Bristle-tail; Sprig-tail; Stick-tail; Spine-tail; Dip-tail; Diver; Dun-bird; Dumb-bird; Mud-dipper; Spoon-billed Butter-ball; Spoonbill; Broad-billed Dipper; Dipper; Dapper; Dopper; Broadbill; Blue-bill; Sleepy-head; Tough-head; Hickory-head; Steel-head; Hard-headed Broad-bill; Bull-neck; Leather-back; Paddy-whack; Stub-and-twist; Lightwood-knot; Shot-pouch; Water-partridge; Dinky; Dickey; Paddy; Noddy; Booby; Rook; Roody; Gray Teal; Salt-water Teal; Stiff-tailed Widgeon.

General Description.— Length, 16 inches. Males are red above and white below; females are brownish-gray above and grayish below. Both sexes have the forehead rather low; the neck thick; the bill long and broad and curving upward, but tip overhanging and curved downward; and the tail composed of 18 stiff feathers, often spiny-pointed.

Color.—ADULT MALE IN SPRING: Forehead, crown, sides of head to below eye and nape, dusky-black; face, lores, chin, and sides of head, pure white; neck all around, upper parts, and sides, rich glossy chestnut; lower parts, silvery-white, "watered" with dusky; wing-coverts, primaries, and tail, blackish-brown; under wing-coverts, white; bill and feet, rather bright bluish-gray, latter with dusky webs; iris, brown; eyelids, bluish. MALE IN FALL, AND ADULT FEMALE: Upper parts, brownish-gray, spotted and traversed with dusky; below, pale gray and whitish, with darker transverse marks on sides; crown and nape, dusky-brown, with two indistinct dusky streaks alongside of head; under tail-coverts, white; bill, feet, and eyes, as in spring male but much duller.

Nest and Eggs.— Nest: In the abandoned homes of Coots or on the shores of lakes, ponds, or streams; a bulky structure of dry reeds, rushes, and grass, so large and buoyant that it will float. Eggs: 9 to 14, creamy or light buff.

Distribution.— North America; breeds from central British Columbia, Great Slave Lake, southern Keewatin, and northern Ungava south to northern Lower California, central Arizona, northern New Mexico, northwestern Nebraska, southern Minnesota, southern Michigan, southern Ontario, and Maine, and rarely and locally in southern Lower California, Kansas, Massachusetts, Valley of Mexico, Lake Dueñas, Guatemala, and in Cuba, Porto Rico, and Carriacou; winters from southern British Columbia, Arizona, New Mexico, southern Illinois, Maine, Pennsylvania, and south to the Lesser Antilles and Costa Rica; rare in migration to Newfoundland and Bermuda.

Drawing by R. I. Brasher

RUDDY DUCK (⅓ nat. size)

A sprightly, comical little Duck, whose flesh is a passable substitute for that of the Canvas-back

The sprightly, comical little Ruddy Duck is a distinctly North American species and is distributed widely over the continent. It is perfectly at home on or under water and dislikes to leave it, often preferring to attempt escape by diving rather than by flying. This makes it easy game for the gunner, as a flock will sometimes remain in a salt pond so small that any part of it may be reached from the shore with a shotgun, diving at every shot until those left alive essay to fly and most of them pay the penalty of their simplicity with their lives. They can dive so quickly that they often escape unharmed. Like the Grebes they possess the power of sinking slowly down backward out of sight, but like them also they rise from the water with some labor and difficulty. They are extremely tough, hardy little birds and gunners know them by such names as Tough-head, Hard-head, Steel-head, etc. Other local names, such as Booby, Noddy, and Fool Duck, indicate a lack of respect for the birds' perspicacity.

When the famous Canvas-back first showed signs of scarcity on the Atlantic coast, a price

Photo by H. K. Job

A PAIR OF RUDDY DUCKS ON BREEDING-GROUND

was put upon the head of the Ruddy Duck to meet the market demand. Unfortunately for its safety it feeds upon delicate grasses and other vegetable aliment in preference to sea-food. Therefore, its flesh is a passable substitute for that of the Canvas-back. So the market gunners have pursued it until its numbers are no longer legion and its chances for extinction are good.

The male is a handsome bird in the breeding season but presents rather a ridiculous appearance in mating time, as he swims pompously about with his head lifted proudly and drawn away back toward the spread tail, which is raised and thrown forward as if to meet it.

This Duck nests in prairie sloughs, where the broods remain until after all the other breeding Ducks have departed. Old and young are regular gourmands and, according to Gurdon Trumbull, gunners near the mouth of the Maumee River told of finding them floundering helplessly fat, on the water and in some seasons floating about dead or dying in numbers. But this was before the days of the market demand for their flesh. They do not have so much time to get fat now.

EDWARD HOWE FORBUSH.

GEESE

Order *Anseres;* family *Anatidæ;* subfamily *Anserinæ*

THE Geese in scientific terminology constitute the subfamily *Anserinæ*, of the family *Anatidæ* (Goose-like swimmers), included in the order *Anseres* (Water fowl). They comprise nine or ten genera and about forty species, of which ten or twelve occur in the United States. Of these, however, only two or three species are actual residents of this country, and the remainder are no more than migratory visitants south of the Canadian boundary.

The group are closely related to the Swans, from which they differ in having the neck shorter than the body, and the lores feathered; they are also closely allied to the Ducks, from most of which they differ in having the tarsus enclosed in small, hexagonal scales, and in the similarity in color of the sexes. They also lack the cere, or soft swollen surface at the base of the upper bill, which is characteristic of the Ducks. Still another marked difference is shown in the feeding habits of the Geese, which often take them into fields far away from water. This habit is due to the fact that Geese walk much more readily than do Ducks, because of their legs being set further forward on their bodies. Their food is almost wholly vegetable. In the water they take seeds and roots of aquatic plants, which they get by searching the vegetation below the surface, an operation which they accomplish by completely immersing the head and long neck, tipping the body meanwhile so that the tail points straight upward. On land they feed in the spring on sprouting grain, and in the fall on corn, oats, wheat, and barley, taken from the stubble fields.

Geese nest invariably on the ground and usually line their nests with their own down to which sometimes soft grasses are added. The eggs, from four to six or eight in number, are white. The coloration of several species of Geese varies greatly according to their habitat and the seasons.

Owing to their great powers of flight the Geese cover immense distances in their annual migrations, many species nesting well within the Arctic Circle, and ranging far to the south in winter.

SNOW GOOSE

Chen hyperboreus hyperboreus (*Pallas*)

A. O. U. Number 169

Other Names.— Wavey; Common Wavey; Little Wavey; White Brant; Lesser Snow Goose; Common Snow Goose; White Goose; Mexican Goose.

Length.— 25 inches.

Description.— Bill, short and high at base. ADULTS: *Pure white,* the head washed with rusty brown; *primaries, gray at base, black at ends;* bill, pale carmine-red with white tip and black cutting edge; feet, pinkish-red; eyes, dark brown. YOUNG: Entire plumage, gray, lightening below; streaked on head and neck very faintly with darker; more or less waved on back with same; secondaries and primaries, dusky, the former with lighter edges; bill and feet, much darker than in adult.

Nest and Eggs.— Unknown.

Distribution.— North America; breeds from mouth of the Mackenzie east probably to Coronation Gulf and Melville Island; occurs on the Arctic coast of northeastern Asia, but not known to breed there; winters from southern British Columbia, southern Colorado, and southern Illinois south to northern Lower California, central Mexico (Jalisco), Texas, and Louisiana, and on the Asiatic coast south to Japan; generally rare in eastern United States.

Drawing by R. I. Brasher

SNOW GOOSE (⅓ nat. size)

Flocks, at rest, appear like banks of snow

The Snow Goose is a western bird, closely resembling the Greater Snow Goose, which is confined mainly to eastern North America. In the old days, about which the ancient hunter loves to tell, great flocks of White Geese, resting upon the western prairies, appeared like banks of snow. The enormous numbers of the past are gone, but the white birds are more or less abundant still in migration in the Far West and they are numerous in winter along the Pacific coast of the United States.

This bird breeds beyond the Arctic circle and reappears in the United States in September. The flocks like to rest on some lake at night and to feed by day in the open fields. Farms where they can pick up waste grain are favorites, and they are destructive to young grain just sprouting from the soil. As the migrating flocks come in at night they present a beautiful and impressive sight. They fly in a wide rank presenting a curved front not so angular as the V-shaped flock of the Canada Goose. Winging steadily along, high and serene, their extended pinions barely moving, their snowy forms borrowing rosy tints from the sunset sky, they seek a harbor of security; but as they seem about to pass on, and leave the placid lake far behind, the flock lengthens, turns upward at an angle of fifty or sixty degrees, and then, hanging on down-bent rigid wings, floats softly down and down, drift-

ing and still falling a thousand feet or more and at the end, with a few quick flaps, dropping to the water, and so they come to rest. Sometimes when near their goal they zigzag down more like a falling Canvas-back. The young are easily distinguished from the adult birds by their grayish plumage.

The Snow Goose is difficult to approach and is not highly regarded by the epicure. Were it not for its taste for sprouting grain it might maintain its numbers for many years.

EDWARD HOWE FORBUSH.

The Greater Snow Goose (*Chen hyperboreus nivalis,* color plate 21) is similar in color to the Snow Goose, but larger in size. It breeds on Whale Island, in Ellesmere Land, and in North Greenland, but its full breeding range is unknown. In the winters it is found from southern Illinois, Chesapeake Bay, and Massachusetts (rarely) south to Louisiana, Florida, and the West Indies. Sometimes during migration it is seen west to Colorado and east to New England and Newfoundland.

Audubon said he found this Goose in fall and winter in every part of the United States that he visited and other early writers record great flocks on the Atlantic coast. Its numbers have been greatly reduced; this is probably due not only to its conspicuousness, but also to the superior flavor of its flesh.

BLUE GOOSE

Chen cærulescens (*Linnæus*)

A. O. U. Number 169.1   See Color Plate 21

Other Names.— Blue-winged Goose; Blue Wavey; Blue Brant; Blue Snow Goose; White-headed Goose; Bald-headed Brant; White-headed Bald Brant; Brant.

General Description.— Length, 28 inches. Head, white; body, gray. Bill, short and high at base.

Color.—ADULTS: *Head and upper neck, white;* face stained with rusty; neck below, back, and breast, dusky-gray fading into whitish below, into fine *bluish-gray on wings,* and into whitish on rump and upper tail-coverts, broadly-barred across the back and on sides with dusky-gray; wing-coverts, pale grayish-brown; most of secondaries, dusky edged with gray;

primaries, black; bill and feet, pinkish-red; cutting edges of bill, black and tip white; iris, dark brown. YOUNG: General color, brownish, streaked on side of neck and barred on back with pale gray; under tail-coverts whitish; wing as in adults; bill and feet, dusky flesh color; iris, brown.

Nest and Eggs.— Unknown.

Distribution.— Eastern North America; breeding range unknown, but probably interior of northern Ungava; winters from Nebraska and southern Illinois south to coasts of Texas and Louisiana; rare or casual in migration in California, and from New Hampshire to Florida, Cuba, and the Bahamas.

Until within a very few years the Blue Goose was generally considered a rare species. In a winter trip to the delta of the Mississippi River,

in 1909–10, I was astonished to find that the immense concourses of Geese, by scores of thousands, which were said to be " Brants," were in

Plate 21

BLUE GOOSE
Chen caerulescens (Linnaeus)
ADULT   IMMATURE
GREATER SNOW GOOSE
Chen hyperboreus nivalis (T. R. Forster)
IMMATURE   ADULT   All ⅓ nat. size

AMERICAN WHITE-FRONTED GOOSE
Anser albifrons gambeli Hartlaub
IMMATURE
ADULT

reality, nine-tenths of them, Blue Geese. The Canada Geese did not consort with them, and there were only a few White-fronted and Snow Geese in their company.

At daybreak they could always be found out on the flats off from the exits of certain "passes" into the Gulf. They kept up a tremendous clamor which could be heard a couple of miles away. Being exceedingly shy, they would rise and disappear up or down the coast if anyone approached within half a mile of them; consequently even the market gunners get very few. Farther westward, on the Wild Life Refuges, they make rendezvous for the night in

Texas, hundreds of thousands being concentrated within a comparatively short coast-line.

In January, 1916, I had a remarkable experience with Blue Geese. On a certain point on the shore of Vermilion Bay, La., there is a rather small gravel-spit, known as "the goose-bank," to which from time immemorial, great numbers of Geese have always resorted during the winter to eat gravel for digesting their food. Wishing to secure photographs and motion pictures of Blue Geese, we built a blind at one end of this spit, scattered corn, and returned some four weeks later. The weather was bad and the Geese did not show up. After five days of dreary waiting

Photo by H. K. Job   Courtesy of Nat. Asso. Aud. Soc.

BLUE GEESE

The photographer waited five days to get this picture

certain localities on the marshes. At Cheniers au Tigres the cattle men complained that these great hordes of Geese, spending the nights, and sometimes days, on the marshes used for pasturing cattle, pulled up every root of the grass from many acres, creating depressions which filled with water and became ponds. The cattle men actually had youths employed to ride about on horseback and shoot at the Geese to drive them off.

They breed very far north, perhaps on the Arctic islands north of the American continent. Very little is known about its breeding habits. It is a remarkable fact that in winter nearly the whole of the species in a body seems to resort to the Gulf coast of Louisiana, or not further than

amid fog and hosts of mosquitoes, patience had its reward.

Hardly was I hidden in the blind that morning before the Geese began to come. After considerable circling they alighted on the shore and came up to get the gravel. The "seance" lasted four hours, and during that time I had upwards of a thousand Blue Geese, and a few Snow Geese, within as near as six feet. They ate, drank, bathed, and dozed, without any suspicion of my presence. Noisy fellows, they talked so much that they seemed not to hear the clattering of the picture machine, even when only a dozen feet away. It was one of the most thrilling experiences of a lifetime.

HERBERT K. JOB.

WHITE-FRONTED GOOSE

Anser albifrons gambeli *Hartlaub*

A. O. U. Number 171a   See Color Plate 21

Other Names.— American White-fronted Goose; Laughing Goose; Harlequin Brant; Gray Brant; Pied Brant; Prairie Brant; Spectacled Brant; Speckled Brant; Yellow-legged Goose; Speckle-belly.

General Description.— Length, 30 inches. Plumage, grayish-brown with dark patch on lower breast. Bill, comparatively low at base.

Color.— *Lores, forehead, and fore-crown, white,* bordered behind by blackish; head, neck, breast, and upper parts in general, dark grayish-brown, feathers of back with lighter edges, forming regular and distinct transverse bars; upper tail-coverts, white; secondaries and ends of primaries, dusky, ashy at base; greater coverts and secondaries bordered with whitish; sides of body below, grayish-brown; a large patch more or less broken of deep blackish-brown on lower breast and abdomen; bill, pink with white tip (the bill is yellow in breeding season); feet, chrome-yellow; iris, dark brown. YOUNG: General tone of color browner, no black below; no white on head; tip of bill, black or dusky; otherwise similar.

Nest and Eggs.— NEST: A shallow depression in the ground, lined with grass, feathers, and down; usually near fresh-water lakes. EGGS: 5 to 7, creamy-white.

Distribution.— Central and western North America; breeds on and near the Arctic coast from northeastern Siberia east to northeastern Mackenzie and south to lower Yukon valley; winters commonly from southern British Columbia to southern Lower California and Jalisco, and rarely from southern Illinois, southern Ohio, and New Jersey south to northeastern Mexico, southern Texas, and Cuba, and on the Asiatic coast to China and Japan; rare in migration on the Atlantic coast north to Ungava.

The White-fronted Goose was formerly an uncommon spring and autumn migrant on our coast (Howe and Allen). Dr. J. A. Allen (1879) terms it a rare migrant, spring and fall, and says that Dr. Brewer states that it was more common thirty or forty years ago, as was the case with many of our other Ducks and Geese. It is now regarded as a mere straggler on the entire Atlantic coast.

It is known as a Brant in some of our western States, where it is abundant in migration.

Formerly it was common as far east as the Ohio River.

The flight of the White-fronted Goose is similar to that of the Canada Goose. There is the same V-shape formation, and at a distance it might be readily mistaken for that of the Canada Goose. Audubon states that in Kentucky this Goose feeds on beechnuts, acorns, grain, young blades of grass, and snails.

EDWARD HOWE FORBUSH, in *Game Birds, Wild-Fowl and Shore Birds.*

CANADA GOOSE

Branta canadensis canadensis (*Linnæus*)

A. O. U. Number 172   See Color Plate 22

Other Names.—Wild Goose; Common Wild Goose; Cravat Goose; Big Gray Goose; Bay Goose; Reef Goose; Black-headed Goose; Canada Brant; Honker; Long-necked Goose.

General Description.— Length, 35 to 43 inches. Head, black; body, brownish-gray. Neck, long and slender.

Color.— Head and neck, black; *a broad circular patch extending from upper side of head around throat to an equal distance on other side,* not reaching lower bill, leaving chin black; rest of plumage, brownish-gray, more ashy below; all feathers with paler edges; *upper and under tail-coverts, white;* bill and feet, black; iris, brown.

Nest and Eggs.— NEST: Usually on a mound in marshes; constructed of grass, reeds, and leaves and lined with down; rarely old nests of Hawks or Eagles are appropriated. EGGS: 6 to 7, dull white.

Distribution.— North America; breeds from limit of trees in valley of the lower Yukon, northwestern Mackenzie, and central Keewatin south to southern Oregon, northern Colorado, Nebraska, and Indiana; formerly bred casually south to New Mexico, Kansas, Tennessee, and Massachusetts; winters from southern British Columbia, southern Colorado, southern Wisconsin, southern Illinois, and New Jersey (rarely southern Ontario and Newfoundland) south to southern California, Texas, and Florida; accidental in Bermuda and Jamaica.

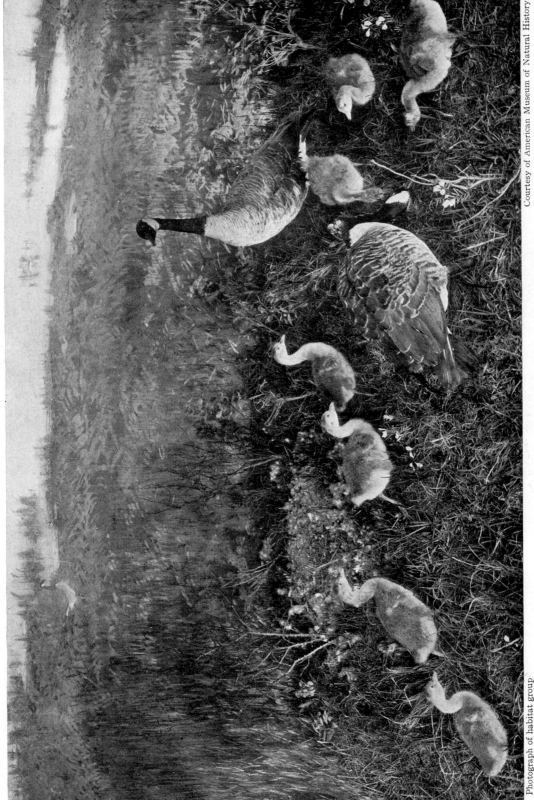

Photograph of habitat group

WILD GEESE ON CRANE LAKE, SASKATCHEWAN

The young birds are about two weeks old

The Canada Goose is the best known member of the subfamily *Anserinæ* in eastern and central North America. Nearly everyone is familiar with the sight of the V-shaped bands of these

Photo by T. G. Pearson　　　Courtesy of Nat. Asso. Aud. Soc.
NEST AND EGGS OF CANADA GOOSE
Stump Lake, North Dakota

splendid birds as they migrate southward in autumn, or in spring when they again turn their wing-beats toward the frozen pole. The great breeding grounds of this Goose are in the British provinces, few, if any, of the eastern flight pausing in spring south of the Canadian border. In the western States, however, they breed commonly in many localities. Thus, I have found their eggs on islands in lakes of North Dakota, and come upon the young attended by the parents in Oregon and northern California. It is a rather curious fact that shortly after the young have hatched, the parents begin a molt of feathers which is frequently so extensive that the birds lose the power of flight. At this season they must of course depend entirely upon their wonderful ability to swim, when in search of food, or endeavoring to escape their enemies.

Canada Geese are not flesh eaters, the grainfields of the great Northwest being their special delight. During the fall migration they often come here in great numbers and feed on the grain scattered among the stubble at harvest time. Along the lower Mississippi River they may often be seen in the fields of Tennessee and Arkansas. Like most Geese, while feeding, they have one or more sentinels constantly on the lookout for danger. Furthermore the members of a feeding flock are continually rising up and looking about, so that there are always a number of heads in the air.

These birds assemble in enormous numbers on favorite feeding grounds in Chesapeake Bay and in the sounds of North Carolina. In Currituck Sound I have seen one flight that was two hours in passing a given point. They came in one long wavy rank after another, from twenty to thirty of these extended lines of Geese being in sight at a time. The Canada Goose is highly esteemed as an article of food, and when one stops to think of the incessant gun-fire to which they have long been subjected, it is hard to understand why their numbers have not materially decreased.　　　　　T. GILBERT PEARSON.

The Canada Geese " feed largely on vegetable matter, the roots of rushes, weeds, grasses, etc., grass, and many seeds and berries, and swallow quantities of sand as an aid to digestion. Geese either feed on shore, when they pluck up grass and other vegetation, or they bring up food from the bottom in shoal water by thrusting their heads and necks down as they float on the surface. Like the Brant, they feed on eel-grass, which grows on the flats in salt or brackish water, in tidal streams, and marshy ponds. Sometimes they are destructive to young grass and grain." (Forbush.)

Hutchins's Goose (*Branta canadensis hutchinsi*) is precisely like the Canada Goose in everything except size; its length is but 25 to 34 inches, and its weight is generally three or four pounds, rarely exceeding six pounds. It breeds in the Arctic region of North America and migrates south in winter chiefly through western

Photo by H. K. Job
NEST AND EGGS OF CANADA GOOSE
Saskatchewan

United States and the Mississippi valley. Sometimes it visits northeastern Asia. Throughout its range it is variously known also as Goose-brant,

Plate 22

Louis Agassiz Fuertes.

WHISTLING SWAN
Olor columbianus (Ord)

CANADA GOOSE
Branta canadensis canadensis (Linnaeus)
BRANT   BLACK BRANT
Branta bernicla glaucogastra (Brehm)   *Branta nigricans* (Lawrence)

All ⅓ nat. size

Little Canada Goose, Little Wild Goose, Small Gray Goose, Little Gray Goose, Short-necked Goose, or Mud Goose.

The White-cheeked Goose (*Branta canadensis occidentalis*) and the Cackling Goose (*Branta canadensis minima*) are other geographical varieties of the Canada Goose. The former is found in the Pacific coast district of North America, breeding from Prince William Sound and Mitkof Island south to northeastern California, and wintering from Washington to south California.

It is like the Canada, but the under parts are darker and the white cheek patches are usually separated by a black throat patch. The Cackling Goose is like the White-cheeked but smaller in size. It breeds in the western Aleutians and Norton Sound south to the northern coast of the Alaskan peninsula. In the winter it may be found from British Columbia south to San Diego county, California; it has sometimes been reported from Colorado, Iowa, Wisconsin, and Illinois.

BRANT

Branta bernicla glaucogastra (*Brehm*)

A. O. U. Number 173a   See Color Plate 22

Other Names.— Common Brant; Eastern Brant; White-bellied Brant; Light-bellied Brant; Brant Goose; Clatter Goose; Crocker; Quink; Black Brant; Brent Goose; Burnt Goose.

General Description.— Length, 24 inches. Color above, brownish-gray; below, ashy-gray and white. Neck, long and slender.

Color.—ADULTS (SEXES ALIKE): *Head, neck, throat, and breast, black; on each side of neck a series of 5 or 6 white streaks;* upper parts, brownish-gray, the feathers lighter edged; rump, darker; upper tail-coverts, white; primaries and secondaries, dusky; lower breast, pale ashy-gray fading on abdomen and lower wing-coverts to white; bill and feet, black; iris, brown. IMMATURE: Similar, but not so much white on sides of

neck and wing-coverts, and the secondaries tipped with white.

Nest and Eggs.— NEST: A depression in the ground on marshy ground or sandy beaches; made of grass, moss, and feathers and lined with down. EGGS: 4 to 6, grayish-white.

Distribution.— Northern hemisphere; breeds on Arctic islands north of latitude 74° and west to about longitude 100°, and on the whole west coast of Greenland; winters on the Atlantic coast from Massachusetts, south to North Carolina, rarely to Florida; has been recorded in the interior from Manitoba, Ontario, Colorado, Nebraska, Wisconsin, Michigan, Indiana, and Louisiana; accidental in British Columbia and the Barbados.

BLACK BRANT

Branta nigricans (*Lawrence*)

A. O. U. Number 174   See Color Plate 22

Description.— Like the Brant, but black of head and breast extending over most of under parts, fading on abdomen and under tail-coverts into lighter; white neck patches usually larger and meeting in front.

Nest and Eggs.— Nesting similar to and eggs indistinguishable from the Brant's.

Distribution.— Western North America; breeds on the Arctic coast and islands from Point Barrow east

to near mouth of Anderson River, north probably to Melville Island; common on Siberian coast, Chukchi Peninsula, and west to New Siberian Islands; winters on the Pacific coast from British Columbia south to San Quintin Bay, Lower California, in the interior of Oregon and Nevada, and on the Asiatic coast south to Japan; recorded as a straggler to Massachusetts, New York, and New Jersey.

The Brant is the smallest of our wild Geese and is known to the United States only as a winter visitor. Its summer home is beneath the very shadow of the frozen pole, for its nest is built well within the Arctic circle. When the

first breath of autumn sweeps over our southland the wild water-fowl begin to appear, and every successive gale from the North brings its teaming thousands. Not among the first arrivals but soon to follow comes the Brant. It does not visit the rivers and lakes of the interior like most of its kin, but follows down the coast to feed principally in the salt and brackish waters of the bays and sounds of Virginia and North Carolina. Here it may be found in thousands and tens of thousands. I recall once sailing through Pamlico Sound from Ocracoke to Cape Hatteras, a distance of thirty miles, and there was not a minute during the entire trip but what newly startled flocks were in the air before us.

When the weather is fair Brants gather in very large companies to feed on the eel-grass grow-

come; they "draw to the idols," the local gunners say. They are awkward, slow-flying birds and poor indeed is the marksman who cannot make a good score with a shotgun under such conditions.

Another popular way of hunting them is by means of a battery. This may be described as a coffin with canvas wings. It is anchored on the Brant's feeding grounds and when the gunner lies down in it he is effectively concealed unless to a bird almost directly overhead. This is probably the most deceptive device used by man to

Drawing by R. I. Brasher

BRANT (¼ nat. size)

The smallest of the wild Geese

ing in the shallow water of the shoals, or at high tide to drift a chattering host upon the bosom of the slow-heaving sound. When strong winds blow these large "rafts" are broken up and small companies of from two to a dozen fly about seeking companionship. It is then that the gunners get in their deadly work. In a small blind erected on four posts standing on a shoal, often three or four miles from land, the hunters take their stand. Anchored in the water about them are from fifty to one hundred wooden decoys representing Ducks and Brant. It is to these dummy sirens that the small flocks of Brant

outwit the wary wild fowl. I have known bags of one hundred Brant to be made from a single battery in a day. In viewing such sights one is led to wonder that any of these game-birds have been able to escape the terrific slaughter to which they have long been subject by the hand of man.

On the Pacific coast of North America the Black Brant is found. It is very similar to the eastern species, but has more black on the underparts and the front of the neck as well as the sides has white markings.

T. GILBERT PEARSON.

EMPEROR GOOSE

Philacte canagica (*Sevastianoff*)

A. O. U. Number 176

Other Names.— Painted Goose; Beach Goose.

General Description.— Length, 28 inches. Head and tail, white; body, bluish-gray. Bill, small and but little elevated at base.

Color.— ADULTS: Head, sides and back of neck, and tail, white, the first two tinged with amber-yellow; throat, blackish; rest of plumage, bluish-gray; feathers above and below with black subterminal crescents white-tipped, producing a scaly appearance; bill, flesh color with white tip; feet, orange-yellow; iris, brown. YOUNG: Head, dusky speckled with white on top; otherwise similar to adult.

Nest and Eggs.— NEST: A depression on marshy islands bordering the sea, at first without semblance of nesting material, but as the number of eggs to be laid nears completion, the depression is lined with grass, leaves, and down. EGGS: 5 to 8, dull whitish.

Distribution.— Coasts of Alaska; breeds from Kotzebue Sound south to mouth of Kuskokwim, on St. Lawrence Island, and also on Chukchi Peninsula, Siberia, near East Cape; winters from the Commander and Near islands east through the Aleutians to Bristol Bay and Sitka; casual in British Columbia and California; accidental in Hawaii.

Edward W. Nelson, who made a special study of the Emperor Goose in Alaska, and prepared for the National Association of Audubon Societies a leaflet in which he records some of his interesting observations, says that this is the " least known and the most beautiful " of all the wild geese which make their summer home in the Far North, in both the Old and the New worlds. For these reasons it seems proper to give here some account of the bird, even though its visits to the United States proper are confined to occasional appearances in northern California.

The main wintering place of the Emperor Goose, according to Mr. Nelson, appears to be on the southern side of the Peninsula of Alaska and the Aleutian Islands, where the Aleuts know it as the " Beach Goose." The Eskimos of the Yukon delta Mr. Nelson found wearing " parkies " or outer garments made of the skins of Emperor Geese, sewed together. Their native name for the bird is " nachau-thluk." As to his observations of the bird's habits in the Yukon region Mr. Nelson writes:

"At first the Emperor Geese were difficult to approach, but as their numbers increased they became less shy. When on the wing, they were easily distinguished from the other Geese, even at considerable distances, by their proportionately shorter necks and heavier bodies, as well as by their short, rapid wing-strokes, resembling those of the Black Brant. Like the latter, they usually flew near the ground, rarely more than thirty yards high, and commonly so close to the ground that their wing-tips almost touched the surface on the down stroke. While flying from place to place, they give at short intervals a harsh, strident call of two syllables, like *kla-ha,*

kla-ha, kla-ha, entirely different from the note of any other Goose I have ever heard. They are much less noisy than either the White-fronted or Cackling Geese, which often make the tundra resound with their excited cries.

" Almost at once after their arrival on the islands, the Emperor Geese appeared to be mated, the males walking around the females, swinging their heads and uttering low love notes; and incoming flocks quickly disintegrated into pairs which moved about together, though often congregating with many others on flats and sandbars. The male was extremely jealous and pugnacious, however, and immediately resented the slightest approach of another toward his choice; and this spirit was shown equally when an individual of another species chanced to come near. When a pair was feeding, the male moved restlessly about, constantly on the alert, and at the first alarm the pair drew near one another, and just before taking wing uttered a deep, ringing *u-lugh, u-lugh;* these, like the flight-notes, having a peculiar deep tone impossible to describe. At low tide, as soon as the shore ice disappeared, the broad mud-flats along shore were thronged with them in pairs and in groups. They were industriously dabbling in the mud for food until satisfied, and then congregated on bars, where they sat dozing in the sun or lazily arranging their feathers.

" Early in June, they began depositing eggs on the flat, marshy islands bordering the sea. The nests were most numerous a short distance back from the muddy feeding-grounds, but stray pairs were found nesting here and there farther inland. One must have lain with neck outstretched on the ground, as I afterward found was their custom when approached, for the Eskimo and I passed within a few feet on each side of her ; but, in scanning the ground for nesting birds, the general similarity in tint of the bird and the obvious stick of driftwood beside her had completely misled our sweeping glances.

" The same ruse misled us several times ; but on each occasion the parent betrayed her presence by a startled outcry and hasty departure soon after we had passed her and our backs were presented. They usually flew to a considerable distance, and showed little anxiety over our visit to the nests. When first laid the five to eight eggs are pure white, but they soon become soiled. When the complement of eggs to be laid approaches completion, the parent lines the depression in the ground with a soft, warm bed of fine grass, leaves, and feathers from her own breast. The males were rarely seen near the nests, but usually gathered about the feeding-grounds with others of their kind, where they were joined now and then by their mates.

" The young are hatched the last of June or early in July, and are led about the tundras by both parents until August, when the old birds molt their quill-feathers and with the still unfledged young become extremely helpless. At this time, myriads of other Geese are in the same condition, and the Eskimos made a practice of setting up long lines of strong fish-nets on the tundras to form pound-traps, or enclosures with wide wings leading to them, into which thousands were driven and killed for food. The slaughter in this way was very great, for the young were killed at the same time. Fortunately, in 1909, President Roosevelt made a bird-reservation covering the delta of the Yukon and the tundra to the southward, which includes the main breed-ground of the Emperor Goose, and thus took a long step toward perpetuating this fine bird."

SWANS

Order *Anseres ;* family *Anatidæ ;* subfamily *Cygninæ*

THE Swans constitute a subfamily (*Cygninæ*) of the family *Anatidæ*, and may be considered as comprising two genera, which include about eight species. The " true " Swans English ornithologists group in a single genus, *Cygnus*, while by American scientists they are called *Olor* from the Latin, meaning Swan. They are large, and almost exclusively aquatic birds and are characterized by the length of the neck, which may be even longer than the body, the number of vertebræ ranging from twenty-three to twenty-five, while the Geese have less than twenty. The Swans are famous for their stately appearance in the water, due largely to the constantly changing but always graceful arching of their necks. The plumage is generally pure white, though the head is sometimes marked with rusty hues.

Like the Geese, the distribution of the Swans is very wide, their range including much of the Arctic regions, where they build their rude nests, composed chiefly of reeds, in which are deposited about six eggs of a greenish hue. Their food consists mainly of the seeds and roots of water plants, though they are accused of destroying great quantities of fish-spawn.

WHISTLING SWAN

Olor columbianus (*Ord*)

A. O. U. Number 180　　See Color Plate 22

Other Names.— Swan ; Common Swan ; Wild Swan ; American Whistling Swan.

Length.— 4½ feet.

Description.— *Nostrils nearer the tip of the bill than the eyes.* ADULTS : Entire plumage, pure white ; bill, black with *a yellow spot at base in front of eye ;* feet, black ; iris, brown. YOUNG : Plumage, ashy-gray, darker on neck where washed with pale rufous ; bill, partly flesh color ; feet, yellowish flesh color.

Nest and Eggs.— NEST : On the ground in or on the borders of marshes ; a large structure of grass, moss, weed stalks, and herbage of different kinds. EGGS : 3 to 6, dull white.

Distribution.— North America ; breeds from north-

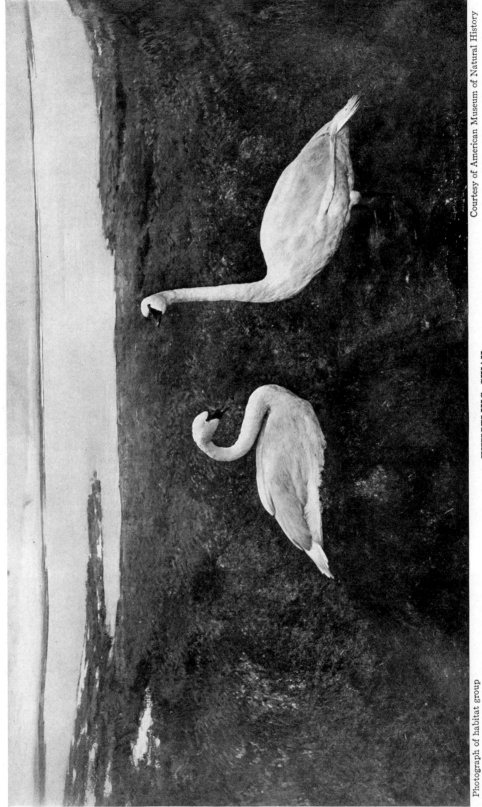

Photograph of habitat group

Courtesy of American Museum of Natural History

WHISTLING SWAN

Incubating on its nest of moss, etc., on Southampton Island, Hudson Bay ern Alaska south to Becharof Lake, Alaska Peninsula, and on Arctic islands from about latitude 74° south to northern Mackenzie and northwestern Hudson Bay; in migration occurs west to Bering Island; winters on the Pacific coast from southern British Columbia, rarely south to southern California, and in the interior from Lake Erie and southern Illinois to coast of Louisiana and Texas, and on Atlantic coast from Delaware and Maryland to South Carolina, rarely north to Massachusetts and south to Florida; casual in northern Mexico; accidental in the British Isles and in the Bermudas.

On the coasts and islands of the Arctic Sea, in far-off archipelagoes of the great frozen North, the Whistling Swan builds its huge nest. When the mother leaves it she covers the eggs carefully with the mossy nest lining to insure warmth and safety. The eggs are hatched by the last of June and the cygnets are led to the water where some high-keyed notes may come from the younger birds but the old males sound the bass horn. As the flock passes over, high in air, the leader utters a high note like that of a flageolet which Elliot describes as sounding like *whŏ-whŏ-whŏ* and this, repeated by flock after flock, may have given the bird its name.

Photograph by H. K. Job   Courtesy of National Association of Audubon Societies
                                                          and of Mr. John Heywood
SWANS IN WINTER ON HEYWOOD ESTATE, GARDNER, MASSACHUSETTS
Showing how waterfowl keep open a hole in the ice

they feed and grow under the midnight sun. Soon the parents molt out all their flight-feathers and, as the whole family is then unable to fly, they often fall victims to the natives who hunt them remorselessly at this season, but native tribes are few; the country is a wide wilderness and many of the birds escape the dangers of the north. Late in September or in October they are on their way southward where they are to face greater perils.

It is hard to see just why this bird is called the Whistling Swan. Its calls have great variety; some high-keyed notes may come from the

The flight seems to divide into three sections; one following the Atlantic coast; another the Mississippi valley, and a third the Pacific coast. The flocks pass mainly overland in an unwavering line at great heights. In fair weather they seem to avoid civilization, flying so high as to be unnoticed by human eyes and making but few stops, therefore they are considered scarce in most of the northern States of the Union. Very rarely, when caught in storms and over-weighted with sleet and snow, they are forced to come to the ground.

Such a catastrophe occurred to the flocks in northwestern Pennsylvania on March 22, 1879. Swans came down in many places in four counties, in ponds, streams, fields, or villages. Large numbers were killed by men and boys with guns, rifles, and clubs. Twenty-five were captured alive in one village, as they were worn out and helpless after their battle with the storm. Most of those that alighted within sight of human habitations were slaughtered wantonly. (George B. Sennett, in *Bull. Nuttall Orn. Club, 1880.*) In some cases the Great Lakes are their refuge, if they can reach those waters, and often they are saved by alighting under the lee of some point or island, but now and then a flock comes down in the Niagara River and is carried over the falls. Whenever this happens and the wearied and often injured birds are cast up against the ice bridge or along the shores, people come in crowds and kill with guns or clubs the birds that have passed alive through the fury of the elements.

There is no safety for a Swan in this country except it be high in air or far out on open water. Such refuge is found on the broad waters of the South. The great flocks that once frequented the coast in winter from Massachusetts to South Carolina are gone, but the species still winters in large numbers on the Carolina coasts.

The song of the dying Swan has been regarded as a pleasing myth for many years, but Elliot asserts that he heard it once at Currituck Sound, when a Swan, mortally wounded in the air, set its wings and, sailing slowly down, began its death-song, continuing it until it reached the water " nearly half a mile away." The song was unlike any other Swan note that he had ever heard. It was plaintive and musical and sounded at times like the soft running of an octave. Inquiry among local gunners revealed the fact that some had heard similar sounds from Swans that had been fatally hurt. Need we wonder that the Swan was a favorite bird of mythology? EDWARD HOWE FORBUSH.

TRUMPETER SWAN

Olor buccinator (*Richardson*)

A. O. U. Number 181

Description.— *Larger than Whistling Swan;* nostrils midway between tip of bill and eyes. ADULTS: Plumage, pure white or with wash of rusty on head; *bill, lores* and feet, *black;* iris, brown. YOUNG: Bill and feet, not perfectly black; plumage, grayish; head and upper neck, rusty. Length, 5 feet.

Nest and Eggs.— NEST: On an elevated knoll near water; constructed of grass, stalks, feathers, and down. EGGS: 5 to 7, dull white.

Distribution.— Interior and western North America; breeds from the Rocky Mountains to western shore of Hudson Bay and from the Arctic Ocean to about latitude 60°; fromerly bred south to Indiana, Missouri, Nebraska, Montana, and Idaho, and casually west to Fort Yukon and British Columbia; winters from southern Indiana and southern Illinois south to Texas, and from southern British Columbia to southern California; casual in migration in the Rocky Mountain region of United States; accidental in New York and Delaware. Now of rare occurrence nearly everywhere.

The Trumpeter Swan, the largest of North American wild fowl, represents a vanishing race. In most parts of North America it is a bird of the past. Formerly it ranged over the greater portion of the continent. Today it is seen rather rarely in the wilder regions of the interior.

Great flights of Swans were observed by the early settlers on the Atlantic seaboard from Maine to Georgia. No one knows what proportion of these were Trumpeters, but, as the Trumpeter was recorded on the Atlantic coast as late as the last half of the nineteenth century, there is some reason for the belief that some of the early flocks were of this species. It was once the prevailing Swan of California and was abundant in Oregon and Washington, but it has now practically disappeared from the Pacific coast. It always was a bird of the fresh waters and did not, like the Whistling Swan, often frequent salt water bays and estuaries. When the country was first setted the Trumpeter bred in the northern United States, and from there northward to the fresh-water lakes and ponds in the vicinity of Hudson Bay, where it was very numerous, and even to the shores of the Arctic Ocean.

Little is known about the breeding habits of

this bird, but, like the Canada Goose, the male guards and defends the female, eggs, and young.

In autumn when the grip of the frost congealed the surface of its native lakes and streams the Trumpeter gathered in mighty flocks, circled high in air and moved southward in great flights using the V-shaped formation so characteristic of migrating Canada Geese. This is written in the past tense as there are no longer any great flights of the species. Then, as now, the Mississippi valley was a highway of bird migration and there, at times, in autumn, when the icy north wind blew, the sunset sky was overcast by clouds of waterfowl moving in dim strata near and far, in varying lines, crossing, converging, ascending, descending, but all trending southward toward waters as yet untouched by the frost. The rushing of their wings and their musical cries filled the air with a chorus of unrelated sounds, blending in rough harmonies. Above them all, in the full light of the setting sun great flocks of Cranes passed along the sky, and higher still in the glowing firmament rode the long " baseless triangles " of the Swans, sweeping across the upper air in exalted and unswerving flight, spanning a continent with the speed of the wind, their forms glistening like silver in the sunset glow. They presented the most impressive spectacle in bird life ever seen in North America. When at last they found their haven of rest they circled with many hoarse trumpetings in wide spirals from that giddy height reconnoitering the country as they swung lower and lower until, their ap-

prehensions at rest, they sailed slowly down to drink, bathe, feed, and rest on quiet, peaceful waters.

Swans feed almost entirely by reaching down in shallow water and pulling up the vegetation from the bottom with the bill. Animal food such as shellfish is taken to some extent, mainly in the spring.

The reason for the rapid decrease of the Trumpeter is not far to seek. It is the largest and most conspicuous of waterfowl. Wherever, in settled regions, Swans were seen to alight, every kind of a firearm that could do duty was requisitioned and all men turned out to hunt the great white birds. They were not much safer in the almost uninhabited North, as the demands of civilization pursued them there. The records of the traffic in Swans' down tell the story of decrease in the territory of the Hudson Bay Company. Just previous to the middle of the nineteenth century about five hundred Swans' skins were traded annually at Isle à la Crosse and about three hundred were taken yearly at Fort Anderson. These were mainly skins of the Trumpeter Swan. The number sold annually by the Company slowly decreased from 1312 in 1854 to 122 in 1877. In 1853 Athabasca turned out 251, in 1889 only 33. In 1889 and 1890 Isle à la Crosse sent out but two skins for each outfit. (Preble, *North American Fauna.*) So the demands of fashion and the blood lust will follow the Trumpeter to the end.

EDWARD HOWE FORBUSH.

ORDER OF LAMELLIROSTRAL GRALLATORES

Order *Odontoglossæ;* family *Phœnicopteridæ*

UNTIL comparatively recent times the Flamingoes were associated by ornithologists — as they still are by many others — with the Storks and Herons. It is now known that they constitute an order which is the link between the order of Lamellirostral Swimmers and that of the Herons, Storks, and Ibises. The Persians recognized this relationship to the Geese when they gave to the Flamingo the name of *Kaj-i-surkh,* or Red Goose.

Of the seven species comprising the Flamingo family, five occur in this hemisphere, but only one comes within the borders of the United States. The family has several peculiar and interesting characteristics. In the first place, the plumage of all Flamingoes is very beautiful, the prevailing colors varying from rosy pink to bright scarlet. Again (and unlike the Herons, Cranes, and Ibises) the Flamingo's long neck is not due to multiplication of the vertebræ, of which there are but eighteen, but to the lengthening of the separate bones. Furthermore, the bird's bill is quite distinct in its structure: the lower mandible is a boxlike affair, broad and deep, into which the upper mandible, which moves freely, closes like a lid, and the sides are fitted with gill-like processes, which act as sieves, while the whole is bent sharply downward near the tip. This curious organ is thrust into the mud in an inverted position, the point being directed backward. In this manner the bird seeks its food, which consists of frogs, shellfish, mollusks, and aquatic herbage, strained from the mud by the sieve apparatus.

Any bird or beast of strange appearance and unusual habits is likely to be credited with almost any weird practice. The Flamingo furnishes an illustration of this in the accounts of its nesting habits which long passed current, and some of which are still believed by many. For probably the oldest and one of the most graphic of these accounts we are indebted to William Dampier, the seventeenth-century English freebooter and explorer, who thus described the nesting of the Flamingo (near Curaçao) in his famous book, *A New Voyage Around the World:*

"They build their Nests in shallow Ponds, where there is much Mud, which they scrape together, making little Hillocks, like small Islands, appearing out of the Water, a foot and a half high from the bottom. They make the foundations of these Hillocks broad, bringing them up tapering to the top, where they leave a small hollow pit to lay their Eggs in; and when they either lay their Eggs, or hatch them, they stand all the while, not on the Hillock, but close by it with their Legs on the ground and in the water, resting themselves against the Hillock, and covering the hollow nest upon it with their Rumps: For their Legs are very long; and building thus, as they do, upon the ground, they could neither draw their legs conveniently into their Nests, nor sit down upon them otherwise than by resting their whole bodies there, to the prejudice of their Eggs or their young, were it not for this admirable contrivance, which they have by natural instinct. They never lay more than two Eggs, and seldom fewer. The young ones cannot fly till they are almost full grown; but they will run prodigiously fast; yet we have taken many of them."

Of course, neither Dampier nor anybody else ever saw Flamingoes incubating their eggs in this manner; what he wrote was what had been told him, or what he conjectured would have to be done by a bird with such tremendously long legs; for we know, as a matter of fact, that Flamingoes cover their eggs very much as other birds do, that is to say, by sitting on them with their legs doubled up and the knees stretched out backward and coming about under the end of the tail. Yet undoubtedly by a great many ornithologies, or by detached articles still in circulation, this absurd invention is still perpetuated.

Photograph of habitat group   Courtesy of American Museum of Natural History

A FLAMINGO COLONY

The nests are made by scooping up mud with the bill and patting it into shape with bill and feet

FLAMINGO

Phœnicopterus ruber *Linnæus*

A. O. U. Number 182

Other Names.— Scarlet Flamingo; American Flamingo.

Description.—ADULTS: Plumage, scarlet; primaries and most secondaries, black legs, lake red; bill, black on end, orange in middle, base and bare skin of head, yellow. This perfect plumage rare; birds as usually seen are mostly dull pink with vermilion and scarlet only on wings. YOUNG: The young are hatched in white down with a straight bill, which gradually acquires the crook. First plumage, grayish-white with dusky wings; this passes through pink, rosy, and red to its full scarlet, several years being required to perfect the plumage. Length of adult, 4 feet.

Nest and Eggs.— NEST: A conical structure on remote inaccessible islands, of mud or marl scraped up by the bird's bill, about 18 inches in diameter at the base and about a foot across the top; from a few inches to more than a foot high. EGGS: 1 or 2, white.

Distribution.— Atlantic coast of subtropical and tropical America, from the Bahamas, Florida Keys, and Yucatan to Brazil, and in the Galapagos; accidental in South Carolina.

The great Scarlet Flamingo is a rare bird in the United States. Occasionally a few are seen at the extreme southern end of Florida and there was undoubtedly a time, many years ago, when they bred in that region. I saw a specimen at Palm Beach in 1908 that had been recently killed near there, but they probably never wander much north of this point. They frequent shallow lagoons or flooded mud flats, and are usually found in flocks.

In 1904 Dr. Frank M. Chapman found and studied a colony of perhaps two thousand pairs that were nesting on the island of Andros in the Bahama Islands. His intimate photographic studies made at this time were the greatest ornithological triumph in bird photography that had then been attained. It may be added that his published notes constitute practically all we know today of the nesting habits of this bird. The nests in this Flamingo city, he tells us, were pillars of dried mud, a foot or more in height, that had been scraped up by the birds from the immediate vicinity.

On each of these one white chalky egg was laid. While incubating, the old birds do not sit astride the nest as shown in many old illustrations, but double their legs under them. There was no cover in the way of trees or bushes for a long distance, but here on the semi-flooded, marl-covered plain the birds were fairly secure from human intrusion, as the region was isolated and particularly difficult to approach.

Upon first entering his photographic blind which he had erected near the field of Flamingoes' nests, Dr. Chapman had grave apprehensions as to whether the birds, all of which had flown to a distance, would return to their eggs.

In *Camps and Cruises of an Ornithologist* he tells us something of their behavior, when, after his companion had departed from the neigborhood, he crouched in his blind and waited.

Drawing by Henry Thurston

FLAMINGOES (⅛ nat. size)

Rare birds in the United States

"Without further delay, the birds returned to their homes. They came on foot, a great red cohort marching steadily toward me. I felt like a spy in an enemy's camp. Might not at least one pair of the nearly four thousand eyes detect something unnatural in the newly grown bush almost within their city gates? No sign of alarm, however, was shown; without confusion, and as if trained to the evolution, the birds advanced with stately tread to their nests. There was a bowing of a forest of slender necks as each bird lightly touched its egg or nest with its bill; then, all talking loudly they stood up on their nests; the black wings were waved for a moment and bird after bird dropped forward on its egg. After a vigorous wriggling motion, designed evidently to bring the egg into close contact with the skin, the body was still, but the long neck and head were for a time in constant motion, preening, picking material at the base of the nest, dabbling in a nearby puddle, or perhaps drinking from it. Occasionally a bird sparred with one of the three or four neighbors which were within reach, when, bill grasping bill, there ensued a brief and harmless test of strength."

T. GILBERT PEARSON.

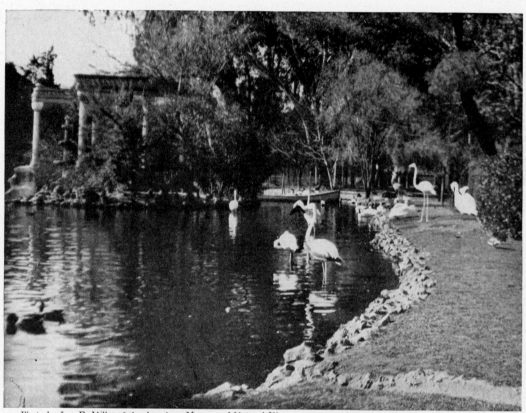

Photo by Leo E. Miller of the American Museum of Natural History

FLAMINGOES IN THE ZOOLOGICAL PARK, BUENOS AIRES

ORDER OF HERONS, STORKS, IBISES, ETC.

Order *Herodiones*

NDER this order are grouped the long-legged wading birds generally found along shores or on muddy flats. Their necks are long, but are easily bent into a strongly curved S-shape. Their wings are rounded, long, and broad, and the tail short. The toes are four in number, all on the same level, long, slender, and without webs. The head is more or less naked with small, elevated nostrils, and the skull slopes gradually to the base of the bill. The bill is variable and divides the order into three suborders: the Spoonbills and Ibises (*Ibides*) have the bill grooved along the side from nostril to tip, a peculiarity not found in the other members of the order; the Storks and Wood Ibises (*Ciconiæ*) have the bill very thick at the base and curved near the tip which is rather blunt; the Herons, Egrets, Bitterns, etc. (*Herodii*) have the bill straight and sharp-pointed. The first of these suborders, as its name indicates, contains two families, and the others one each.

Their food is principally fish, reptiles, amphibians, mollusks, and other aquatic animals. The food is seized by a quick, straight thrust of the bill. Because of the structure of their feet, they are naturally good perchers and generally nest in trees. The nests are clumsy and crude, the eggs few. The young are naked, or nearly so, when hatched, and are fed and cared for in the nest by the parents.

SPOONBILLS, IBISES, AND STORKS

Order *Herodiones;* families *Plataleidæ, Ibididæ,* and *Ciconiidæ*

THE Spoonbills are distributed quite generally throughout the tropical and subtropical regions and are grouped in three genera including five or six species, of which the only American representative is the Roseate Spoonbill. As a family they are gregarious, especially during the breeding period, when they gather sometimes in very large colonies in marshes and bayous and build platform-like nests in low trees or bushes. The eggs number from three to five, and are white, spotted with varying shades of brown.

Structurally the Spoonbills are similar to the Ibises, except in their possession of the curious spoon-shaped bill which gives them their name. This is plainly a special adaptation, and is made use of by the bird in obtaining its food, which consists of frogs, aquatic insects, shellfish, mollusks, and small fish, and which the bird captures by submerging its bill and swinging it from side to side in a semicircular sweep imparted by a corresponding movement of the body. While thus feeding the birds stalk about with grave and dignified mien, seldom making long pauses, as do the Herons, to wait for their prey to approach. While resting, either in a tree or on land, they often stand for an hour or more on one leg, after the manner of many of their kind. Their flight is accomplished by an easy flapping operation, and is accompanied by some soaring, with head and legs outstretched meanwhile.

The plumage of the Spoonbills varies from almost pure white to the beautiful combination of white and rose or pinkish tints which characterize the species found in this country. During the breeding season the adults develop a fine crest, which depends from the nape of the neck. Spoonbills have no true vocal organs, though the windpipe is very long, and at the lower end coils approximately in the form of a figure eight, somewhat after the manner of that of the Cranes. The common call is a harsh *quack*, and the birds often make a clattering sound by snapping their mandibles together.

As the Spoonbills differ from the Ibises in the peculiar structure of their bill, so the Ibises are unlike the Storks, their close relatives, in the differentiation of the same organ, which is evenly curved, somewhat slender, more or less cylindrical, and comparatively soft, except at the tip, while that of the Storks is generally straight, rigid, and hard. Of the eighteen or more members of the Stork family scattered over the warmer parts of the earth, only one, the Wood Ibis, is regularly found in America north of the southern boundary of the United States.

Certain of the Ibis species are gregarious in the breeding season, while others are rather solitary. The nests may be placed in low bushes, on trees, or occasionally among reeds, or even in holes in ledges or cliffs. They are composed of plant-stems and sticks, and may or may not be lined with straw, roots, or herbage. The eggs are from two to four in number and may be greenish-blue, pale blue, olive-green, greenish-white, or sometimes brownish, while some of the lighter-colored forms may show brownish or reddish markings. The range of the Ibis is virtually cosmopolitan. About thirty species are known, and these are referable to about twenty genera. About one-third of the species are of New World occurrence.

Remarkable variation in both proportions and coloration are shown in this family; some species are graceful in their outlines and others are clumsy and uncouth, while plumage colors range from neutral or dull tints to gaudy and brilliant hues. Most of the species walk with marked grace and deliberation, while the flight is generally like though perhaps rather more rapid than that of the Spoonbills. The Ibises' diet includes aquatic insects, shellfish, mollusks, worms, small fish, frogs, grasshoppers, beetles, and lizards. In their search for their food, when it is in the water, the birds sweep the bill to and fro, though they also use it frequently for probing in mud or soft sand.

The Ibis was one of the most sacred birds of the ancient Egyptians, and as such was the subject of many myths and superstitions. Even to-day it is one of the characteristic birds of the Nile valley, and in lower Egypt it is called *Abou-mengel*, "Father of the Sickle," the reference being, of course, to its curved bill. Herodotus credited the bird with being a destroyer of snakes, and Cuvier recorded finding the remains of a reptile in the stomach of a mummied Ibis, but it seems clear that such creatures do not form part of the bird's normal diet.

ROSEATE SPOONBILL

Ajaia ajaja (*Linnæus*)

A. O. U. Number 183

Other Names.— Pink Curlew; Rosy Spoonbill.

General Description.— Length, 32 inches. Plumage, white with some pink or red. Adults have the head and throat bare.

Color.— Upper neck and back, white, sometimes tinged with pink; *wings and under parts, delicate rose-madder;* plumes of lower foreneck, lesser wing-coverts, upper and under tail-coverts, rich carmine; shafts of wing- and tail-feathers, carmine; tail, brownish-yellow with a patch of same color on sides of breast; the skin of the bald head varied with dull green, orange, and black; bill, with various shades of green, blue, yellow, and black; legs, lake red; iris, carmine. YOUNG: Head, feathered; general plumage, white tinged with pink on wings, tail, and abdomen; edge of wing, dark brown. Three years are required to reach the perfect adult plumage.

Nest and Eggs.— NEST: A platform of sticks in dense tropical marshes, usually in cypress trees or mangrove bushes, from 8 to 20 feet above ground. EGGS: 3 or 4, white or buffy, blotched and spotted with various shades of brown.

Distribution.— North and South America, from Texas, Louisiana, Florida, and Georgia south to Patagonia and the Falkland Islands; formerly casual north to Pennsylvania and the lower Ohio valley (Indiana and Illinois); accidental in California, Colorado, Kansas, and Wisconsin.

There is no large wading bird of North America that bears such brilliant feathers as the Roseate Spoonbill. The general plumage is pink with the lesser wing-coverts of the adult a bright carmine color. This part of the plumage is known as the "drip." The bill is long and flatly spoon-shaped. The bird gets its food by wading, swinging its opened bill from side to side through the mud and water, as it advances. Formerly the Spoonbills, or "Pink Curlews," as the Florida hunters know them, were extensively shot and their feathers shipped to Jacksonville where they were made into fans to sell to winter tourists. Today the birds are extremely rare, thanks to the energy of the plume-hunter and the bird-shooting tourist. But for the wardens employed by the National Association of Audubon Societies they would probably now be extinct in Florida. A few are sometimes seen in Louisiana and possibly a thousand are left in Florida, but unless public sentiment in that State should receive a radical and sudden shift toward conservation, the bird will probably not long survive.

Spoonbills travel in flocks, sometimes in company with Ibises. They fly in long diagonal lines, each bird being behind and just to one side of the one in front. When seen among the dark green foliage of the mangrove trees, or while in flight, their wings reflect the sunlight and they show to advantage and make an unusual appeal to the bird-student. For the most part they are silent, although when feeding or when about their nests a low croaking note is constantly uttered, as though the birds were conversing among themselves.

Dr. Frank M. Chapman, speaking of the actions of the young in a nesting colony he visited in Mexico, says:

"When their parents returned they were all attention and on the alert for food. On such occasions they usually stood in a row on the edge of the nest facing the old birds, and in a most comical manner swung the head and neck up and down. I have seen balanced mechanical toys which would make almost exactly the same motion. The toys, however, were silent, while the little Spoonbills all joined in a chorus of tremulous, trilling whistles, which grew louder and more rapid as the parent approached.

Drawing by Henry Thurston

ROSEATE SPOONBILL (⅓ nat. size)

One of the rarest and most brilliant waders of the South

"What their parent brought them I could not see, nor for that matter, could they. But with a confidence born of experience, the bird that had first opportunity pushed its bill and head far down into its parent's mouth to get whatever was there. This singular operation sometimes lasted as long as ten seconds, and it was terminated only by the parent which, much against the will of its offspring, disengaged itself; then after a short rest a second youngster was fed and thus in due time the whole family was satisfied."

T. GILBERT PEARSON.

WHITE IBIS

Guara alba (*Linnæus*)

A. O. U. Number 184

Other Names.— Spanish Curlew; Stone Curlew (young); White Curlew.

Length.— 26 inches.

Color.— ADULTS: *Plumage, pure white; tips of several outer primaries, glossy black;* bare face, bill, and legs, orange, red, or carmine, the bill tipped with dusky; iris, pale bluish-white. YOUNG: Dull grayish-brown; rump, base of tail, and under parts, white; bare space on head, restricted and dull yellowish; bill, yellowish-orange; legs, bluish-gray; iris, brown.

Nest and Eggs.— NEST: Usually in mangrove thicket; constructed from twigs of those bushes. EGGS: 3 to 5, grayish-blue or whitish, blotched and spotted with dull yellow, rufous, and umber-brown.

Distribution.— North and South America, from Lower California, Texas, and South Carolina south to West Indies, Brazil, and Peru, and casually to Great Salt Lake, South Dakota, Illinois, Vermont, Connecticut, and Long Island; winters from Gulf of Mexico southward.

Some years ago the National Association of Audubon Societies purchased as a bird-reservation a portion of Orange Lake, Florida, that con-

Drawing by Henry Thurston

WHITE IBIS (⅓ nat. size)

A flock returning to their nests at evening is a pretty sight

tains an island which has long been the breeding place of innumerable water-birds. Those years when the water is not too high to cover their food White Ibises to the number of about nine thousand pairs come here to breed, as do the Egrets, Herons, and Water Turkeys that are present every season. Their nests are built in the low alder trees that cover the island and are placed at all heights from one to fifteen feet. They are bulky and their weight added to that of the heavy birds plays sad havoc with the branches. The eggs are beautifully spotted; the young are crested with black down. At times the trees are so covered with White Ibises that at a distance they appear to be weighted down with snow.

The birds, of course, have their natural enemies. This island literally swarms with water moccasins in summer. They take many of the eggs and perhaps some of the newly hatched

young. Vultures roost on the island and they devour many young. The most annoying of all the creatures that disturb the Ibises, however, are the Fish Crows. Numbers of them are on the island all day long and the quantities of eggs they consume is astonishing. When the nest is robbed these birds will lay again, and the Crows keep them producing eggs for many weeks. The warden in charge estimated that in the summer of 1913 every female Ibis laid an average of eleven eggs, although four is the normal number for a bird each season.

These birds fly in long ranks and make a very pretty sight when towards evening they begin coming in from their feeding grounds which are often many miles away. Low over the water to avoid the wind they come into view, rank after rank as far as the eye can see. With black-tipped wings sweeping up and down with never a pause the birds advance until near the island when they rise in unison and scatter about among the trees to spend the night.

In the United States the White Ibis breeds as far north as the swamp country of southern Illinois and the rice regions of South Carolina. I have seen them on the coast as far north as

Photo by T. H. Jackson   Courtesy of Nat. Asso. Aud. Soc.

NEST AND EGGS OF WHITE IBIS

At Orange Lake, Florida

Beaufort, North Carolina, but only in the late summer, and only then the immature birds who exhibit the same wanderlust as the young of some species of Herons. The young birds before they assume the adult plumage are called "Stone Curlews" by the fishermen, and the old birds, which are popularly supposed to be of a different species, are usually referred to as "Spanish Curlews"

or "White Curlews." The White Ibis is in no sense a Curlew, but its long, rounded, curved bill has doubtless suggested this name to many interested but unscientific observers.

T. GILBERT PEARSON.

GLOSSY IBIS

Plegadis autumnalis (*Linnæus*)

A. O. U. Number 186

Other Names.— Bay Ibis; Green Ibis; Ord's Ibis; Liver; Black Curlew.

Description.— Length, 24 inches. ADULTS: *Rich purplish-chestnut* shading on head, back, wings and tail, to glossy purplish-green; sides and under tail-coverts dusky-green; primaries, greenish-black; bare skin around eye slaty-blue; *no white feathers on face;* bill, dusky; legs, dark grayish; iris, brown. YOUNG: Head and neck, grayish-brown streaked with whitish; upper parts, dull dusky-green; below, grayish-brown.

Nest and Eggs.— NEST: In marshy ground or low bushes; constructed of dead reeds, plant stems, etc.; rather well built and well cupped. EGGS: 3, deep dull bluish-green.

Distribution.— Tropical and subtropical regions, mainly of eastern hemisphere; rare and local in southeastern United States from Louisiana to Florida, and in the West Indies; casual north to Missouri, Wisconsin, Michigan, Ontario, and Nova Scotia.

Photo by O. E. Baynard   Courtesy of Nat. Asso. Aud. Soc.

GLOSSY IBIS

Two adult birds, one nest, and four young, Bird Island, Orange Lake, Florida

WHITE-FACED GLOSSY IBIS

Plegadis guarauna (*Linnæus*)

A. O. U. Number 187

General Description.— Length, 24 inches. Predominating color, rich purple.

Color.—ADULTS: Head, neck, and entire under parts, rich purplish-chestnut tinged with iridescent violet on head and nape; back and wing, iridescent violet-green and purple; shoulders, rich wine-red, less lustrous than wing; primaries, green with brassy luster; rump, upper tail-coverts, and tail, green with purplish reflections; lower tail-coverts, similar, contrasting with chestnut abdomen; *bare area on head, lake red; a margin of white feathers surrounding bare space on head,* including chin; bill, dusky, reddening on tip; legs and

feet, dull reddish; iris, red. YOUNG: Plumage, entirely green; bill, dusky, blotched or banded with pinkish-white; legs, black; this coloration changing through brownish or grayish to the mature iridescent plumage.

Nest and Eggs.— NEST: On reed beds; constructed of dead reeds attached to upright stalks of living ones; very well and compactly built with a well-shaped cup. EGGS: 3 or 4, deep bluish-green.

Distribution.—Temperate and tropical America from southern Oregon, Arizona, Texas, and Florida south through Mexico to southern South America; casual north to British Columbia, Wyoming, and Nebraska.

The Glossy Ibis and the White-faced Glossy Ibis are identical in appearance, except that the former does not possess the small patch of white feathers in the region about the base of the bill.

Both birds are inhabitants of tropical and subtropical America. They are extremely rare in eastern United States and appear to be confined largely to Florida. The only place they have been known to nest in that State in many years is on the Audubon Society's bird-island in Orange Lake. As many as seven pairs have built their nests here in a season.

In April, 1914, I hid in the top of a willow

Courtesy of Am. Mus. Nat. Hist.

WHITE-FACED GLOSSY IBIS (⅛ nat. size)

He is capable of a flight of ten or twenty miles in search of breakfast

tree on this island to watch the actions of the thousands of nesting Herons and White Ibises in the bushes below and about me. While thus concealed I had the good fortune to see six of

these rare birds. At a distance they appear to be dull black, but upon coming closer the plumage was seen to possess a rich metallic luster that shone with various hues of green and purple as the birds turned in the sunlight. One that lit in a bush nearby had a white face which marked it as a White-faced Glossy. The nests were built in the bushes in a manner similar to that of the other Herons and Ibises. They were very substantial structures of sticks and twigs.

The Glossy Ibis is the species most generally supposed to be found in the West Indies and Florida, the White-faced Glossy on the other hand being regarded as a western bird. The latter breed in the extensive marshes of Malheur Lake in southeastern Oregon, making their nests in the interminable jungles of the tule reeds that here cover the marshes far and wide.

They are gregarious birds at all times and after the nesting season wander about from one feeding ground to another. The people of the Malheur country esteem them highly as food, and despite the law they are at times killed and eaten. In the coastal regions of Texas these Ibises are met with in various sections and here also they are shot. " Black Curlew " is the name by which gunners usually know them. They frequent the low, moist grounds about lakes, or over-flooded meadows. Often the feeding grounds are long distances from their nests, but the Glossy Ibis is a good flyer and quite capable of taking a flight of ten or twenty miles to get its breakfast. The food consists of crustaceans, especially crawfish, and water insects of various kinds. Frogs at times fall beneath the lightning stroke of the long curved bill. There should be a strong law in every State where this elegant wader is found, making the deed of killing one a misdemeanor punishable by heavy fine — and the law should be rigidly enforced.   T. GILBERT PEARSON.

WOOD IBIS

Mycteria americana *Linnæus*

A. O. U. Number 188

Other Names.— American Wood Stork; Colorado Turkey; Goard, or Gourd, Head; Iron Head; Gannet.

Description.— Length, 4 feet. ADULTS: *White; wing-quills, primary coverts, and tail, glossy greenish-black;* the bald head and neck, grayish-blue, creamy, and yellowish; bill, dusky along ridge, dingy yellowish on sides and below; legs, bluish-gray; iris, dark brown. YOUNG: Dark gray with blackish wings and tail; head and neck, downy feathered, becoming bald after first molt.

Nest and Eggs.— NEST: A platform of sticks in trees, sometimes 100 feet up; the same sites are occupied every year and the nests sometimes become very bulky from the addition of material each season. EGGS: 2 or 3, white.

Distribution.—Temperate and tropical America from southern California, Arizona, Texas, Ohio valley, and South Carolina south to Argentina; casual north to Montana, Wisconsin, New York, and Vermont.

Of all the various species of Storks known to inhabit the earth, only two are found in North America. One of these, the Jabiru (*Jabiru mycteria*) of tropical America, occasionally wanders north to Texas, but the other species, the Wood Ibis, is with us in goodly numbers. They breed in the southern United States, chiefly in Florida. They are gregarious at all times, although now and then small bands wander away from the main flock. I once saw at least five thousand of these birds in a drove feeding on a grassy prairie of central Florida. When disturbed by the report of a gun they arose, a vast white and black mass, and the roar of their wings coming across the lake resembled nothing so much as the rumbling of distant thunder.

They breed in colonies numbering hundreds or thousand of pairs, and they always select the tallest trees for nesting sites. For several years the Audubon Society has been guarding a colony in " Big Cypress " swamp of south Florida. In the rookery nearly every tree has its nest and some of the cypresses with wide-spreading limbs hold six or eight of them. This colony occupies an area of from two hundred to five hundred yards wide and about five miles in length. Here, as in other rookeries, Fish Crows are a great scourge. All day a stream of Crows can be seen flying from the pine woods to the swamp, or returning with eggs stuck on the end of their bills.

I had the opportunity to witness the rather odd manner in which these birds sometimes get their prey. The water was low at this season and in the pine flats various ponds, which ordinarily cover many acres, were partially or entirely dried up. One of these, now reduced to a length of about one hundred feet and with a width perhaps half as great, contained many small fish

crowded together. Thirty-seven Wood Ibises had taken possession of this pool and seemed to be scratching the bottom, evidently for the purpose of making the already thick water so muddy that the fish would be forced to the surface. The numerous downward strokes of the bare, bony heads fully demonstrated the effectiveness of their enterprise. " Goard Head," " Iron Head,"

Photo by H. K. Job   Courtesy of Doubleday, Page & Co.

YOUNG WOOD IBIS

and " Gannet " are the appellations given to these birds by many swamp-dwellers to whom the name Wood Ibis is unknown.

After the breeding season these Storks wander north as far as Pennsylvania and Michigan. Often one may find them on the wide marshes, either salt- or fresh-water, standing perfectly still for an hour or more at a time, the long heavy bill pointed downward and resting on the skin of the thick, naked neck. On such occasions they seem to represent the personification of dejection.

T. GILBERT PEARSON.

HERON FAMILY

Order *Herodiones;* suborder *Herodii;* family *Ardeidæ*

"A S hungry as a Heron" is a simile which should mean much to a student of birds, for Herons as a class are gaunt and voracious creatures who always seem to be half famished, and actually are more or less emaciated, no matter how plentiful is their food supply.   Structurally the family is characterized by the possession of four toes, with the hind one on the same plane as the three front ones, and the claw of the middle one equipped with a comb-like process on the inner side; a slender body, long neck, and a long and sharply pointed bill; comparatively long but noticeably rounded wings; and a bare space about the eyes and on the sides of the head.   There is great variation in the plumage, which is free and pliable, and is likely to be extended on the back, as in the case of the beautiful nuptial plumes of the Egrets.   On the abdomen, rump, and certain other parts are curious patches of down which are characteristic of the family.

Several of the American Herons are gregarious during the breeding period, when large colonies place their bulky nests near together in tree-tops; but in their feeding habits they usually are solitary.   Some species capture their prey by standing motionless and waiting for it to come within reach; others pursue on foot frogs, crawfish, and the like in shallow water. Their flight is deliberate, but powerful and certain, and is accomplished by incessant flapping, and little or no sailing or soaring.   Unlike the Cranes and Ibises, the Herons in flight carry the neck folded and the head drawn in near the shoulders.   Their eggs number from three or four to six, are unspotted and are whitish or bluish-green in color.   Of the true Herons there are about twelve species, which are from one foot to four feet and more in length.   The family is represented in virtually all parts of the North American continent excepting the regions of continuous cold or drought.

Drawing by R. I. Brasher

BITTERN (¼ nat. size)

It is an adept at concealment

Plate 23

GREEN HERON *Butorides virescens virescens* (Linnaeus)   LEAST BITTERN *Ixobrychus exilis* (Gmelin)
IMMATURE   ADULT   FEMALE   MALE
AMERICAN BITTERN *Botaurus lentiginosus* (Montagu)
All ¼ nat. size

BITTERN
Botaurus lentiginosus (*Montagu*)
A. O. U. Number 190   See Color Plate 23

Other Names.—American Bittern; Stake Driver; Thunder Pumper; Butterbump; Mire Drum; Bog Bull; Indian Hen; Marsh Hen; Poke.

General Description.—Length, 24 to 34 inches. Color above, brown, blackish, white, and tawny mixed; below, yellowish.

Color.—Crown, dull brown with buffy stripe over eye; rest of upper parts, streaked and minutely *freckled with brown, blackish, white, and tawny*; chin and upper throat, whitish; under parts, yellow and tawny-white, each feather with a brown darker-edged stripe; center of throat and neck, white with brown streaks; a brown mustache on side of throat; wing-quills, greenish-black with a glaucous shade and tipped with brown; tail,

brown; bill, pale yellow with dusky ridge; *legs, dull greenish-yellow*; iris, yellow.

Nest and Eggs.—NEST: On the ground among reeds in a swamp; roughly and loosely constructed of dead rushes. EGGS: 3 to 5, brownish with a gray shade.

Distribution.—North America; breeds from central British Columbia, southern Mackenzie, central Keewatin, southern Ungava, and Newfoundland south to southern California, northern Arizona, Kansas, the Ohio valley, and North Carolina, and less frequently in southern United States; winters from California, Arizona, southern Texas, the Ohio valley, and Virginia south to Cuba and Guatemala, and casually to the Bahamas, Porto Rico, Jamaica, and Great Britain.

Thoreau says that the Bittern is the genius of the bog. It frequents the ooze, and delights in the quaking false bottom where the first unwary step may plunge the adventurer into slimy depths. Here it steals about, hidden among the rank marsh growth; here it makes its nest and woos its mate. But it is not confined to the marsh; it is common in large meadows and may even be seen hunting grasshoppers in nearby upland pastures. The Bittern is an adept at concealment. It has a habit of standing among the grass or reeds with its bill cocked up at such an angle that even when in full sight it remains unnoticed because of its close resemblance to a rail or a stake. Its penciled foreneck imitates the reeds and all its colors are inconspicuous. It has learned the art of moving almost as slowly as the minute hand of a clock so as to escape observation while changing position.

The most remarkable characteristic of the Bittern is its song, but the result of its efforts can hardly be called musical. While producing the sound the bird looks as if trying to rid itself of some distress of the stomach and the resulting melody sounds much like the sucking of an old-fashioned wooden pump when some one tries to raise the water. The bird suddenly lowers and raises its head and throws it far forward with a convulsive jerk, at the same time opening and shutting the bill with a click. This is accompanied by a sound which resembles a hiccough. This is repeated a few times, each time a little louder than before, while the bird seems to be swallowing air. This is succeeded by the pumping noises which are in sets of three syllables each resembling *plunk-a-lunk* or, as some people will have it, *plum pudd'n*. The lower neck seems to dilate with the air taken in and remains so

until the performance is over, when the neck is deflated.

There is a peculiar acoustic property about the sound. Its distance and its exact location are very hard to gage. The volume seems no greater when near than when at a consider-

Photo by H. K. Job   Courtesy of Outing Pub. Co.
BITTERN ON NEST

able distance, but as the distance increases the sound is no longer heard and in the place of each set of syllables there comes to the ear only a single note closely resembling the driving of a stake, which can be heard from afar. Hence the name " Stake Driver," often applied to this bird. These notes, although common in spring, particularly at morning and evening, are not noticeable and their resemblance to pumping and stake-driving is a protection to the bird.

Another remarkable characteristic consists of white nuptial plumes upon the sides of the neck or breast, which appear to be always concealed, except when the birds are performing their mating antics, when a plume is raised on each side high above the shoulder and becomes conspicuous against the darker plumage of the upper parts. The young — helpless, homely, and awkward — are exposed to many dangers in their lowly nest. Minks, muskrats and water snakes roam about them; keen-sighted Hawks, Eagles, and Owls sweep over the marsh; but the watchful mother is ever ready to defend them, and with her dagger-like bill and long neck she is no mean antagonist. When danger threatens she bristles to twice her usual size and with glaring eyes and ready, open beak becomes a dauntless defender.

EDWARD HOWE FORBUSH.

LEAST BITTERN
Ixobrychus exilis (*Gmelin*)

A. O. U. Number 191   See Color Plate 23

Other Names.— Dwarf Bittern; Little Bittern; Least Heron.

General Description.— Length, 11 to 14 inches. Color above, greenish-black; below, brownish-yellow.

Color.— ADULT MALE: Crown, back, and tail, glossy greenish-black; a streak down back of neck; most of wing-coverts, and outer edges of inner secondaries, pure chestnut; other wing-coverts, brownish-yellow; primaries, dusky, tipped with chestnut; front and sides of neck and under parts in general, brownish-yellow; white streaks along throat line; sides of breast with a broken brownish-black patch; a whitish streak on upper side of shoulder-feathers; bill, pale yellow with dusky ridge; skin of lores, light green; legs, dull greenish; iris and toes, yellow. ADULT FEMALE: Crown, brownish; back, brownish-chestnut with 2 white streaks along shoulders; wings, similar, but coverts more spotted with brown.

Nest and Eggs.— NEST: Usually in a bunch of cattails; a rough platform of dead reeds, raised above the water on a bed of decayed rushes. EGGS: 3 to 6, bluish-white.

Distribution.— Temperate North America and northern South America; breeds from southern Oregon, southern Saskatchewan, southern Manitoba, southern Quebec, and Nova Scotia south to the West Indies and Brazil; winters from Florida and Gulf of Mexico southward.

Photo by A. A. Allen

LEAST BITTERN

On its nest in the marsh

Reed-grown ponds, grassy margins of lakes, and expanses of fresh-water marshes form the abiding places of the Least Bittern. Only a little over a foot in length, it is the smallest of all our Herons. Because of its retiring habits and secretive disposition it is known to few besides the inquisitive ornithologist, whose enthusiasm for the subject leads him into the forbidden haunts of the Bittern. Even then it is rarely seen until suddenly it springs from its hiding, at times almost beneath your feet, and in an awkward and laborious manner flies away a few rods and drops again into the marsh. More rarely it may be seen clinging to the stem of some rush or reed much in the manner of a Wren. It has not been given to many to hear the soft cooing spring notes of the male, but most summer marsh-waders are familiar with the startled *qua* with which it begins its flight when disturbed.

Although the Least Bittern is found in summer as far north as Maine and Manitoba, it is much more abundant in the southern States. A few pass the winter in Florida, but the bulk of these birds migrate farther south. In spring they arrive in the Carolinas and Arkansas by middle April, and a few weeks later their summer dis-

position in the northern States is complete. A
fairly compact platform of plant stems and
grasses serves as a nest, on which from three to
six elliptical pale bluish eggs are laid. It is
usually situated in clusters of tall grass or reeds
and at a distance varying from one to four feet
from the water.

In many of the fresh-water ponds of Florida
certain small areas, near the shore, are covered
with a thick growth of buttonwood bushes.
These are popular places for small colonies of
the Boat-tailed Grackle, the big shiny Blackbird
of the country. In the midst of these Blackbird
villages one may often find a Least Bittern's nest.
They do not assemble in colonies like most members of the family, the two or three nests sometimes found in the same neighborhood evidently
having been placed close together more because
the different pairs chanced to like the location,
than from any desire for the companionship of
their kind. Although I have always found these
Bitterns partial to fresh water in the summer,
Arthur T. Wayne states that in South Carolina
they also breed regularly in salt marshes, and
that during migration they constantly frequent
such locations.

To find a nest full of young Least Bitterns is
an event to remember. Standing at their full
height with bills pointed skyward they remain as
motionless as though cast in bronze. The alter-
nate light and dark streaks on their breasts and
throats blend perfectly with the coloring of the
reeds about them. Evidently they know that so
long as they are still they are perfectly hidden.

A rare and closely allied bird variously known
as Cory's Least Bittern (*Ixobrychus neoxenus*),
Cory's Bittern, or Cory's Dwarf Bittern, has been
found in Florida, Ontario, Michigan, and perhaps elsewhere.

                          T. GILBERT PEARSON.

Drawing by R. I. Brasher

LEAST BITTERN (⅔ nat. size)

The smallest of the Herons in " the frozen position "

GREAT WHITE HERON

Ardea occidentalis *Audubon*

A. O. U. Number 192

Other Name.— Florida Heron.

General Description.— Length, 48 to 54 inches.
Head not crested, but in breeding season with a few
feathers long and flowing; plumage, *pure white;* bill,
yellow, greenish at base; legs and feet, yellow; iris,
chrome yellow; bare space around eye, bluish and green.

Nest and Eggs.— NEST: In low bushes or high trees;
a simple platform of sticks. EGGS: 3 to 5, bluish-green.

Distribution.— Region bordering Gulf of Mexico
from southern Florida south to Cuba, Jamaica, and
Yucatan; casual north to Anclote River and Micco,
Florida.

The Great White Heron is equal in size to the common and well-known Great Blue Heron. It is not the proud possessor of beautiful aigrette-plumes, such as adorn the Egrets, and consequently has not been so extensively shot. It occurs mainly on the islands of Jamaica and Cuba, but is not uncommonly found along the coast of Florida. In 1911 I discovered a colony of seven pairs breeding on the island in Tampa Bay, on the Gulf coast of Florida. This appears to be the northern limit at which they have thus far been found in the nesting period. The nests were about twelve feet above the water and rested among the stronger topmost limbs of mangrove trees. They were huge affairs, made of sticks, and those examined contained either three or four eggs. The little colony covered a territory about eighty feet in diameter. One hundred feet away a number of Florida Cormorants and Louisiana Herons were beginning to build their nests. Apparently the three species were dwelling together in harmony.

Cruising among the Florida Keys and coral reefs near Cape Sable one may often see these giant Herons feeding in the shallow places which everywhere abound. They haunt such localities in south Florida, but one need not look for them inland. Their great size and white plumage render them conspicuous marks which may be seen for a long distance. I have always found the Great White Heron extremely shy and difficult to approach. Its judgment seems never at fault in determining what is the exact range of a hunter's rifle.   T. Gilbert Pearson.

Photo by H. K. Job   Courtesy of Houghton Mifflin Co.

YOUNG GREAT WHITE HERON

In nest, Florida Keys

GREAT BLUE HERON

Ardea herodias herodias *Linnæus*

A. O. U. Number 194   See Color Plate 24

Other Names.— Red-shouldered Heron; Blue Crane; Crane; Common Blue Crane.

General Description.— Length, 42 to 50 inches. Color above, slaty-blue; below, black. Head, crested and with long plumes.

Color.— Adults: Forehead and top of head, white; *sides of crown and crest, black;* neck, pale gray, marked on throat with white, rusty and black streaks; chin and cheeks, white; *upper parts, slaty-blue;* shoulders, grayer; tail, slaty-blue; inner wing-quills, slaty-blue shading into black primaries; plumes of lower neck and breast, gray; abdomen, black with white and rufous streaking; under tail-coverts, white; bill, yellow with dusky ridge; legs and feet, dusky, soles yellow; bare space around eye, greenish and blue; iris, chrome yellow. Young: No crest or lengthened feathers on head; entire crown, blackish; general color above, brownish-slate, the feathers edged with rufous; lesser wing-coverts, reddish-brown; below, ashy.

Nest and Eggs.— Nest: Usually in tall trees along river banks; a large and bulky structure of limbs, twigs, and some dry grass. Eggs: 3 to 6, blue or greenish-blue.

Distribution.— Western hemisphere; breeds from southeastern British Columbia, central Alberta, central Manitoba, northern Ontario, and Prince Edward Island south to southern Lower California, northern Texas, and South Atlantic States (except Florida); winters from Oregon, the Ohio valley, and Middle States south to the West Indies, Panama, and Venezuela.

The Great Blue Heron is the largest of the American herons, and is known as a most stately, dignified, and interesting bird by those who have observed it in other ways than over the sights of a shotgun or rifle. This pursuit is legalized in certain regions where the bird is believed to be even more destructive to the spawn and young of game fish than to its other prey of frogs, crawfish, small snakes, salamanders and various water creatures which are more harmful than useful, not to mention grasshoppers and meadow mice. Under these conditions it becomes difficult to approach one of these alert and far-sighted birds even to within field-glass range. A stalk of this kind is, however, well worth while if it brings the observer to within observation distance, for his reward will be an exhibition of stealthy and skillful fishing which is bound to command his admiration.

Much of this fishing the Heron does without stirring from the position he takes in shallow water among reeds or near the shore. Motionless as a statue he stands, his long neck doubled into a flattened S and his keen eyes searching the water nearby. As a frog or fish approaches he holds his rigid position until the creature comes within striking range, and the Heron knows what that is to a small fraction of an inch. Then suddenly the curved neck straightens out and simultaneously the long, rapier-like bill shoots

Photo by W. L. Finley and H. T. Bohlman

GREAT BLUE HERON

The largest of the American Herons

downward with a stroke which is quicker than the eye can follow and seldom misses its mark. In a second the fish or frog has disappeared, and

the fisherman has resumed his statuesque pose. Again, the great bird may be seen stalking slowly through shallow water, lifting each foot above

Photo by H. K. Job   Courtesy of Outing Pub. Co.

A COLONY OF GREAT BLUE HERONS

the surface, and sliding it into the water again so gently as to cause hardly a ripple; and woe to the crawfish or salamander that does not observe that approach.

Like most Herons, the Great Blue is a solitary bird in its habits except during the breeding season. Then the birds show a strongly marked gregarious instinct by forming colonies, generally in isolated swamps, where they build their huge nests and bring up their young, which are fed by regurgitation. These heronries are most interesting institutions for the bird-student. Occasionally several nests are placed in a single tree, and frequently colonies are found which include 150 or more nests. Unless the birds are seriously molested they are likely to return for many successive years to the same nesting-site.

It is well known that members of the Heron family feed to a great extent on fish and other forms of aquatic life, and consequently do not live far from water. The Great Blue Herons at times depart from this family trait and visit hillsides, cultivated fields, and drier meadows in search of pocket gophers, ground squirrels, and field mice, which they greedily devour. Pellets collected in an inland nesting colony of these Herons showed that a very large proportion of the food of the young is made up of these injurious rodents. The Herons, like other flesh-eating birds, digest their food rapidly and are disposed to gorge themselves when opportunity offers. It is fair to assume as a low average that a pair of Herons with four or five young will consume twelve to fifteen gophers per day.

GEORGE GLADDEN.

EGRET

Herodias egretta (*Gmelin*)

A. O. U. Number 196   See Color Plate 24

Other Names.—American Egret; White Heron; White Egret; Greater Egret; Great White Egret; Great White Heron; Long White.

Description.— Length, 41 inches. No crest, but a magnificent train of long plumes springing from back and extending a foot or so beyond tail in breeding season; *plumage, entirely white;* bill, yellow; legs and feet, black; lores and iris, yellow.

Nest and Eggs.— Nest: Merely a platform of sticks in mangroves or in trees. Eggs: 3 to 5, plain bluish-green.

Distribution.— Temperate and tropical America; breeds in Oregon and California, and from North Carolina, Florida, the Gulf coast, and Mexico south to Patagonia; formerly bred north to New Jersey and Wisconsin; winters from the Gulf of Mexico southward; casual in Manitoba, Quebec, New England, and Nova Scotia.

The treatment which man has accorded the Egret is not only an evidence of his power over weaker animals, but stands as a blot on this country's history. The long white plumes, which this bird bears on its back in the mating and nesting season, have long been sought as adornments for women's headwear. The only way to get these "aigrettes" is to shoot the bird, and shoot it at the time it is engaged in the care of its nestlings. At other seasons it is wild, and only with great difficulty can one approach to within shooting distance, before it takes wing.

The plumes are acquired early in the year but not until the birds have accumulated in colonies, and laid their eggs, can the hunter hope for success. Even then the wise millinery agents wait until the rookery is ripe. By "ripe" they mean when the eggs have hatched. If the shooting begins in a colony before this time, the birds will frequently desert their nests and eggs. Thus in order to get the most satisfactory results the plume-hunter must be content to wait until the young appear, and the instinct of parental care is so aroused that the old birds will return again and again despite the fact that they see their companions falling all about them before the guns of the inhuman hunters. This method of attack on any species if long continued means its doom. When old and young alike perish no chance remains to perpetuate the species.

In the far West a few Egrets still are found, but very rarely. They appear never to have reached the abundance there that they did in the Southern States. At one time the lake-shores of Florida teemed with tens of thousands of these elegant, long-legged white creatures. Several years ago I visited rookeries containing great numbers of them, but even then the work of destruction was going on. While visiting a plume-hunter's camp in 1886 I was told that the New York feather dealers paid ninety cents for the plumes of every bird. Since that time the price has gone up and up until recently tourists at Miami and Palm Beach have been paying $10 and more for the scalp of each bird brought in by the white hunters and Seminole Indians of the Everglade country.

For several years past the National Association of Audubon Societies has been employing guards to protect the few remaining breeding colonies as far as they are known. These nesting places are distributed from the coastal region of North Carolina southward to the Florida Keys, but it is debatable whether the species can be saved, although without the efforts of the Audubon Society the bird would probably have disappeared entirely by this time.

This member of the Heron family often associates in the nesting season with other Herons. The loose nests of twigs are placed in the top of bushes or on the limbs of cypress trees high above the waters of the sequestered swamps into which these birds have long since been driven.

T. GILBERT PEARSON.

Photograph of habitat group   Courtesy of American Museum of Natural History

EGRETS

These birds have been brought to the verge of extinction by plume hunters

SNOWY EGRET

Egretta candidissima candidissima (*Gmelin*)

A. O. U. Number 197

Other Names.— Little Egret; Lesser Egret; Common Egret; Snowy Heron; Little Snowy; Little White Egret; Little White Heron; Bonnet Martyr.

Description.— Length, 24 inches. Plumage, pure white; bill and legs, black; toes, yellow; bare space around eye, greenish-yellow; iris, chrome yellow. A long crest on crown, another from back of about 50 feathers, the latter recurved, and another on lower neck.

Nest and Eggs.— NEST: Usually among mangroves or in swampy willow ponds; a simple platform of sticks. EGGS: 2 to 5, pale bluish-green.

Distribution.— Temperate and tropical America; formerly bred from Oregon, Nebraska, Indiana, Illinois, and New Jersey south to Chile and Argentina; now breeds locally in the United States from North Carolina to Louisiana; winters from Florida southward; casual in British Columbia, Ontario, Massachusetts, and Nova Scotia.

Much smaller than the Egret, the Snowy Egret is nevertheless adorned in the breeding season with "aigrettes," growing on the back between

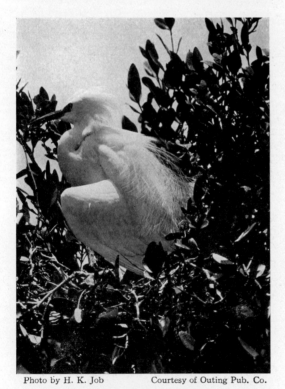

Photo by H. K. Job   Courtesy of Outing Pub. Co.

SNOWY EGRET ON NEST

Showing " aigrette " plumes

the wings, that are quite as valuable in the market as those produced by the larger bird. The plume-feathers are much shorter, more delicate, and are recurved at the end. They are the " cross aigrettes " of the millinery trade. To the plume-

hunters the bird is known as the " Little Snowy," to distinguish it from the larger species called by them the " Long White."

Snowy Egrets once bred as far north as New Jersey, but now their northern breeding limit is North Carolina. Although found inland in Florida, they are elsewhere in their range in the United States more distinctively inhabitants of the tide-water regions. Owing to protection afforded them from the millinery feather hunters of recent years by Audubon Society wardens, they appear to be increasing in a few sections, notably about Charleston, South Carolina. Apparently the largest gathering of breeding birds is in a splendid Heron colony that has developed under the special care of E. A. McIlhenny at Avery Island, Louisiana. The rookery is in the trees and bushes of a small artificial pond within 200 yards of Mr. McIlhenny's house, and among the many interesting entertainments he gives his guests is to take them out to the edge of the yard of a spring evening that they may watch the Herons and Snowy Egrets coming home to roost or to relieve their mates on guard at the nests.

Like that of other Herons the food of this bird consists of such small forms of life as inhabit the sloughs and marshes of their territory. The young are fed extensively on small fish that are regurgitated into their throats by the parent bird. The Snowy Egret has a plumage of spotless white. The legs are black and the feet are bright yellow. By observing the coloring of the feet and legs one need never mistake it for the immature Little Blue Heron, which, except for the absence of " aigrettes," it much resembles.

T. GILBERT PEARSON.

LOUISIANA HERON

Hydranassa tricolor ruficollis (*Gosse*)

A. O. U. Number 199

Other Names.— Lady of the Waters; Demoiselle.

General Description.— Length, 27 inches. Color above, slaty-purple; below, white. The lengthened feathers of head and neck, sharp with well-defined edges; the back train-feathers, fringe-like.

Color.— ADULTS (SEXES ALIKE): Crown, sides of head, most of neck, back, and wings, slaty-purple; chin and throat, white, broken behind with color of head; the long feathers of crest, white; lower back and rump, white but concealed by feathers of train which extends beyond tail; *lower parts, mostly white*; bill, black — bluer toward base; legs, grayish; iris, red; bare space around eye, light lilac. YOUNG: No crest or plumes. Neck and back, brownish-red; rump, center of throat, and under parts, white; wings and tail, pale lavender-blue; legs, dusky green. Individuals show variations between this and adult plumage but *are never white*.

Nest and Eggs.— NEST: In mangrove or willow swamps; in communities or in company with other Herons; a frail platform of sticks. EGGS: 3 to 5, bluish-green.

Distribution.— Southern North America; breeds from North Carolina and the Gulf States to the West Indies, Mexico (both coasts), and Central America; winters from South Carolina southward; casual in Indiana, New Jersey, and Long Island.

Though characteristically a southern species, the Louisiana Heron ranks among the most abundant Herons in this country, since in the Southern States it is decidedly the most abundant of the numerous Herons. In every way it is a beautiful bird, distinct and distinguished in its royal purplish garments contrasted with sharply defined white under parts. It is graceful and gentle, not shy, and is quite well known, feeding along the edges of swamps and meadows, or on the borders of streams and ponds.

Of social disposition, its nesting is mainly in rookeries, sometimes of large size. In E. A. McIlhenny's celebrated Egret and Heron colony at Avery Island, La., this is the most abundant species, many thousands of them nesting in this forty-acre tract. Reasons for their abundance are primarily that the plumes which grow from their backs at the nuptial season, though quite pretty, fortunately have not been in demand for millinery purposes. Then, further, they are tamer in disposition than some others, and apparently are not so easily frightened from a locality by human intrusion.

The rookeries are usually in a wooded swamp, generally among low, rather thick trees, and par-

Courtesy of Am. Mus. Nat. Hist.

LOUISIANA HERON (¼ nat. size)

The most abundant Heron in North America

ticularly on small wooded or bushy islands, where such can be found. On the Louisiana Coast reservations, where the islands were treeless, these Herons were content to nest directly on the ground, or on the smallest of bushes, sometimes hardly a foot up. The nests are frail platforms

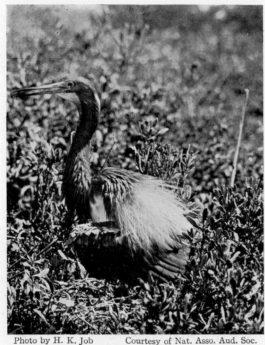

Photo by H. K. Job   Courtesy of Nat. Asso. Aud. Soc.
LOUISIANA HERON
On nest on ground

of sticks, and are similar to those of most other Herons, as are their eggs, which are blue, rather small, and from three to five in number.

On various occasions I have pitched my little photographic tent among their nests, preferably at night, leaving it till morning, when I would enter it and have a companion withdraw. The birds had soon become accustomed to it as a part of the landscape, and, not being able to "count noses," would soon return and settle down to brood their eggs or small young, or would come to feed the latter. It was most interesting and exciting to sit there, as though a member of the tribe, and watch all the singular, remarkable ways and actions, selecting the quaintest of these for photographic records.

These rookeries are the more interesting in that it is usual for various species of Herons to congregate together. In such colonies I have found, besides representatives of this species, the Snowy and American Egrets, Black-crowned and Yellow-crowned Night Herons, Little Blue and Great Blue Herons — certainly a lively assortment. Since, however, the Louisiana Heron is the most abundant of all, there are plenty of rookeries, especially the smaller ones, where it is found alone. In such places there is the wildest of confusion when one enters. The larger young climb from the nests from branch to branch, using both bills and feet to aid them. The less said about cleanliness and odor the better. Yet despite their slovenly ways it is remarkable how clean and trim the Herons look! They spend hours preening their feathers, so that, after all, in their own peculiar way they are orderly.

Most of them retire beyond our borders in winter, but on the Gulf coast I have seen a few of them at that season, still wading in the shallows and striking swiftly with their sharp bills at the small fish and other aquatic forms which constitute their bill of fare.   HERBERT K. JOB.

LITTLE BLUE HERON

Florida cærulea (*Linnæus*)

A. O. U. Number 200

Other Name.— Blue Egret.

Description.— Plumes on shoulders and throat. OLD ADULTS: General plumage, dark slaty-blue shading to purplish-red on neck and head; bill, black shading to bluish at base; legs and feet, black; iris, yellow. YOUNG ADULTS: In perfect plumage, pure white, but usually showing traces of blue, especially on end of primaries. Length, 24 inches.

Nest and Eggs.— NEST: In trees or bushes over or near swamps; constructed like those of the rest of the genus. EGGS: 2 to 4, bluish-green.

Distribution.— North and South America; formerly bred from Missouri, Indiana, Illinois, and New Jersey to western Mexico and south to Argentina and Peru; in the United States now breeds locally on the coast from North Carolina to Texas; wanders casually to Nebraska, Wisconsin, Ontario, New England, and Nova Scotia; winters from South Carolina southward.

In that portion of the United States that the Little Blue Heron inhabits it is one of the most common members of the Heron family. It is generally seen in flocks, inhabiting the shallow ponds and grassy lake-sides of the Southern States. With slow deliberation they wade carefully along, their bright yellow eyes scanning the shallows in quest of the fish, water-insects, or frogs upon which they subsist. Upon the approach of evening they take flight and with measured wing-strokes pass across the country, sometimes for several miles, to a favorite roosting place in the trees of a swamp, or on some island. In spring they assemble in colonies, often by hundreds, and build their nests in the small trees or bushes of some isolated and favorite pond. These "rookeries" are usually inhabited also by other species of Herons and sometimes by other varieties of water birds.

The young are first covered with white down which later is replaced by white feathers. Not until two years of age do they assume the blue plumage of the adult. During the second summer individuals may be seen representing all stages in this change of feathers. Some are white with only a few blue feathers showing, while others, further developed, are entirely blue except for scattering spots of white. The Little Blue Heron is one of the comparatively few birds that mates and rears young while yet clothed in the feathers of youth. I recall visiting a colony of perhaps forty pairs on one occasion, every bird of which was still in the white phase of plumage.

Because of their white appearance they are often mistaken for Egrets and many times these rarer birds are reported as being seen in a neighborhood, when a closer inspection by a competent observer would easily reveal the mistake.

After the nesting season the birds wander all over the country hunting for good feeding grounds. It is an odd fact worthy of mention, that the young take trips farther afield than do their parents; and thus it happens that in the late summer immature Little Blue Herons are constantly recorded far to the north of their breeding grounds, where the adult birds are seen only at very rare intervals, if at all. Old Herons

VOL. I — 14

possess a very pretty tuft of long plumes on their backs in summer, but these decorations never appear on the bird while in the white plumage.

Being fish eaters their flesh is not at all esteemed as a table delicacy, but in remote regions the colonies are often raided for their eggs for which some people profess a fondness. Their

Photo by H. K. Job   Courtesy of Houghton Mifflin Co.

LITTLE BLUE HERON

chief natural enemies appear to be water moccasins and alligators, with which most rookeries are infested. The former climb into the trees and swallow the eggs, the latter devour the young when they fall from the nest.

T. GILBERT PEARSON.

GREEN HERON

Butorides virescens virescens (*Linnæus*)

A. O. U. Number 201   See Color Plate 23

Other Names.— Little Green Heron; Green Bittern; Fly-up-the-creek.

General Description.— Length, 18 inches.   Color above, dark green; below, dark brown.

Color.— ADULTS: Crown (including a long soft crest), lengthened feathers of back and shoulders, *lustrous dark green*; the back plumes with a glaucous cast; *wing-coverts, green* with well-defined tawny edges; neck, rich dark purplish-chestnut; center of throat, white with dusky streaks; below, dark brownish; abdomen, streaked with white; primaries, secondaries, and tail, greenish-dusky; edge of wing, white; bill, dusky-greenish, yellow at base below; bare space around eye, bluish-green; legs, yellow; iris, yellow. YOUNG: No crest; top of head, brown; sides of neck and body,

brownish streaked with lighter; throat and center line of neck, white with dusky streaks; back, plain greenish-brown; wing-coverts and secondaries, with white edgings and white tips; under tail-coverts, grayish-white; bill, greenish with dusky ridge; legs, pale greenish-gray; iris, yellow.

Nest and Eggs.— NEST: Frequently in the woods but usually near water; a frail platform of twigs in a tree or bush. EGGS: 3 to 6, pale greenish.

Distribution.— Eastern North America; breeds from southern South Dakota, northern Wisconsin, southern Ontario, southern Quebec, and Nova Scotia south to the West Indies; winters from the West Indies southward, and rarely in southeastern United States; casual in Colorado.

Though a comparatively small Heron, the Green Heron is perhaps the best known member of his family in this country, and probably most people who see him dismiss him as a gawky, awkward, and rather stupid bird with habits which are not exactly tidy. This is because he is usually seen when he utters his harsh alarm note and flops clumsily along to a nearby perch, where he stretches his neck, jerks his tail, and gazes around in a fuddle-headed manner.

Those who really know the bird, however, realize that when he is about his business of

Photograph by R. W. Shufeldt

GREEN HERON

Perhaps he is the best known member of his family in this country

Photograph by A. A. Allen

GREEN HERON

At its nest in the willows fringing a pond

catching fish, frogs, salamanders, and the like, he is very far from stupid or clumsy. Then he steps along in the shallow water or through the weeds with true Heron stealth, and the thrust of his long bill, as he seizes his prey, is as accurate as and a great deal quicker than that of an expert swordsman. When flushed to a perch, the bird has a curious habit, if it sees it is observed, of suddenly becoming absolutely rigid, or "freezing," to use the term commonly employed. This apparently is done for the purpose of escaping further observation. It is an interesting fact that young Herons, at a signal from the old bird, often employ the same ruse, and stand as motionless as statues, sometimes until the intruder has approached to within a few feet.

Unlike other members of its family, the Green Heron is not gregarious in its breeding habits. Occasionally a few birds place their nests near together, but this apparently is accidental, for there are no true rookeries of Green Herons, and the birds lead a distinctly lonely life.

Photo by S. A. Lottridge

YOUNG GREEN HERONS

Removed from the nest by the photographer

BLACK-CROWNED NIGHT HERON
Nycticorax nycticorax nævius (*Boddaert*)
A. O. U. Number 202   See Color Plate 24

Other Names.— Night Heron; American Night Heron; Qua-bird; Quawk; Squawk; Gardenian Heron.

General Description.— Length, 26 inches. Color above, black and ashy-gray; below, white. Head crested and, in breeding plumage, with a few long white cord-like plumes from back of crown.

Color.— ADULTS: *Crown, back, and shoulders, black;* rest of upper parts, wings, and tail, pale ashy-gray; forehead, sides of head, and throat, white shading into very pale lavender on neck; rest of under parts, white; bill, black; legs, yellow; iris, red; bare space around eye, yellowish-green. YOUNG: Entire plumage, grayish-white, streaked on head, breast, and beneath with dark brown; streaked and spotted on back with rusty and whitish; wing-coverts, brown with conspicuous white triangular tips; primaries, dusky-brown; bill, dull yellowish; feet, pale greenish-yellow; iris, brown.

Nest and Eggs.— NEST: In trees, bushes, or on ground; a large but loosely constructed affair of branches and twigs. EGGS: 3 to 6, pale sea-green.

Distribution.— North and South America; breeds from northern Oregon, southern Wyoming, southern Manitoba, northern Quebec, and Nova Scotia south to Patagonia; winters from northern California and Gulf States southward; casual in winter north to Massachusetts and southern Illinois.

Though not strictly a nocturnal bird, as it moves about more or less in the daytime, the Black-crowned Night Heron feeds chiefly in the evening or after the night has fallen. As the twilight deepens it may be seen flying heavily toward its favorite feeding places, and now is most frequently heard the loud and raucous *quawk* from which is has received one of its popular names.

The bird's preferred hunting grounds are shallow tidal creeks, the edges of ponds, and swamps which include pools. Here it hunts, usually alone and often at a distance of several miles from its breeding place, so that the feeding of the young frequently involves long flights from the hunting ground to the nest.

Its hunting methods differ from those of its relative, the Great Blue Heron. Instead of

Photo by W. L. Finley and H. T. Bohlman

BLACK-CROWNED NIGHT HERON ON NEST

Plate 24

Louis Agassiz Fuertes

AMERICAN EGRET
Herodias egretta (Gmelin)
SANDHILL CRANE
Grus mexicana (Müller)

BLACK-CROWNED NIGHT HERON
Nycticorax nycticorax naevius (Boddaert)
ADULT   IMMATURE
GREAT BLUE HERON
Ardea herodias herodias Linnaeus
ADULT IN SUMMER   IMMATURE

All ½ nat. size

standing rigid, and knee-deep in water, as that big fisherman does, the Night Heron moves

Photo by H. T. Middleton
YOUNG NIGHT HERONS

about briskly, holding its head lowered and its neck curved, all ready for the quick stroke which means death to the frog or fish at which it is aimed.

This Heron's most interesting characteristic is its gregariousness, which causes it to collect in large colonies during the nesting period. These heronries usually are situated in an isolated patch of woods, and their population may include several hundred pairs of birds, not to mention as many groups of four or five young birds. Indeed, as a pair will frequently raise two broods in a season, it is not uncommon to find the adult birds feeding at the same time two sets of youngsters, one composed of fledglings in the nest and the other of birds able to clamber about in the branches.

YELLOW-CROWNED NIGHT HERON
Nyctanassa violacea (*Linnæus*)
A. O. U. Number 203

General Description.— Length, 24 inches. Plumage, bluish-gray, lighter below. Head, crested and, in breeding plumage, with a few long white cord-like plumes from back of crown.

Color.— Adults: Top of head and patch under eye, creamy white; sides of head and chin, black; rest of plumage, bluish-gray, darker on back, the feathers with black centers and pale edges; lighter below; head and neck, and most of crest, white *tinged with very pale tawny*; wings and tail, dusky-slate; bill, black; feet, black and yellow; iris, orange; lores and space around eye, greenish. Young: Above, brownish-gray with a strong olive tinge, streaked and spotted with brownish-yellow; below, streaked with brown and white; sides

of head and neck, yellowish-brown streaked with darker; top of head and neck variegated with white; bill, black with much greenish-yellow below; lores and legs, greenish-yellow; iris, yellow.

Nest and Eggs.— Nest: A platform of sticks in trees of swampy areas. Eggs: 4 to 6, dull bluish.

Distribution.— Warm temperate and tropical America; breeds from southern Lower California, Kansas, southern Illinois, southern Indiana, and South Carolina south to Brazil and Peru; casual north to Colorado, Ontario, Massachusetts, Maine, and Nova Scotia; winters from southern Lower California and southern Florida southward.

Although the name of Yellow-crowned Night Heron suggests that this bird is a " night " bird, in reality it is quite as diurnal in its habits as any of the more common Herons. Many times I have come upon it in the fresh-water marshes or on mud flats by the sea where it was evidently feeding and it would fly away with all the assurance of a bird whose sight was unimpaired by the sunlight. It is a solitary species and is little known to many bird-students. Rarely are more than two or three found at a time and generally they are seen singly. It is a southern species and probably never breeds north of Illinois and North Carolina. Wayne states that they " breed only in small colonies of two or three pairs." This refers to the South Carolina birds of which he writes, but in Florida I have found the facts to be otherwise. In that State I have examined several of their colonies and they numbered from twelve to twenty pairs in each instance. Ap-

Drawing by Henry Thurston
YELLOW-CROWNED NIGHT HERON (⅛ nat. size)
A solitary and little-known species

parently they do not associate in colonies with other Herons, but always form their own village.

In Hillsboro County, Florida, some years ago, I waded out in a large pond thickly grown with trees through the foliage of which the sun rarely

Photo by H. M. Laing   Courtesy of Outing Pub. Co.

NOT SINGING, BUT HUNGRY

Young Night Herons

pierced to the dark scum-water beneath. The object of my venture was to discover whether any Egrets were breeding among a company of

Herons, whose squawks told me they were nesting in the trees surrounding an open place in the center of the pond. Submerged logs, fallen limbs and aquatic moss made the going difficult. The place was infested with water-moccasins and alligators, and the nervous strain soon began to tell. Upon reaching a point perhaps sixty yards from shore where the water and slime was breast deep, I was startled beyond all description by a sudden hoarse cry and heavy flapping directly overhead. Unknowingly I had waded into the midst of a colony of Yellow-crowned Night Herons.

While occupying the same pond with the other Herons, they were at least two hundred feet from the nearest nest of any other species. Before leaving I counted sixteen nests, all of which appeared to be occupied.

These birds are supposed to feed largely upon mussels and crawfish and along the coast many small crabs are consumed. They retire to the far south in the autumn and do not reappear in the northern part of their range until March. After the nesting season many of the young wander far inland and in North Carolina I have seen them during the month of August more than two hundred miles from the coast.

T. GILBERT PEARSON.

Photo by G. N. Leek

NEST OF GREAT BLUE HERON

Showing the four bluish eggs

ORDER OF MARSH-DWELLERS

Order *Paludicolæ*

BIRDS of this order vary greatly in size and appearance—the Little Black Rail is but five inches long, while the Cranes average about four feet. Structurally all are alike in having the hind toe elevated. Two habits are common to the entire order. The first of these is that of dwelling in marshy places, and the second is that of always flying with the neck extended. The young are hatched with a covering of down and are able to run about soon after leaving the shell, although requiring more or less attention from the parents.

The order is divided into two suborders: the Long-legged Marsh-dwellers (*Grues*), which includes two families, the Cranes and the Courlans; and the Henlike Marsh-dwellers (*Ralli*), which consists of the single family of Rails, Gallinules, and Coots.

CRANES AND COURLANS

Order *Paludicolæ;* suborder *Grues;* families *Gruidæ* and *Aramidæ*

THOUGH superficially similar to the Herons in some respects, the Cranes constitute a distinct group in a different order. They are the family *Gruidæ* of the Marsh-dwellers and are really more closely related to the Rails than to the Herons. When in flight they may be distinguished from the Herons by their habit of carrying the neck extended at full length. But they are similar to the Herons in having the head more or less bare, while they differ from them in that their plumage is dense and compact, rather than loose. The family includes about twenty species, of which only three occur on this continent. Their favorite habitats are marshes and plains, and their diet includes not only frogs, snakes, field mice, and lizards, but grain and considerable vegetable food. Most of the Cranes have singularly loud and resonant cries, this being especially true of the Sandhill Crane. This resonant quality of the Crane's cry is due probably to the curious peculiarity and great length of the bird's windpipe. Though this organ is about normal in the chick just hatched, it becomes elongated and coiled as the bird matures, and is accommodated in the keel of the breastbone. In the Whooping Crane, when this development is complete, nearly thirty inches of the trachea may be thus packed away, and the entire length of the organ, from the throat to the lungs, may be fully five feet.

Another distinguishing characteristic of the Cranes is the fact that the chicks are covered with down when they are hatched, and are able to run about a few hours after they leave the shell. The American species range over the entire continent as far south as Cuba and Mexico. They are migratory from the northern portions of their range, but less so or not at all in the south.

The Courlans comprise another family, the *Aramidæ*, of the Marsh-dwellers. But two species are known: one found in South America, and the other, the Limpkin, in Central America, Mexico, the West Indies, and Florida.

WHOOPING CRANE

Grus americana (Linnæus)

A. O. U. Number 204

Other Names.— White Crane; Great White Crane; Garoo.

General Description.— Length, 4½ feet; spread of wings, 7½ feet. Plumage, white. Head with bare spot on each side below eyes, *extending to a point on back of crown* and sparsely covered with short hairs.

Color.— ADULTS: *White; primaries and coverts, black;* bare part of head, carmine; bill, dusky-greenish; legs, black; iris, yellow. YOUNG: Entire head, feathered. General plumage, whitish, variegated with rusty-brown.

Nest and Eggs.— NEST: On the ground; a well-built structure of marsh grass and reed stems, from one and a half to two feet in diameter and eighteen inches high. EGGS: 2, olive or buffy, blotched with large irregular spots of brown.

Distribution.— North America; bred formerly from northern Mackenzie south to Illinois and Iowa; now mainly restricted to southern Mackenzie and northern Saskatchewan; in migration formerly not rare on the Atlantic coast from New England to Florida and casual west to Colorado and Idaho; winters from the Gulf States to central Mexico.

The Whooping Crane was named and described by Linné in the eighteenth century. Previous to that time all three American species were lumped together as Cranes.

Many of the narratives of the early voyagers and settlers tell of Cranes migrating and nesting along the Atlantic coast. During the first century after the discovery of the country, Cranes evidently were more or less numerous all along this coast, from Florida to New England, but the word has been used so frequently to denote the larger Herons that one might be inclined to place little faith in the statements of sailors and colonists were it not for two facts: (1) In those days Cranes were well-known and conspicuous birds in England and other countries of which these voyagers were natives, or which they had visited, and undoubtedly they were familiar with these birds, and could distinguish them from Herons. (2) In the lists of birds given by these early adventurers, Herons, "Hearnes" and "Hernshaws," "Bitterns," and "Egrets" or "Egrepes" are also referred to, showing that they distinguished the Cranes from the Herons. The common European Heron was a large species (resembling the Great Blue Heron of America) which, at that time, was called the Hernshaw, Hearneshaw, or Heronshaw. It is often impossible to determine which species of Crane was referred to in these early narratives and lists of birds, as usually no description is given; but now and then we find a reference to a bird that must have been the Whooping Crane.

The Whooping Crane is the only bird of North America that can be described as "almost as tall as a man." The Whooping Crane stands about five feet high when stretched to its full height, but being white it appears taller, while the Sandhill Crane is not so conspicuous on account of its color and does not appear so large.

Probably there were few Cranes inhabiting Massachusetts when the Pilgrim Fathers landed at Plymouth, except along the coast, on the islands, and on the meadows and marshes of the river valleys, for most of the State was then covered with primeval forest; and while Cranes are sometimes found in open woods, they are shy and wary birds, and prefer the open country, where they can discern their enemies from afar.

The fact that they sometimes ate the corn proves that they were actually Cranes, not Herons, and also helps to explain their early disappearance from Massachusetts. They paid with the death penalty for eating the corn. Also, as these birds occupied the only natural open lands — those that were first sought by settlers — they were driven out within a few years after settlement began. Even had they not attacked the corn they must soon have succumbed because of their large size, their white color, and their general conspicuousness. In the early days the Indians used to steal upon the Cranes and shoot them with arrows. Now the few survivors of this species in the West will hardly come knowingly within a mile of the white man.

John Lawson, in his *History of Carolina*, says that Cranes are sometimes "bred up tame" and are excellent in the garden to destroy frogs and other vermin.

This bird is long-lived and grows wary as the years go by; it now frequents prairies, marshes, and barren grounds, over which it stalks, always alert and watchful. It flies low, its wings sometimes almost brushing the grass tops, but in migration it rises to such tremendous heights that it may pass over a large region unnoticed by man.

Courtesy of American Museum of Natural History

Photograph of habitat group

THE SANDHILL CRANE IN FLORIDA

When standing erect it is nearly the height of a man

[199]

It feeds on frogs, fish, small mammals, and insects, and is said to take corn and other cereals and the succulent roots of water-plants.

Nuttall, describing the flights of the Whooping Crane up the Mississippi valley in December, 1811, says, "that the bustle of their great migrations and the passage of their mighty armies fills the mind with wonder." It seemed, he says, as though the whole continent was giving up its quota of the species to swell this mighty host, and the clangor of their numerous legions, passing high in air, was almost deafening. His state-

ment, that this great host of Cranes was passing nearly all night, will give some idea of the immensity of this great flight.

The Whooping Crane is doomed to extinction. It has disappeared from its former habitat in the East and is now found only in uninhabited places. It can hardly be said to be common anywhere except perhaps locally in the far North. Only its extreme watchfulness has saved thus far the remnant of its once great host.

EDWARD HOWE FORBUSH, in *Game Birds, Wild-Fowl and Shore Birds.*

SANDHILL CRANE

Grus mexicana (*Müller*)

A. O. U. Number 206   See Color Plate 24

Other Names.— Brown Crane; Upland Crane; Field Crane; Southern Sandhill Crane.

General Description.— Length, 4 feet; spread of wings, 6½ feet. Plumage, slaty-gray. *Head with bare spot forking behind,* not reaching on sides below eyes, and thinly sprinkled with hair.

Color.— ADULTS: Plumage, *slaty-gray;* primaries and their coverts, ashy-gray but little darker than general color; cheeks and throat, lighter inclined to whitish; bill and feet, black; iris, brown. YOUNG: Head, feathered. Plumage, variegated with rusty and brown.

Nest and Eggs.— NEST: On the ground, usually on a slight knoll of open grassy flats; generally a mere depression in the ground, lined with dry grass and weed stems. EGGS: 2, from pale olive to buffy-brown, marked over entire surface with spots of burnt-umber.

Distribution.— North America; resident in Louisiana and Florida; bred formerly from southern British Columbia, Saskatchewan, Manitoba, and western Ontario south to California, Colorado, Nebraska, Illinois, and Ohio; formerly in migration east to New England; now rare east of the Mississippi, except in Florida, and rare as a breeder in the southern half of its former breeding range; winters from California, Texas, and Louisiana south to Mexico.

The virtual extermination, or at best the extreme rarity, of the great Whooping Crane, leaves the much smaller Sandhill Crane by far the largest representative of that interesting family in America. For it should be remembered that the various Herons — notably the Great Blue Heron — which are commonly called "Cranes," not only are not Cranes at all, but differ radically from them in both disposition and habits.

If not in size, then in its conspicuous and striking characteristics, the Sandhill Crane is a fit successor to his towering relative, whose days seem to be numbered. Nor is the bird a weakling at that, for the height of the male when he stands erect is nearly that of a man of average stature, while the bird's great wings carry his compact and muscular body with perfect ease and at a high speed. The bird's wariness bespeaks intelligent caution rather than weakness or fear.

Indeed, when the Sandhill Crane is crippled by a broken wing or otherwise, he may become an exceedingly ugly antagonist for the man who attempts to overpower him, because of the skill, strength, and quickness with which he will then employ his long and dagger-like bill in defending himself. Many a hunter's dog has been blinded or otherwise badly injured by the vicious thrusts of this very dangerous weapon, which the Crane does not hesitate to use when he is at bay and fighting for his life.

Unlike the Herons, this Crane spends much of its time, and gets the food which it seems to relish most, on dry land. Hence it is often found on the plains and prairies, sometimes in small flocks but oftener in pairs or singly. Its diet includes a large percentage of roots, bulbs, grains, and the like; and it is especially fond of corn which it takes from the shock. Insects, frogs, lizards, snakes, and mice are also included in its bill of fare, but not in sufficient numbers to make its flesh "strong" as is that of the Herons and other wading birds. In fact, this Crane's flesh is excellent for the table, and it has been persistently hunted for food.

On the fenceless prairies and the treeless marshes, where its keen eyes can detect afar off the approach of an enemy, the demeanor and habits of this fine, brave bird challenge the admiration of the man who appreciates alertness, courage, and strength in wild life. Not for an instant is the great bird off his guard. Moving in deliberate and dignified strides he pauses occasionally and lowers his head to thrust his long bill into the soft earth, or to seize a dozing frog or an unwatchful insect; but in a few seconds up again comes his head, and his eyes search the surrounding country. If the approach of his chief enemy, man, is discovered, the Crane surveys the intruder for a few minutes and then, with a few long, running strides takes to his wings, at the same time sounding his wild and defiant cry.

This cry of the Sandhill Crane is a veritable voice of Nature, untamed and unterrified. Its uncanny quality is like that of the Loon, but is more pronounced because of the much greater volume of the Crane's voice. Its resonance is remarkable and its carrying power is increased by a distinct tremolo effect. Often for several minutes after the birds have vanished, the unearthly sound drifts back to the listener, like a taunting trumpet from the under-world.

GEORGE GLADDEN.

The Little Brown Crane (*Grus canadensis*) is like the Sandhill Crane except for its smaller size. It breeds from northern Alaska, Melville Island, and Boothia Peninsula south to central Alaska, southern Mackenzie, and central Keewatin. During migration it occurs through the interior of the United States and winters south to Texas and Mexico.

LIMPKIN

Aramus vociferus (*Latham*)

A. O. U. Number 207

Other Names.—Courlan; Crying-bird; Clucking-hen; Carau.

Description.— Length, 28 inches. Color, olive-brown, paler on face, chin, and throat, streaked or spotted everywhere with white; bill, dusky; legs, greenish-dusky; iris, brown. The young are paler and duller than the adults.

Nest and Eggs.— NEST: On the ground near water, sometimes a short distance above ground in a maze of vines or thick bushes; constructed of grass, leaves, dead vines, moss, and other old vegetation. EGGS: 4 to 7, usually 5 or 6, varying from pure white to buffy, spotted and splashed with brown and gray.

Distribution.— Florida, Greater Antilles, and both coasts of Central America; casual north to South Carolina; accidental in Texas.

Of the Courlan family only two species are known, one of these being the Limpkin of Central America, Mexico, the West Indies, and Florida. It may be described as a very large Rail with many of the habits of an Ibis. In the Everglades of Florida it is a common bird and while crossing that vast waste in the month of May I found many flocks, some of which numbered as high as forty individuals. Their flight is peculiar. With dangling legs the bird springs from the glades and goes off on wings that have a jerky motion, strongly suggestive of the movements of the wings of a mechanical beetle. In alighting the wings are held high above the back and in this attitude the bird drops from sight. The food consists largely of the big fresh-water snail found in many parts of the State. These snails in places abound in the shallow waters and are easily procured by this long-legged wading bird. In the cypress swamps I have come upon piles of empty shells from which the snails had been extracted by these birds. In doing this the shell is rarely broken.

In the swamps along the Oklawaha River, lumbermen of recent years have cut much of the timber. Stumps, from four to ten feet in height, are everywhere left standing. The jungle hates a bare place and soon these stumps are covered with vines. Here, on the top of these vine-clad pillars, the Limpkins often build their nests. Farther south you may find them in tall bunches of saw-grass or isolated custard-apples bushes in the glades. The nests are made chiefly of such varieties of twigs and leaves as are obtainable in the neighborhood. From four to seven brown spotted eggs are laid.

Limpkins at times are very noisy creatures. Their usual call possesses a quality of unutterable sadness, as though the bird was oppressed beyond measure by the desolateness of its surroundings. For this reason the name "Crying-bird" is usually given them by the natives. In the spring and early summer they largely haunt the swampy shores of streams and lakes, but in the autumn they gather in great numbers in the more open savannas. Thousands thus pass the winter months on the pond-covered prairies about the headwaters of the Caloosahatchee River, west of Lake Okechobee. The Limpkin is highly esteemed for food, but owing to the difficulties of hunting them in their retreats there is strong likelihood of the species persisting in Florida for many years to come.

A few years ago many were to be found in the swampy country of northern Florida, within fifteen or twenty miles of the Georgia line, and two or three specimens have even been taken in South Carolina.   T. GILBERT PEARSON.

Courtesy of Am. Mus. Nat. Hist.

LIMPKIN

A long-legged wading bird of Florida and tropical America

RAILS, GALLINULES, AND COOTS

Order *Paludicolæ;* suborder *Ralli;* family *Rallidæ*

ABOUT fifty genera, embracing one hundred and eighty species constitute this family, the *Rallidæ,* which includes the Rails (*Rallinæ*), Gallinules (*Gallinulinæ*), and Coots (*Fulicinæ*). The distribution of these birds is virtually cosmopolitan, and about fifteen species occur, regularly or casually, in North America. They are from small to fair-sized birds, with noticeably compressed bodies,— well adapted to rapid progress through thickly growing reeds and rushes,— long necks, small heads, short, rounded wings, short tails, and long, strong legs and feet. The bill is short and henlike in the Coots and Gallinules, but long and slightly curved toward the end in the Rails. The plumage is subdued and blended in color. A family peculiarity is that of running, rather than flying, to escape danger, a trait apparently responsible for the extermination of certain species which had lost the power of flight through disuse of the wings, and the steady diminution of others for the same reason.

"Rails and Gallinules are marsh birds, very secretive in habits, keeping well under cover of the dense rushes and grasses, except at night or in the twilight, when they venture out on the muddy shores. When silently floating along the marshy stream, one may often see them standing motionless near their favorite coverts, or walking deliberately along the margin flirting their upturned tails and bobbing their necks in henlike fashion. Their cries are also loud, and remind one of the different notes of our domestic fowl. Consequently all our species of the family, from the Virginia Rail to the Coot, have received the common name of Mud Hens. The flight of Rails and Gallinules is feeble and hesitating. They usually take wing as a last resort, and then proceed with dangling legs, in a direct course, low over

Plate 25

Louis Agassiz Fuertes.

VIRGINIA RAIL
Rallus virginianus Linnaeus

DOWNY YOUNG   ADULT

KING RAIL
Rallus elegans Audubon

IMMATURE

CLAPPER RAIL
Rallus crepitans crepitans Gmelin

All ½ nat. size

the tops of the rushes, dropping abruptly in a few rods amidst the grass, as if exhausted by their unwonted exertion. They are perfectly at home on the ground, and dart among the dense weeds with marked freedom, the long toes keeping them from sinking in the mud or submerged vegetation, their thin bodies gliding easily between the reeds." (Eaton.)

All of the Rails, Gallinules, and Coots nest on the ground, and as a rule lay large sets of eggs. The young are covered with down when hatched, and are able to run about very soon after leaving the shell.

KING RAIL
Rallus elegans *Audubon*
A. O. U. Number 208   See Color Plate 25

Other Names.— Fresh-water Marsh Hen; Great Red-breasted Rail; Mud Hen.

General Description.— Length, 19 inches. Upper parts, tawny-olive streaked with darker; lower parts, chestnut. Forehead entirely feathered down to base of bill; bill long and slender.

Color.— ADULTS: Crown, sides of head, back of neck, and rest of *upper parts, tawny-olive* streaked from center of neck to tail with blackish-brown; an indistinct whitish line from bill over and behind eye; chin and upper throat, white; *neck and breast, rich chestnut;* rest of under parts, white traversed by broad bars of olive-brown; wing-coverts, olive-brown; secondaries, dusky-brown edged with lighter; primaries, plain dusky-brown; a narrow white semi-circle below eye; bill, yellowish, dusky on ridge and tip; legs, pale dusky-greenish; iris, reddish-brown. DOWNY YOUNG: Glossy black.

Nest and Eggs.— NEST: On the ground in marsh grass; built of dead reeds and grass, well concealed from above by interlacing of surrounding grass. EGGS: 6 to 12, dull white to pale buff, thinly spotted with reddish-brown and lilac.

Distribution.— Eastern North America; breeds from Nebraska, southern Minnesota, Ontario, New York, and Connecticut south to Texas, Florida, and Cuba; winters mainly in the southern part of its breeding range; casual north to South Dakota and Maine.

This large and handsome Rail, the King Rail, closely resembles the Virginia Rail except in size. Its retiring habits probably account for our lack of knowledge regarding it. Little seems to be known of it except that it appears to prefer fresh marshes to salt marshes. I have never seen it alive.

Dr. Bachman, in South Carolina, seems to have had a better opportunity of observing its habits than any one else who has written about it. He states that he found twenty pairs breeding within a space having a diameter of thirty yards, and that the nests were placed on the ground, being raised up six or eight inches by means of withered weeds and grasses; but Wayne, who has also found numerous nests, finds them in rushes or buttonwood bushes, from eight to eighteen inches over water. He noted that the female laid an egg each day after 11 A. M. and on laying the twelfth began at once to incubate. This Rail frequents the swampy borders of rivers and fresh-water ponds overgrown with vegetation. The stomach of one specimen was filled with seeds of *Arundo tecta;* that of another contained a quantity of oats.

EDWARD HOWE FORBUSH, in *Game Birds, Wild-Fowl and Shore Birds*.

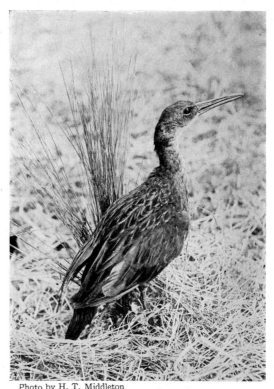

Photo by H. T. Middleton

KING RAIL

CLAPPER RAIL

Rallus crepitans crepitans *Gmelin*

A. O. U. Number 211   See Color Plate 25

Other Names.— Common Clapper; Marsh Clapper; Mud Hen; Sedge Hen; Meadow Hen; Salt-water Marsh Hen.

General Description.— Length, 16 inches. Color above, brownish-gray; below, lighter. Forehead entirely feathered down to base of bill; bill, long and slender.

Color.— ADULTS: Forehead, dusky; crown, sides of head, neck, upper parts, and lower parts as far as abdomen, *pale olive-ash* streaked on back, shoulders, and rump with olive-brown; lores and throat, whitish; abdomen and under tail-coverts, pale brownish-white traversed with broad indefinite bars of brownish-gray;

wing-quills and tail, plain dusky-brown; bill, yellow, dusky on ridge and tip; feet, pale greenish-dusky; iris, reddish-brown. There is much variation in the shades of plumage, fall and winter birds being much darker and with browner shades. DOWNY YOUNG: Glossy black.

Nest and Eggs.— NEST: A platform of dead reeds and grasses on the ground in meadows. EGGS: 6 to 15, white to buff, dotted and blotched with chestnut and some lavender.

Distribution.— Salt marshes of the Atlantic coast; breeds from Connecticut to North Carolina; winters mainly south of New Jersey; casual north to Maine.

Grassy salt marshes are the haunts of the Clapper Rail. From Connecticut southward to the Florida Keys they are undoubtedly more numerous than any other species found in these marshes. One does not find them everywhere in their range but in the localities they like best the grass seems to swarm with them. It is ordinarily very difficult to flush them and one may wade or push a boat through the marsh for hours and

never see one while all the time their tantalizing calls are heard near and far. Their facility in keeping out of sight is most remarkable. From Virginia southward they are much hunted during the months of September and October. They are shot from small boats when the tide is high and the flooded marshes afford no shelter wherein the birds may hide. While one man poles the boat a second stands in the bow and fires at the

Drawing by R. I. Brasher

CLAPPER RAIL (⅓ nat. size)

A noisy salt-water marsh bird

slow-flying game as it rises from the scant cover of the exposed tops of the grass.

During the breeding season one may find many nests within a small area. The following description of one of their favorite nesting colonies is quoted from my notes made at the time of my visit:

"'Jacks Grass' is a low island of perhaps twenty acres on the North Carolina coast near New Inlet. It has no trees, but is covered generally with grass eight or ten inches long. Small clumps of rushes growing rarely over three feet high are scattered over the island, and in nearly every one of these a Clapper Rail's nest was found. These were composed of marsh-grass blades and stalks, and were built from six to eight inches above the wet sod. The fragments of grass used varied from four to six inches in length, shorter pieces being employed for the top layers. The nests measured about eight inches across the top, and were of uniform width from the bottom. On May 13 two of the nests examined each held eight slightly incubated eggs, and one nest of ten eggs was seen. One was found with two freshly deposited eggs, and another had four incubated eggs. Egg-shells from which the young had but shortly departed were found in one instance. Usually the nests were not screened from view by any arching of the rushes above them. Along the banks of the tide creeks that traversed the island the marsh grass was often two or more feet in length. Here were many covered runways of the birds, some of which were several yards in length."

Three distinct subspecies, or climatic varieties, of this Clapper Rail have been recognized by naturalists. One is the Louisiana, or Henshaw's, Clapper Rail (*Rallus crepitans saturatus*), chiefly distinguished by having its feathers darker

colored than the common variety; the Florida Clapper Rail (*Rallus crepitans scotti*), a form that is still darker; and Wayne's Clapper Rail (*Rallus crepitans waynei*), found from North Carolina southward. Two closely allied but distinct species occurring elsewhere in North America are the California Clapper Rail (*Rallus*

Photo by P. B. Philipp   Courtesy of Nat. Asso. Aud. Soc.
NEST AND EGGS OF CLAPPER RAIL
Stone Harbor, New Jersey

obsoletus), of the salt marshes of the Pacific coast, and the Caribbean Clapper Rail (*Rallus longirostris caribæus*), found in Texas and the West Indies. The general habits of all are very similar to the more familiar eastern bird.

T. GILBERT PEARSON.

VIRGINIA RAIL

Rallus virginianus *Linnæus*

A. O. U. Number 212   See Color Plate 25

Other Names.— Little Red-breasted Rail; Small Mud Hen; Fresh-water Marsh Hen; Long-billed Rail.

General Description.— Length, 11 inches. Like the King Rail except for smaller size.

Color.— ADULTS: Crown, back of neck, and upper parts, pale olive-brown, streaked on back and rump with

dark brownish-black; *sides of head and cheeks, ashy;* lores and a narrow semi-circle below eye white; chin and upper throat, white; *neck and breast, rich chestnut;* abdomen and under tail-coverts, dusky with narrow white traverse bars; wing-coverts, chestnut; secondaries, brownish-black edged with olive; primaries and tail, plain brownish-black; *bill, flesh color,* dusky on ridge and tip; legs, dark flesh color; iris, reddish-brown. IMMATURE: Darker above than adults; under parts, blackish. DOWNY YOUNG: Sooty black with yellowish bill.

Nest and Eggs.— NEST: In a tuft of grass or reeds in meadows; rather compactly constructed (for a Rail) of dry reeds. EGGS: 6 to 12, cream or buffy, thinly spotted with chestnut or lavender.

Distribution.— North America; breeds from British Columbia, southern Saskatchewan, southern Keewatin, Ontario, southern Quebec, and New Brunswick south to southern California, Utah, Kansas, Missouri, Illinois, New Jersey, and eastern North Carolina, and in Toluca valley, Mexico; winters from Oregon, Utah, and Colorado to Lower California and Guatemala, also in the lower Mississippi States, and from North Carolina (casually Massachusetts) to Florida; occurs casually north to northern Quebec and Newfoundland.

In general habits I have not noticed any very distinctive difference between the Virginia Rail and the Sora, unless it be that birds of the former species are more inclined to keep by themselves in solitude or in pairs, whereas a good many photographs. Despite all my care I found it next to impossible to see the bird on the nest before pulling the thread attached to the shutter. So I laid my line of communication further off and pulled at a venture, after waiting a reasonable

Courtesy of S. A. Lottridge

VIRGINIA RAIL

It hides away in marshes and is little known

Soras may be found, even during breeding time, in the same bog. The nesting is entirely similar. With neither species, as a rule, can one flush the sitting bird directly from the nest, for it slips off upon hearing the approach. In a few cases, where I came up very silently, I have seen them slip off through the grass, especially when I approached with caution nests already located.

On one occasion, by concealing my camera in a bower of rushes near a nest, I secured some time. In each case except one I secured my subject.

The young, as with other kinds, are tiny black creatures, which have a most amazing way of disappearing in a bog. Seeing the sprite in the grass, we may do our best to make a grab, but the reward is likely to be only a handful of grass and black slime.

Though it is hard to see the nesting bird for identification, the eggs of both the Virginia Rail and the Sora are distinct and characteristic. Though of the same size, those of the former are lighter in ground color, being yellowish-white, whereas those of the Sora are a more decided buff in hue. The birds, too, are distinct, the Sora having a little short bill, while the subject of our sketch has quite a long bill and a redder shade of plumage.

This bird is one of the coterie, always to be associated together, which are found in the bogs and meadows — Virginia Rail, Sora, Red-winged Blackbird, both Marsh Wrens, Bittern and Least Bittern, sometimes Swamp Sparrow, and, in the West, the Coot and Yellow-headed Blackbird, as well as Redhead, Ruddy Duck, Canvas-back, and others. It is a most interesting fraternity, and the fascination of their company has made and keeps me a regular "bog-trotter."

HERBERT K. JOB.

Photo by H. K. Job   Courtesy of Outing Pub. Co.

VIRGINIA RAIL ON NEST

SORA

Porzana carolina (*Linnæus*)

A. O. U. Number 214   See Color Plate 26

Other Names.— Carolina Rail; Common Rail; Soree; Meadow Chicken; Carolina Crake; Little American Water Hen; Chicken-billed Rail; Chicken-bill; Rail-bird; Ortolan; Mud Hen.

General Description.— Length, 9 inches. Color above, olive-brown; below, gray. *Bill short and stout;* forehead entirely feathered down to base of bill.

Color.—ADULTS: Forehead, lores, face, *chin, and throat* (narrowly), *black;* crown, neck, and upper parts, including tail, *olive-brown;* back with dark-brown traverse bars and streaked narrowly with white; line over eye, sides of head, and *under parts, pure gray,* more olive on sides of body where barred with white transversely; abdomen barred with white; tail-coverts, whitish, tinged with rufous; bill, yellow, with extreme tip black; feet, light yellowish-green; iris, carmine.

IMMATURE: *No black on foreparts;* throat and abdomen, whitish; *neck and breast, washed with cinnamon.* DOWNY YOUNG: Glossy black, with a tuft of orange-colored bristly feathers on the breast.

Nest and Eggs.— NEST: On the ground in meadows; a carelessly constructed affair of grass and weeds. EGGS: 7 to 13, more rarely 16, pronounced drab, spotted with chestnut and lavender over entire surface.

Distribution.—North America; breeds from central British Columbia, southern Mackenzie, central Keewatin, and Gulf of St. Lawrence south to southern California, Utah, Colorado, Kansas, Illinois, and New Jersey; winters from northern California, Illinois, and South Carolina through the West Indies and Central America to Venezuela and Peru; accidental in Bermuda, Greenland, and England.

The Soras are curious birds, which remind one of very tiny dark-colored bantam hens. They spend their lives mainly in slipping through the tangles of the fresh-water bogs, in the universal search for something to eat. Success in their mission is demonstrated by the fact that, though slenderly built, supposedly "thin as a rail," by autumn they are quite generally loaded with fat. From their arrival in May until their final departure south in October they live in close retirement and are seldom seen. But throw a stone into one of these seemingly tenantless bogs, and it is surprising what a chorus of yells and cackling sounds may arise, as though its coverts sheltered a sizable poultry farm.

During my boyhood I had constant opportunity to study Soras and Virginia Rails in an almost bottomless "cat-tail" bog, in the suburbs of Boston, Mass., on the edge of the town of Brookline, now groomed up into a fine city park and lake. It was my delight to flounder through it with boy companions, and find many sorts of nests. I shall never forget how one day a boy tried a short cut to a nest, contrary to my advice, got in all over, and finally, in tears, floundered ashore, swimming through black ooze of the consistency of New Orleans molasses. His return home through the city was a constant ovation, as may be imagined.

Here I found many a Sora's nest, including one

which contained sixteen eggs, the largest number that I ever found in a Rail's domicile, eight to ten being usual, and thirteen not infrequent. The

Courtesy of Am. Mus. Nat. Hist.

SORA

Their peculiar flight makes them easy targets for gunners

nests are little platforms of dry grass or rush leaves, quite well hollowed. Sometimes they are in a cluster of reeds or rushes, a little above the level of the water, or under a thick tussock of meadow grass. But, after much searching, I found that the more typical location, both for the Sora and the Virginia Rail, was just out of the bog, in open meadow, where, on comparatively firm ground, rather short meadow-grass grew from just a little water. There the Rails constructed a little pile or island of grass, raised

slightly above the water. The stems of the rather sparse grass held it together, and the ends were twisted and tied by the birds to form over it a sort of rounded canopy. In walking over the meadow I learned to find nests by noting this arching of the grass, even at some distance. Rails are nocturnal, and toward dusk one may watch them at the edges of the bog trotting out to feed. Their migrations are quite mysterious. Some frosty morning the meadows suddenly are found to be alive with them. Then the gunners get their innings. In some localities, such as the meadows along the Connecticut River, near its mouth, Rail shooting becomes a regular industry. At high tide boatmen pole flat skiffs through the grass. The Rails flutter up with their characteristic flight, making easy marks.

In Louisiana I found this species common in winter on the marshes back from the Gulf coast, on the reservations. Toward evening I could watch them from the windows of our camp, as well as during cloudy days. They came out from the reeds and fed on the rice which we scattered, sometimes venturing even under the house.

HERBERT K. JOB.

Photo by H. K. Job

NEST AND EGGS OF SORA

YELLOW RAIL

Coturnicops noveboracensis (Gmelin)

A. O. U. Number 215   See Color Plate 26

Other Names.— Little Yellow Rail; Yellow Crake.

General Description.— Length, 7 inches. Prevailing color, brownish-yellow, paler below and streaked above with dark. Forehead entirely feathered to base of bill; bill short and stout.

Color.— ADULTS: Crown (narrowly), neck, and upper parts, broadly and regularly streaked with *yellowish brown and burnt umber,* this fusing on crown and shading on sides of neck and sides of breast into reddish-brown spots; the dark streaks of back and wings,

Plate 26

YELLOW RAIL
Coturnicops noveboracensis (Gmelin)
ADULT
DOWNY YOUNG of Little Black Rail

BLACK RAIL
Creciscus jamaicensis (Gmelin)
ADULT   All ¼ nat. size

SORA
Porzana carolina (Linnaeus)
ADULT   DOWNY YOUNG

crossed by narrow white semi-circles, *the wings, show-ing considerable white in flight;* sides of head and neck, chin, throat, breast, and abdomen, yellowish-brown; under tail-coverts, plain brownish; sides of body, with some traverse spots of brown and white; lores and a streak below eye extending on side of face, brown; bill, yellow; feet pale yellowish flesh color; iris, brown-ish-red. DOWNY YOUNG: Black.

Nest and Eggs.— NEST: On the ground in meadows; constructed of dry grass. EGGS: 6 to 10, creamy-buff, spotted with fine rusty-brown.

Distribution.—Chiefly eastern North America; breeds from southern Mackenzie, central Keewatin, and south-ern Ungava south to Minnesota and Maine; winters in the Gulf States, rarely in California, Illinois, and North Carolina; casual in Nevada, Utah, and Bermuda.

The Yellow Rail is seen rather rarely in Massa-chusetts. I have met with it alive only once. It probably is more common in migration than is believed generally, as it is very small and its habits are secretive. It is even more reluctant than the other Rails to take wing; hence it is seen rarely, but is sometimes caught by dogs and cats. When forced to take wing it flies in the same hesitating, fluttering manner as the other Rails, but rather swifter and sometimes to a consider-able distance. It can swim and dive well in case of necessity.

Wayne states that in South Carolina he found it nearly impossible to flush these birds with a dog when their only cover was short dead grass. His dog caught nine and flushed but one. Fresh-water snails were found in their stomachs.

EDWARD HOWE FORBUSH, in *Game Birds, Wild-Fowl and Shore Birds.*

BLACK RAIL

Creciscus jamaicensis (*Gmelin*)

A. O. U. Number 216   See Color Plate 26

Other Names.— Little Black Rail; Black Crake.

General Description.— Length, 6 inches. Upper parts, black barred with white; head, throat, and chest, slate color. Forehead entirely feathered down to base of bill; bill short and stout.

Color.— ADULTS: Forehead and crown, dusky; hind-neck and fore-back, dark chestnut; rest of *upper parts, deep brownish-black,* finely barred with white; head, neck, and breast, dark slate; abdomen and under tail-coverts, deep blackish-brown, traversed with narrow

Drawing by R. I. Brasher

BLACK RAIL (⅔ nat. size)

The smallest of the American Rails

white bars; lores and a line through and back of eye, dusky; wing-quills and tail, dusky with some white spots. Downy Young: Black.

Nest and Eggs.— Nest: A very well-made and deeply cupped structure of fine grasses and weed stems; well concealed in a depression of the ground. Eggs: 6 to 9, white, sparsely spotted with small chestnut dots.

Distribution.— Eastern North America; breeds from southern Ontario and Massachusetts south to Kansas, Illinois, and South Carolina; winters from Texas east through the Gulf States and south to Jamaica and Guatemala; casual in Bermuda.

The Black Rail, the smallest Rail in America, is believed to be a very rare bird in New England, where it has been recorded only from Maine, Connecticut, and Massachusetts, in which States it possibly breeds. So far as our present information goes, Massachusetts appears to be near the northern limit of its breeding range on the Atlantic coast, but it may go farther north.

Records are received with caution, as the black, downy young of larger Rails are mistaken for Black Rails. Wayne appears to be the first observer who has actually seen the female Black Rail on her nest in the United States, and recorded it. The nest was in an oat field, and the standing grain, where the nest was, had been cut. The bird is so secretive that, as related by Wayne, two men and a dog searched four hours for the male in the oat field before it could be secured, although it was calling incessantly. This bird may not be as rare as it is rated.

The Black Rail runs swiftly, like a mouse, through the herbage, and seldom flies, although in migration it has reached the Bermuda Islands. Gosse quotes a Mr. Robinson who says that in Jamaica it is so foolish as to hide its head and cock up its tail, thinking itself safe, when it is easily taken alive.

EDWARD HOWE FORBUSH, in *Game Birds, Wild-Fowl and Shore Birds.*

Courtesy of Am. Mus. Nat. Hist.

BLACK RAIL

PURPLE GALLINULE

Ionornis martinicus (*Linnæus*)

A. O. U. Number 218   See Color Plate 27

Other Name.— Sultana (Jamaica).

General Description.— Length, 14 inches. Head, neck, and under parts, purplish; upper parts, olive-green. Head with frontal shield extending from base of bill and covering forehead; toes slender and without lobes; bill shorter than head.

Color.— Adults: Head, neck, and under parts, *deep purplish-blue;* abdomen black; *under tail-coverts white;* back and upper parts in general, olive-green; wing-coverts, blue-edged; wing- and tail-feathers dusky with outer webs bluish-green; frontal shield, pale cobalt; basal half of bill, carmine, front half yellow; a narrow white streak on side of face at base of bill; legs, chrome-yellow; iris, red. Immature: Upper parts, washed with brownish; under parts, mottled with white. Downy Young: Glossy-black with numerous white hair-like feathers on head.

Nest and Eggs.— Nest: Placed in reeds over water; constructed of dead rushes. Eggs: 6 to 10, creamy, thinly spotted and dotted with brown and lavender.

Distribution.— Tropical and subtropical America; breeds from Texas, Tennessee, and South Carolina south through Mexico and the West Indies to Ecuador and Paraguay; winters from Texas, Louisiana, and Florida southward; irregularly north in summer to Arizona, Nebraska, Wisconsin, Ontario, Quebec, Nova Scotia, and New Brunswick; accidental in England and Bermuda.

The Purple Gallinule has been richly endowed with beautiful feathers. With the single exception of the male Wood Duck it must be regarded as possessing the most striking colors of any of our southern water-birds. On the rice plantations along the Ashley River above Charlestown, South Carolina, I found this species very abundant and often saw them run across the road ahead of our buggy. There was much water about and they seemed to pass frequently from one pond or ditch to another, their stout, fairly long legs sending them forward at a good speed when haste was desired.

With much vividness do I recall one spring morning when, while I was fishing from a boat in Levy Lake, Florida, these birds were much in evidence. It was during the mating season and they were the personification of activity. There was here an abundant growth of water lilies, and the birds seemed to take the greatest pleasure in walking over the lily pads, their yellow legs twinkling in the sunlight. As they walked, their tails jerked in a most pert and amusing manner. When springing from pad to pad their wings would be held high above the head. One of them clucking and displaying his superb plumage to every possible advantage approached some bushes which grew near shore and climbing the limbs proceeded with many flutters and loud bursts of guttural notes to climb upward until it

Photo by T. H. Jackson   Courtesy of Nat. Asso. Aud. Soc.

NEST AND EGGS OF PURPLE GALLINULE

Orange Lake, Florida

reached the branches of a dense magnolia tree. Here from a height of twenty feet its purple plumage shone with a most resplendent beauty under the full glare of the morning sun. The whole performance combined to make a picture not easily forgotten.

When making short flights, and especially when chasing each other, the legs hang down as if ready for immediate use in case of emergency. They swim well although they are not web-footed. The long slender toes must be very

Drawing by R. I. Brasher

PURPLE GALLINULE (¼ nat. size)

A southern water bird of superb plumage

serviceable in aiding them to run over the insecure pathway paved only with the floating leaves of the water lilies or to climb among the tangles of grass and water-plants.

The Purple Gallinule appears in its summer home in April or May and after a perfectly proper period of courtship nest building is begun. This interesting receptacle for the eggs is usually built in reeds or rushes a few feet above the water. Not long ago I examined six nests in a pond in lower Louisiana. Without exception these were constructed of grass-stems and rushes, each being built in a separate bunch of thick rushes. The surrounding stalks were pulled down in such a manner as to hide each nest completely from view. They were located above the water at heights varying from two to five feet. In the Mississippi valley the Purple Gallinule does not breed much north of Missouri. In the East and South (except Florida) it is confined largely to the tide-water sections.

T. GILBERT PEARSON.

FLORIDA GALLINULE

Gallinula galeata (*Lichtenstein*)

A. O. U. Number 219   See Color Plate 27

Other Names.— American Gallinule; Common Gallinule; Red-billed Mud Hen; Water Hen; Water Chicken.

General Description.— Length, 14 inches. Prevailing color, blackish. Forehead covered by naked shield at base of bill; toes slender and without lobes; bill slender, sharp, and nearly as long as head.

Color.— ADULTS: Head, neck all around, breast, and under parts, *dark slate,* duskier on head and neck, and whitening behind; upper parts, brownish-slate; wings and tail, dusky; sides of under tail-coverts, edge of wing, outer web of first primary, and stripes on flanks, white; *bill, frontal plate, and a ring around upper part of leg, red;* tip of bill, yellow; a narrow white stripe on face at base of bill; legs, greenish-yellow; iris, red. YOUNG: Similar to adults, but duller,

with whitish under parts, and brownish bill and forehead.

Nest and Eggs.— NEST: In the marshes; constructed of dry reeds; often placed on a buoyant platform of the same material, capable of rising and falling with the water; in some places it is built on dry parts of the meadow. EGGS: 6 to 12, buffy-white, rather sparsely spotted with brown.

Distribution.— Tropical and temperate America; breeds from central California, Arizona, Nebraska, Minnesota, Ontario, New York, and Vermont south through the West Indies and Mexico to Chile and Argentina, and in the Galapagos and Bermuda; winters from southern California, Arizona, Texas, and Georgia southward; casual in Colorado, Quebec, Nova Scotia, New Brunswick, and Maine.

Photograph by A. A. Allen

A FLORIDA GALLINULE TURNING ITS EGGS

Plate 27

PURPLE GALLINULE
Ionornis martinicus (Linnaeus)

FLORIDA GALLINULE (Lichtenstein)
Gallinula galeata (Lichtenstein)

All ⅗ nat. size

AMERICAN COOT
Fulica americana Gmelin
ADULT

DOWNY YOUNG

So hen-like in many of its movements is the Florida Gallinule that one can readily understand why its near relative in Europe should be named the Moor Hen. In habits it much resembles both the King Rail and the Coots, and its home is in the same character of country occupied by both of these species. It is a bird of the ponds and marshes of our southern country, although it occasionally breeds as far north as Minnesota and Maine. Like the Rails it often has more or less favorite pathways through the thick marsh grass, and like the Coot is sometimes seen swimming about in shallow weed-grown waters. When thus occupied the head bobs back and forth with each stroke of the feet. They cannot

of despondency, and the questioning explosive *chuck* of inquiry. They are very noisy birds and their notes are among the most familiar and constantly heard calls of the rush-grown lakeside. When the incubation of the eggs begins, the volume of sounds decreases perceptively. Rarely have I heard one call at night, for this bird is not so nocturnal as the Rails and many of the Herons.

Like most birds, the Gallinule is very cleanly and bathing is one of its frequent diversions. In flight it is most ungainly and when flushed its passage through the air is attended with every indication of extreme weariness.

The Gallinule's nest is worth a wade in the

Drawing by R. I. Brasher

FLORIDA GALLINULE (⅔ nat. size)

The source of many of the henlike noises heard in fresh-water marshes

rightly be said to assemble in flocks, although as many as a dozen are at times seen feeding near together. Often they come on shore for food or assemble in small companies to sun and rest at some favorite rendezvous. At a distance they somewhat resemble the Coot, but a nearer view will reveal the difference. The bright scarlet bill and head-shield is a field mark for identification quite distinct from the white bill of the Coot.

Florida Gallinules possess a wonderful repertoire in the matter of calls. They are all very harsh, but they suggest the entire range of passions. For example, there is the appealing *ticket, ticket* of the lovelorn male, the petulant *tuka, tuka*

pond to discover. It is made of flags or rushes, and is placed from just above the water to a height of a foot or two. It is wedged in among a clump of rushes or in a rush-hidden bush. Frequently it is a foot and a half in diameter and several inches thick. The central cavity is slightly sunken and is just large enough to hold the six to twelve spotted eggs that are laid. Incubation begins as soon as egg-laying commences, with the result that some young appear from a week to twelve days before the others. Among their enemies may be mentioned the cotton-mouth moccasin that swallows their eggs and the frogs and alligators that snap up the young when swimming. T. GILBERT PEARSON.

COOT

Fulica americana *Gmelin*

A. O. U. Number 221   See Color Plate 27

Other Names.—American Coot; Mud Hen; Water Hen; Marsh Hen; Moor-head; Meadow Hen; Water Chicken; Pond Hen; Mud Coot; Ivory-billed Coot; White-bellied Mud Hen; White-bill; Hen-bill; Crow-bill; Sea Crow; Pond Crow; Crow Duck; Flusterer; Blue Peter; Splatter; Shuffler; Pelick; Pull-doo.

General Description.— Length, 16 inches. Prevailing color, slate, dark above and light below; forehead, covered by naked shield at base of bill; bill stout, nearly as long as head; *toes lobed along edges.*

Color.—ADULTS: Entire plumage, dark slate-gray, blackening on head and neck, tinged with olive on back; under tail-coverts, edge of wing, *tips of secondaries,* and ends of some primaries, *white; bill, white* with small spots of reddish near end and at base of frontal shield; frontal shield, brown; *feet, pale olive-greenish;* iris, red. DOWNY YOUNG: Blackish above, whitish below, with numerous orange-colored hair-like feathers on throat and upper parts. IMMATURE: Similar to adults, but lighter below, and bill flesh color.

Nest and Eggs.— NEST: Constructed of dead reeds, grasses, and bits of decayed vegetation; afloat on the water or in the reeds nearby. EGGS: 7 to 16, creamy, finely and regularly spotted over entire surface with specks of dark brown and black.

Distribution.— North America; breeds from central British Columbia, southern Mackenzie, Manitoba, Quebec, and New Brunswick south to northern Lower California, Texas, Tennessee, and New Jersey, and also in southern Mexico, southern West Indies, and Guatemala; winters from southern British Columbia, Nevada, Utah, the Ohio valley and Virginia south to Colombia; casual at Fort Yukon, Alaska, and in Greenland, Labrador, and Bermuda.

Many people think that the Coot is a Duck because it is usually seen swimming. As a matter of fact, however, it belongs to the Rail tribe. Its feet are not webbed straight across, but each toe has a sort of scallop of lobes, which answer just about as well in paddling. Another popular mistake is to apply the name Coot to those marine Ducks which are properly called Scoters, not "Sea Coots."

The real Coot, while having some limitations, is notably versatile with its feet. Not that it is exactly a feathered Pavlowa, but with marked ability it can run, walk, swim, and "skitter." In the "Mud Hen skitter," which might well be

Photo by W. L. Finley and H. T. Bohlman

COOTS
Their odd ways make one laugh

made a new dance for society, it can beat even the celebrated dancer, for it is practiced on a peculiar floor, the surface of the water — as the flock flutter away, pattering with their feet as they go.

The favorite haunts of the Coots are the shallow ponds or bogs, where reeds or rushes grow from the water. In such places they make their nests, which are platforms of dead stems woven together in a sort of wicker-basket fashion, piled up from the bottom of the water, and partly supported by the stems of the aquatic plants, being rather deeply hollowed. The eggs number from seven or eight to fourteen or sixteen, and are distinguishable by the small

If there is a more amusing bird anywhere, I should like to see it!

Though the Coot is rather tame, it is difficult to see it on the nest, but it is easy to watch it swim away, bobbing its head after the approved fashion of the skittering fraternity. Numbers breed, scattered about, in the same slough. On migration they are seen mostly in small parties, or often singly. They breed from the northern States north, and in winter are abundant in swampy parts of the southern States where they gather in large flocks.

In Louisiana I found them in great numbers in winter on the fresh-water marshes. When I "baited a blind," to photograph wild Ducks, it

Photograph by H. K. Job   Courtesy of National Association of Audubon Societies

COOTS AND TEALS

The Ducks used the Coots as buffers for danger

"pepper-spot" markings evenly sprinkled over them. One egg is laid each day and incubation begins with the first egg. Consequently they hatch one by one, each youngster promptly leaving the nest to swim off, probably to be tended by the other parent.

The young are singular creatures, covered with a sort of black down with orange-colored hairs projecting from the neck and head, the latter being bald on top, and the bill and adjacent parts bright red. I have hatched some in incubators and reared them to maturity. At first small and feeble, they become active and bold, rushing at me and shrieking for food with raucous screams.

was always the Coots which ventured up first to try the food. The Ducks used them as buffers for danger, and swam up after the Coots proved to them that it was safe. They often came up on the steps of the camp to get food, and were known to walk into the house, perhaps thinking they heard the dinner-bell.

They are easily kept in captivity, but in the breeding season are said at times to make a rather too free use of their sharp bills. However, their odd ways make one laugh, and I recommend the funny Coot as an antidote for "the blues."

HERBERT K. JOB.

ORDER OF SHORE BIRDS

Order *Limicolæ*

HORE birds include seven closely related families — so closely related that no suborder has been established within this order. The various species frequent open areas, usually along watercourses, ocean beaches, or marshes. They average small in size, the largest North American species being the Long-billed Curlew, and the smallest being the Least and Semipalmated Sandpipers, or Peeps, so abundant in the spring, summer, and fall everywhere in the maritime districts. In color they are generally brown or blackish above, mottled and streaked with buff or whitish. The wings are long and pointed, the primaries graduating rapidly from outer to inner, the secondaries reversing this order — this giving a V-shape to the open wing. Many species are capable of sustained flight, and perform almost incredible journeys during migration. The tail is short. The legs are long and thin with long, slender, usually unwebbed, toes.

The food of the Shore Birds is the mollusks, crustaceans, and insects, found in the mud or along the moist strand of their habitat. They nest on the ground, usually laying four eggs, which are so well spotted or blotched with dark colors that they are quite inconspicuous among the grass or pebbles. When hatched the young are covered with down of a gray or brown color marked with blackish. At the approach of an " enemy " these downy chicks lie flat on the ground in an endeavor to escape detection.

Shore Birds have mellow, piping or whistling, voices, which can be heard for some distance. They are greatly prized as game birds and have been hunted to such an extent that it is not uncommon to hear them spoken of as " our vanishing shore birds."

PHALAROPES

Order *Limicolæ;* family *Phalaropodidæ*

ITTLE swimming Sandpipers " the Phalaropes were aptly called by Dr. Coues. They are essentially birds of the northern hemisphere, and all of the three species occur in North America, though only one, Wilson's Phalarope, is actually a permanent resident of this continent. A peculiar and interesting characteristic of the family is that the usual differences between the sexes of most species are reversed in the case of the Phalaropes; which is to say, the females are not only the larger and have the more striking plumage, but they are the aggressors in the courtship performances and the males do the nest-building and incubate the eggs.

All of the Phalaropes are comparatively small birds — from seven to nine inches long — and have noticeably thick, duck-like plumage to protect their bodies from the freezing waters in which they are often found, and a bill in which the lateral groove is prolonged nearly to the hardened and pointed tip, while the bill itself is as long as or longer than the head. The toes are equipped with marginal webs. The legs are normally long and slender. The wings are long, flat, and pointed, with the outer primaries longest and the inner secondaries elongated, giving the wing in flight a V-shaped appearance. The tail is short, stiff, broad, and rounded.

Dr. Coues's popular name for the Phalaropes is in recognition of their pelagic, or at least aquatic, habits, which often take them many miles out to sea, even in the dead of winter. The nests are mere depressions in the ground and sometimes are thinly lined with grass. Three or four eggs are laid but only about two young are successfully hatched and raised.

Plate 28

Louis Agassiz Fuertes.

RED PHALAROPE *Phalaropus fulicarius* (Linnaeus)

MALE

All ⅔ nat. size

FEMALE

AUTUMN AND WINTER PLUMAGE

The baby Phalaropes are covered with down at birth and within a short time after leaving the shell are able to run about.

The Northern and Wilson Phalaropes are known to be of great economic value, because they destroy immense numbers of more or less harmful insects. The investigations of W. L. McAtee, a Government biologist, showed that 53 per cent. of the food of twenty-eight Northern Phalaropes consisted of mosquito larvæ, the insects eaten including the famous mosquito of the marshland of New Jersey. Wilson's Phalarope is known to feed upon bill-bugs, which often do considerable damage to corn. Undoubtedly far more has been done by the Phalaropes and other shore birds toward the extermination of mosquitoes in New Jersey than has been accomplished by the State's expenditure of large sums of money. Mr. McAtee's investigations showed that the Phalaropes also feed freely upon the crane flies ("leatherjackets"), grasshoppers, the clover-root curculio, the wireworms and their adult forms, the click beetles, the diving beetles which are a nuisance in fish hatcheries, and various species of marine worms which prey upon oysters.

RED PHALAROPE

Phalaropus fulicarius (*Linnæus*)

A. O. U. Number 222   See Color Plate 28

Other Names.—Whale-bird; Red Coot-footed Tringa; Gray Phalarope; Flat-billed Phalarope; Sea Snipe; Bank-bird; Brown Bank-bird; Gulf-bird; Sea Goose.

General Description.— Length, 8 inches. In summer, upper parts mottled and striped with black and pale brown, under parts entirely red; in winter, gray above and white below; but always distinguishable from other Phalaropes by the short, stout, tapering bill (dagger-shaped). The front toes have lobed or scalloped webs.

Color.— ADULT MALE IN SUMMER: *Forehead, lores, chin, lower side of head, throat, and entire under parts, dull cinnamon-brown;* crown, nape, back of neck, and upper parts, yellowish-brown; crown streaked with brownish-black; rest of feathers above, with broad dark centers; wing-coverts dusky, the greater coverts showing white for most of their exposed portions; primaries brownish-black; a white ring around eye and a whitish area above and behind eye; basal half of bill, yellow, end dusky; feet, yellowish; iris, brown. ADULT FEMALE IN SUMMER: Forehead, crown, chin, nape (narrowly), back of neck, wings, and middle tail-feathers, sooty-brown; lores, cheeks, sides of head, over eye and larger part of greater wing-coverts, white; *throat, neck (broadly), breast, and entire under parts, rich wine-red;* back, shoulders, and long inner coverts ochery-white, each feather with a broad center streak of brownish-

black; primaries and wing-coverts, dusky, the latter edged with dull white; bill, yellowish, tipped with black; feet, yellowish-brown; iris, deep brown. ADULTS IN WINTER: Forehead, most of crown, sides of head, throat, breast, and rest of *under parts, pure white;* back of head, a spot in front of, another below, and one behind eye, a narrow streak down back of neck, upper back and primaries, plain dusky-gray; lesser and middle wing-coverts, grayish-ash edged with white, center coverts showing white space as in summer; rest of upper parts, *nearly uniform pale grayish-ash,* some of the feathers with darker centers; bill, mostly dusky; feet, dull yellow; iris, brown.

Nest and Eggs.— NEST: A hollow in ground; sometimes thinly lined with moss and dry grass. EGGS: 3 to 4, dull greenish or yellowish-gray, spotted with various shades of brown.

Distribution.— Northern and southern hemispheres; in North America breeds from northern Alaska, Melville Island, and northern Ellesmere Land south to mouth of the Yukon, northern Mackenzie, central Keewatin, Hudson Strait, and southern Greenland; winter home unknown but probably on the oceans, at least as far south as Falkland and Juan Fernandez islands; migrates along both coasts of United States; casual in migration in interior south to Colorado, Kansas, Illinois, and Maryland.

It is unfortunate that the Red Phalarope breeds far in the north, for the chance of studying its habits would be unusually interesting. After depositing the eggs the female loses her interest in home-ties and the smaller, more protectively-colored male meekly performs the household duties of incubation and assumes all the care of starting the youngsters toward maturity, while his mate looks on or gads about the country seeking new feeding grounds.

"When migrating this is a bird of the open waters, usually the sea, where it feeds and rests in flocks, swimming as gracefully and safely as a duck, and found along the shore only when driven in by storms." (Barrows.)

Their food is worms, soft, small marine animalcula, insects, and crustacea, which live in their marshy habitat. In the North it feeds on the animal-life which forms the food of the right whale — hence its name of Whale-bird.

NORTHERN PHALAROPE

Lobipes lobatus (*Linnæus*)

A. O. U. Number 223   See Color Plate 29

Other Names.— Sea Goose; Mackerel Goose; Web-footed Peep; Bank-bird; White Bank-bird; Sea Snipe; Whale-bird; Hyperborean Phalarope; Red-necked Phalarope.

General Description.— Length, 7 inches. Color above, ashy-gray; bill very slender, cylindrical, and sharp (needle-like); front toes with lobed or scalloped webs.

Color.— ADULT MALE IN SUMMER: Forehead, throat, breast, and *lower parts, pure white;* crown, sides of head, back of neck, upper back, ashy-gray; forehead and front part of crown, mottled with ashy; lores, dusky; *a broad area of rufous extending from nape downward across upper breast, interrupted on upper breast with dusky streaks;* sides of breast much mottled with ashy-gray and white; flanks and sides marked with arrowhead-shaped dusky spots; shoulders, rufous-brown, each feather with blackish center and white tipped; wing-coverts and primaries, dusky, the greater coverts with rear portion white; a white semi-circle above and another below eye; bill, black; iris, brown; feet, dusky gray. ADULT FEMALE IN SUMMER: Head from chin, back of neck, shoulders, and back, plain grayish-ash; throat and lower side of head, white, bordered behind and below with a large patch of rich tawny, this color including upper breast; under parts, white, broken on side of breast, sides, and flanks, with ashy-gray; *a broad V-shaped stripe of yellowish-brown on back; two narrow ones of same color on shoulders;* wing-coverts and primaries, dusky, the greater coverts broadly white on ends, forming a conspicuous bar, a white semi-circle above and another below eye; bill, black; legs and feet, bluish-gray; soles of feet, greenish-yellow; iris, deep brown. ADULTS IN WINTER: *Forehead, broad line over eye running along side of head and meeting white of chin, breast, and lower parts, pure white;* a broad streak behind eye, crown, back of neck, and *upper parts, plain light ash,* varied with white edges of feathers, these lighter edges forming a V-shaped mark on back and more extensive on shoulders, becoming narrower on longer wing-coverts behind; sides of breast, mottled with ash; sides and flanks, with a faint tinge of gray, thinly spotted with darker; wing as in summer; a wash of pale rufous on sides of neck; a

Drawing by R. I. Brasher

NORTHERN PHALAROPE (female; ⅔ nat. size)

She leaves all the family duties to the less handsome, more modest male

Plate 29

Louis Agassiz Fuertes.

FEMALE

MALE

NORTHERN PHALAROPE *Lobipes lobatus* (Linnaeus)

AUTUMN AND WINTER PLUMAGE

All ⅗ nat. size

dusky spot in front of eye; eye-ring, white interrupted before and behind; bill, bluish-black; feet, livid; iris, deep brown.

Nest and Eggs.— NEST: A hollow in ground lined with grass or leaves. EGGS: 4, greenish or buffy, thickly blotched with various shades of brown.

Distribution.— Northern and southern hemispheres; in North America breeds from northern Alaska, Mel- ville Island, and central Greenland south to Aleutian Islands (including Near Islands), valley of the upper Yukon, northern Mackenzie, central Keewatin, southern James Bay, and northern Ungava; winter home un- known, but probably the oceans south of the equator; in migration occurs nearly throughout the United States and in Mexico, Central America, Bermuda, and Hawaii.

Like the Red Phalarope, the Northern Phal- arope breeds in the extreme north. It has a curious habit of whirling around several times in succession on the surface of the water, creating miniature whirlpools, evidently with the intention of stirring up the tiny marine life on which it feeds. I have seen many flocks on the ocean, well off the shore of the New England coast, dur- ing August and September, floating like thistle- down but not going through the gyrations they perform on the shallow inland ponds, which would indicate that in the latter they find food absent in the former.

R. I. BRASHER.

Photo by W. L. Finley and H. T. Bohlman

NORTHERN PHALAROPE

Female in summer plumage

WILSON'S PHALAROPE

Steganopus tricolor *Vieillot*

A. O. U. Number 224	See Color Plate 30

Other Name.— Summer Phalarope.

General Description.— Length, 9 inches. Color above, gray; bill longer than head and very slender; front toes with marginal webs, but the membrane not scalloped.

Color.— ADULT MALE IN SUMMER: Forehead, crown, and upper parts in general, including wings and tail, dull grayish, streaked on back, shoulders, and wing-coverts with darker gray; lores and a broad stripe over and behind eye, whitish; throat and a patch on nape, white; rest of under parts, dull white, washed on side with pale yellowish; a rusty area on side of neck, bordered above with dusky; dusky spot in front of eye and an indistinct one of the same color, behind; bill, dusky; feet, dull horn; iris, brown. ADULT FEMALE IN SUMMER: Crown, pale ash changing to white on a narrow stripe on back of neck, this color changing again on back to *ash*, continuing down and becoming white on rump and upper tail-coverts; *a broad black area commencing behind eye, running halfway down neck where widening and changing into rich purplish-chestnut, extending along back in a narrower streak;* shoulders, the same color, bordered on each side with grayish; wings, pale grayish-brown; primaries, dusky; tail, mottled with gray and white; chin and throat, pure white; rest of *under parts, white;* sides of neck, breast, and flanks washed with pale rufous; a large white spot over eye, bordered in front with black streak; a smaller spot of white below eye; bill, dusky; feet, horn blackish; iris, brown; *no white patch on wing.* ADULTS IN WINTER: Crown, back of neck, and upper parts, ashy-gray, each feather usually edged with whiter; wing-coverts and secondaries, dusky-gray edged with pale yellowish-white; primaries, plain dusky; upper tail-coverts, line over eye, and under parts, white, shaded on sides of breast with grayish; a dusky spot in front of eye; an indistinct streak behind eye of light dusky; bill, dusky; legs, yellow; iris, brown. YOUNG: Brownish-black above, this soon succeeded by coloring of winter adult.

Nest and Eggs.— NEST: A slight depression in the ground; lined with grass. EGGS: 3 or 4, creamy, buff, or drab, spotted, specked, and scratched with brown of different shades.

Distribution.— North and South America; breeds from central Washington, central Alberta, and Lake Winnipeg south to eastern California, southern Colorado, southern Kansas, northern Iowa, and northwestern Indiana; winters from central Chile and central Argentina south to Falkland Islands; casual in migration on Pacific coast from southern British Columbia to Lower California and on Atlantic coast from Maine to New Jersey.

Photo by W. L. Finley and H. T. Bohlman

MALE WILSON'S PHALAROPE RETURNING TO HIS TASK OF INCUBATING

Plate 30

Louis Agassiz Fuertes.

WILSON'S PHALAROPE   *Steganopus tricolor* Vieillot

MALE

FEMALE

AUTUMN AND WINTER PLUMAGE

All ⅔ nat. size

Though I have met the other two kinds of Phalaropes out on the open Atlantic well off-shore, to find Wilson's Phalarope one has to journey to the northwest interior. There I have found these beautiful, gentle birds breeding beside the marshy sloughs of North Dakota, Manitoba, and Saskatchewan. The best-known, most widely advertised peculiarity of Phalaropes is their family relationship. The female is the larger and brighter-colored, and is said to do the courting; the demure little male — mere man — incubates the eggs and cares for the young, while the wives flock together in the sloughs as though they had organized women's clubs or other social coteries. Thus I have watched parties of these giddy little ladies sporting about, and then, tramping through the meadow grass on the prairie a few rods back from some other slough, have flushed the male from the nest so well hidden in the grass. The four eggs are decidedly pointed and are very boldly and thickly streaked with black.

To the credit of the female it must be said that she is not entirely without the heart of the mother. The cries of her husband, in times of seeming danger, soon bring her to the rescue, and she runs or flies about with him, scolding, though he usually leads in the performance of the various protestations.

On one occasion, during the spring migration, in early June, I met a considerable flock of Northern Phalaropes on a shallow alkaline slough in northern Manitoba, but at the most I have only seen Wilson's Phalarope in small parties. Like all the tribe these are graceful in every motion, notably in swimming, bobbing their heads and necks prettily forward as they progress.

Despite the above reversals of social usage, the female is far from being a virago. The birds

Photo by H. K. Job   Courtesy of Outing Pub. Co.

WILSON'S PHALAROPE

The male of this species attends to the work of raising the family

are gentle in manner and inconspicuous, and the average person passing through their haunts probably would not notice them. Though small, they are, like other shore birds, swift and strong in flight, and in winter they journey as far south as Chile and Argentina.

HERBERT K. JOB.

AVOCETS AND STILTS

Order *Limicolæ;* family *Recurvirostridæ*

THE Avocets and Stilts include eleven or twelve species which occur, usually in flocks, throughout the warmer regions of the world. As a family they are comparatively large birds, and have exceedingly long legs, long necks, and long, slender bills, curved more or less upward, in which the nostrils are set within the quarter nearest the base.

Of the Avocets, there are four species, one occurring in North America, another in South America, a third in Europe, and a fourth in Australia. Each of these has a rudimentary hind toe, and the front toes webbed, in which latter respect they differ from most wading birds. Their wings are rather short and their tails are short and square. Their plumage is thick and duck-like. They feed on aquatic insects, shellfish, and the like, which they capture chiefly in shallow water by sweeping the bill from side to side with a movement which suggests the swinging of a scythe. The Avocets swim easily, when they need to, and usually are comparatively tame. They are from fifteen to eighteen inches long and in coloration are generally black and white, with the legs of a bluish tinge. They build rude nests on the ground in swampy places; the eggs are three or four in number, of olive or buff color profusely marked with dark brown spots.

Of the true Stilts there are seven or eight species, only one of which occurs in America. The family differs from the Avocets in having no web between the middle and inner toes; in being considerably smaller, with an average length of about thirteen inches; and in having the wings long and pointed. The common American species occurs in both continents and is found most often in small flocks on muddy flats, where the bird walks with long, deliberate strides, probing the mud with its long bill or catching fish in the shallow waters. Physically and in their habits, there is considerable general similarity between the Stilts and the Avocets.

The young of both Avocets and Stilts are covered with down at birth and shortly after leaving the shell are able to run about. This natal down is soon replaced by the first or juvenal plumage.

AVOCET

Recurvirostra americana *Gmelin*

A. O. U. Number 225

Other Names.— American Avocet; Blue Stocking; Blue Shanks; Irish Snipe.

General Description.— Length, 18 inches. Color, white with some black areas; bill, flattened and upturned; three front toes webbed.

Color.— ADULTS IN SUMMER: *White, changing imperceptibly to chestnut-brown of head and neck;* shoulders and wings, black; some secondaries and coverts, white; tail, pearl-gray; bill, black; legs, dull blue; iris, red or brown. ADULTS IN WINTER: Head and neck, pearl-gray; otherwise like summer plumage. YOUNG: Head and neck, washed with chestnut, the black feathers edged with same color; bill, nearly straight.

Nest and Eggs.— NEST: In the marshes, hidden in the grass and constructed of grass and weed stems. EGGS: 3 or 4, pale olive or buffy, uniformly and thickly spotted with burnt umber and other shades of brown.

Distribution.— North America; breeds from eastern Oregon, central Alberta, and southern Manitoba (rarely north to Great Slave Lake) south to southern California, southern New Mexico, northwestern Texas, northern Iowa, and central Wisconsin; winters from southern California and southern Texas to southern Guatemala; casual from Ontario and New Brunswick to Florida and the West Indies, but rare east of Mississippi River.

Courtesy of American Museum of Natural History

AVOCET

The most showy of North American shore birds

The Avocet stands out among North American shore birds as the most showy of them all. Its white body and black and white-striped wings reveal its presence at a great distance. It is a large bird, being about a foot and a half long. This, added to the fact that it makes a most acceptable dish when served on the table, is responsible for the extended persecution to which it has been subjected by gunners. One of the names by which shooters know it is "Blue Shanks," the color of its long, bare legs being responsible for this. While searching for wild Ducks' nests on the marshes of the Klamath River in Oregon I first came upon these remarkable birds. Evidently a small group was nesting in the neighborhood, for upon our appearance three birds came into view and at once set up a great outcry. Our first view of them was when they came flying toward us giving vent to their alarm and resentment at our approach. They flew overhead and circled about much as is the custom of Willets under like circumstances. Their screaming soon brought others, who may have been their mates called from the nests by the general alarm. At times they alighted on the ground at a safe distance, or settled in the water of the slough. Here the maneuvers of head-bobbing and wing-waving were most amusing. Sometimes the body would be all but submerged and with head laid out along the water the bird would swim away just as a wounded wild Goose will often try to escape the fowler.

The Avocet's nest is a depression in the ground in the vicinity of water and is lined with grass. The young upon emerging from the spotted eggs are able to run almost at once.

Audubon has this to say in reference to their feeding habits:

"They search for food precisely in the manner of the Roseate Spoonbill, moving their heads to and fro sideways, while their bill is passing through the soft mud; and in many instances, when the water was deeper, they would immerse their whole head and a portion of the back, as the Spoonbill and Red-breasted Snipe are wont to do. When, on the contrary, they pursued aquatic insects, such as swim on the surface, they ran after them, and, on getting up to them, suddenly seized them by thrusting the lower mandible beneath them, while the other was raised a good way above the surface, much in the manner of the Black Shearwater [Black Skimmer], which, however, performs this act on wing. They were also expert at catching flying insects, after which they ran with partially expanded wings."

In the United States the Avocet is to-day confined almost entirely to the territory lying west

Photo by H. T. Bohlman   Courtesy of Nat. Asso. Aud. Soc.

NEST AND EGGS OF AVOCET

of the Mississippi River. The Federal Migratory Bird Law extends protection to it at all times, and it is to be hoped this splendid game bird may be spared the melancholy fate of the Eskimo Curlew and the Whooper Swan.

Like several other shore birds, the Avocet makes itself very useful by destroying diving beetles, which are predatory in their habits and do much damage to fish hatcheries by feeding upon insects which are the natural diet of fishes. It also feeds freely upon grasshoppers and upon bill-bugs, which injure the corn crops. Snails and marine worms also part of its diet.

T. GILBERT PEARSON.

BLACK-NECKED STILT

Himantopus mexicanus (*Müller*)

A. O. U. Number 226

Other Names.— Stilt; Longshanks; Lawyer.

General Description.— Length, 13 inches. Color above, black, sharply contrasting with the white of under parts; legs very long.

Color.— ADULTS: *Back, shoulders, and wings, glossy*

black, *continuing up back of neck*, on crown, enlarging on side of head, and including the eyes; a spot over and behind eye, one beneath eye, forehead, forepart of crown, lores, chin, sides of head below eye, sides of neck, entire under parts, rump, and upper tail-coverts, white; tail, ash; bill, black; iris, red; legs, flesh color. White of rump covered by the wings in life. In the female the black is often dingy. Young: Upper parts, brown, marked with whitish.

Nest and Eggs.— Nest: A depression in the sand or a frail structure of grass and small stems hidden in a bunch of weeds. Eggs: 3 or 4, buffy or olive-brown, thickly spotted and blotched with dark brown.

Distribution.— Temperate North America and northern South America; breeds from central Oregon, northern Utah, and southern Colorado to southern California, southern New Mexico, southern Texas, coast of Louisiana, and in Mexico, and from central Florida and Bahamas throughout the West Indies to northern Brazil and Peru; formerly bred north to New Jersey; winters from southern Lower California, southern Texas, southern Louisiana, and southern Florida south through Central America and the West Indies to northern Brazil, Peru, and the Galapagos; casual in migration to Nebraska, Wisconsin, and New Brunswick.

The Black-necked Stilt has been brought to verge of extermination along the Atlantic coast by the spring and summer shooting. It is not uncommon in the West and South, being particularly abundant about the alkaline lakes and pools of the Great Basin, where it is often seen in the company of the Avocet.

" On the ground, whether walking or wading, the bird [the Black-necked Stilt] moves gracefully, with measured steps; the long legs are much bent at every step (only at the joint, however) and planted firmly, perfectly straight; except under certain circumstances, there is nothing vacillating, feeble, or unsteady, in either the attitudes or the movements of the birds. When feeding, the legs are bent backward with an acute angle at the heel joint to bring the body lower; the latter is tilted forward and downward over the center of equilibrium, where the feet rest, and the long neck and bill reach the rest of the distance to the ground." (Coues.)

When the birds light they raise their wings straight up above the body for a moment, then close them slowly over the back. Many water birds have this same habit; and it is undoubtedly a recognition mark to keep in touch with the rest of the flock as the pose is a very conspicuous one, enabling the bird to be seen from a long distance.

The Black-necked Stilt's diet is known to include in considerable quantities several species of the predacious diving beetles which, because they prey upon insects that are the natural food of fishes, are counted a nuisance in all fish hatcheries. In this respect its economic value is a matter of fact, not of theory. Grasshoppers are destroyed in large numbers by this bird, and also bill-bugs which feed upon corn.

R. I. Brasher.

Courtesy of S. A. Lottridge

BLACK-NECKED STILT

The bird walks with long deliberate strides

Plate 31

AMERICAN WOODCOCK *Philohela minor* (Gmelin)

⅞ nat. size

SNIPES, SANDPIPERS, ETC.

Order *Limicolæ;* family *Scolopacidæ*

THE Snipes, Sandpipers, and the closely allied species which form the family *Scolopacidæ* of the order of Shore Birds, or Wading Birds, are represented in all the habitable parts of the world, but during the breeding season they are found with few exceptions only in the northern parts of the northern hemisphere. There are about one hundred species in the family, about half of which number occur regularly or occasionally in America.

The members of this family vary greatly in size, shape, and color, but in general they are of small or medium size and never reach the average size of Herons. Usually the bill is long and soft-skinned, generally straight, roundish, and slim, but sometimes curved either upward or downward and in one species, the Spoon-bill Sandpiper of eastern Asia, the end is spoon-shaped. The head is feathered to the bill. The legs are of moderate length. The wings are normally long, flat, and pointed. The tail is rather short, stiff, broad, and rounded.

As indicated by the name of the group in which this family has been placed, its members are seldom found far from the shores of bodies of water or from moist lands. They migrate and pass the winter in flocks, but during the breeding season are not gregarious. Like other shore birds, they all, with the exception of the European Green Sandpiper and the American Solitary Sandpiper, nest on the ground. The eggs usually number four, but seldom does a pair succeed in bringing more than two young birds to maturity during a season. The babies are clothed with down when hatched, and are precocial, that is, they are not cared for in the nest by their parents, but are able to run about within a very short time after leaving the shell.

Many of the species in this group are greatly prized as game birds, and to this fact is due to a large extent the decrease in their numbers. The development of land for agricultural purposes has restricted their breeding grounds, and this is an indirect, but nevertheless another, cause for their lessening numbers. Not only because of their food value are the birds entitled to protection, but also because of their usefulness. They search out and destroy many creatures that are detrimental to man's interests. Among the pests which they eat are grasshoppers, army worms, cutworms, cabbage worms, cotton worms, boll weevils, rice weevils, Texas fever ticks, horseflies, and mosquitoes.

WOODCOCK

Philohela minor (*Gmelin*)

A. O. U. Number 228   See Color Plate 31

Other Names.—American Woodcock; Woodhen; Big-headed Snipe; Big Mud Snipe; Blind Snipe; Whistling Snipe; Wood Snipe; Night Partridge; Night Peck; Timber Doodle; Hookum Pake; Labrador Twister; Bogsucker; Bog-bird; Pewee; Whistler; Bigeyes.

General Description.— Length, 11 inches; color above, brown; below, pale orange-brown; head, large; neck, short; *eyes, large* and set far back and high; *bill, very long* and compressed, the lower section shorter than the upper into which it fits at the tip, and the upper section capable of being flexed like a finger; wings, short and rounded; *three outer primaries,* *scythe-shaped; legs, short and stout with thighs feathered;* toes, without webs.

Color.— Above, finely blended and varied with black, warm browns, gray, and russet, the brown predominating, the gray tending to form streaks above and below shoulders; forehead, grayish; *three square patches of black extending from top of crown to nape and separated by narrow gray bars;* a black stripe from gape to eye; chin, whitish; rest of under parts, pale orange-brown with a few black spots on sides of chest; primaries, plain brownish; bill, brownish flesh color, dusky on ridge and tip; feet, flesh color; eye-ring, white; iris, dark brown.

Nest and Eggs.— Nest: On ground, on brushy bottoms or in open woods, usually not far from water; a depression in the leaves without lining. Eggs: 3 or 4, buffy to grayish-white, irregularly and thickly spotted with pale reddish-brown.

Distribution.— Eastern North America; breeds from northeastern North Dakota, southern Manitoba, north-ern Michigan, southern Quebec, and Nova Scotia south to southern Kansas, southern Louisiana, and northern Florida; winters from southern Missouri, the Ohio Valley, and New Jersey (rarely Massachusetts) south to Texas and southern Florida; ranges casually to Saskatchewan, Keewatin, Colorado, Newfoundland, and Bermuda.

During the day the Woodcock sits quietly in a shadowy retreat, usually in the swamps, but often in open upland woods. It may also be flushed in "slashings," where will be found the "form" of old leaves where it had nestled. The swampy coverts which "Mr. Big-eyes" prefers are clean, sweet localities, where alders and willows like to grow. The bird is by no means confined to such resorts for it may be found nesting well up in the hills, though even there a favorite resort is generally not far away, to which it travels in the evening and forages for its nocturnal supper. Often in the evening I have seen it against the fading west, bound for its own particular restaurant. Even after night had fallen its familiar *scape* could be heard.

Some of our birds are enveiled in mystery and the Woodcock is not the least strange of this coterie. It often lives where its presence is unsuspected. One of the best Woodcock covers I have known was within the limits of the city of Brooklyn. Fortunately this knowledge was not shared by others, so the birds were little hunted. Into this retreat the birds would come silently some April night, and from it they would disappear some October day as mysteriously.

The flight is swift though short, sometimes accompanied with a clattering sound, at others as silent as an owl's. I have frequently seen them collide with limbs when flushed. This may be due to the fact that the birds' eyes are placed far back in the head, or it may be because they are watching the intruder and cannot look forward and behind at the same time.

Drawing by R. I. Brasher

WOODCOCK (⅔ nat. size)

A game bird that is not disturbed by the advent of agriculture

The mother Woodcock has a curious and interesting habit of flying off, when disturbed, with a young chick grasped between her feet or between her thighs. If she has an opportunity, she will convey all her babies, one at a time, to a place of security.

At courting time, and all through the period of incubation, the male indulges in a curious aërial dance. Soon after sunset he whirls up in spirals, chirping and twittering, to a height of fifty or sixty feet, then circles horizontally and descends, giving voice to his ecstasy in a continuous "cheeping" until he reaches the ground where he struts like a tiny turkey-gobbler, with drooping wings and upright spread tail, changing his notes to a series of rather hard *paiks*. On moonlight nights, I have listened to this serenade until after 9 o'clock.

A dish of angleworms can hardly be considered appetizing; but, transmuted in the Woodcock's interior machinery (he is really one hundred per cent. angleworm), there seems to be no difference of opinion among epicures when the bird is brought to the table on toast.

The Woodcock's diet includes also in considerable quantities such harmful insects as the crane fly ("leather-jacket"), and various species

Photo by H. K. Job   Courtesy of Outing Pub. Co.

WOODCOCK ON NEST

Its nest is a depression among fallen leaves

of more or less destructive grasshoppers. To this extent its feeding habits are of distinct benefit to man.   R. I. BRASHER.

WILSON'S SNIPE

Gallinago delicata (*Ord*)

A. O. U. Number 230   See Color Plate 32

Other Names.— Common Snipe; English Snipe; American Snipe; Meadow Snipe; Marsh Snipe; Bog Snipe; Gutter Snipe; Jack Snipe; Shadbird; Alewifebird; Shad Spirit.

General Description.— Length, 12 inches. Color above, mainly brownish-black; bill long and slender, upper section overlapping under. Seldom found away from fresh-water marshes.

Color.— Ground color of head, neck, throat, and breast, *pale brownish-white;* sides of head, neck, and breast, *spotted with pale and dark brown;* two dusky stripes from bill over crown to back of head; another from gape to eye and extending a little behind and a small patch on cheeks; back and shoulders, brownish-black mixed with chestnut and brown; shoulder-feathers, broadly edged with brownish-white, forming two longitudinal stripes on each side; wing-coverts, brownish, feathers edged with whitish, secondaries with brown spots coalescing along shaft; primaries and their coverts, dusky-brown, the outer one white-edged; upper tail-coverts, brown with narrow black bars; *tail-feathers, black at base, then bright rufous with a* *narrow subterminal black bar* and white-tipped; abdomen, white; *sides of body, shaded with brown, barred with numerous traverse streaks of dusky;* under tail-coverts, rufous with dusky bars; bill, brownish flesh-color, dusky on ridge and tip; feet, greenish-gray; iris, brown surrounded by white ring interrupted in front and behind.

Nest and Eggs.— NEST: A grass-lined depression in marshy ground. EGGS: 3 or 4, grayish-olive, spotted and streaked with chestnut, burnt umber, and black.

Distribution.— North America and northern South America; breeds from northwestern Alaska, northern Mackenzie, central Keewatin, and northern Ungava south to northern California, southern Colorado, northern Iowa, northern Illinois, Pennsylvania, and New Jersey; winters from northern California, New Mexico, Arkansas, and North Carolina through Central America and West Indies to Colombia and southern Brazil; remains in winter casually and locally north to Washington, Montana, Nebraska, Illinois, and Nova Scotia; accidental in Hawaiian Islands, Bermuda, and Great Britain.

As its scientific name implies, the Wilson's Snipe is truly a delicacy, and in many more ways than from the culinary standpoint. Every phase of its life assumes a peculiar interest, when one comes to know it well. Sportsmen, naturally, are fond of it, and refer to it familiarly as "Jack Snipe."

In the breeding season its ways are most singular and entertaining. It breeds on the northern borders of the United States and north to the Arctic Sea. On the Magdalen Islands I have watched it with both amusement and amazement. The background is of the mossy bogs and marshes, interspersed with shallow ponds and clumps of small spruce. There, in May and June, we may see and hear the male bird darting about in wide circlings up in the sky, like a sort of feathered meteor, producing with its wings a humming, murmuring sound, not unlike that accompanying the flight of the "Whistler" or Golden-eye. Then the mode of the performance changes. The singular, long-billed creature now flies low, emitting a vocal yelping or cackling, in general form not very different from that of the Yellow-legs, only continuous, lasting for several minutes at a spell. Presently it alights on a spruce tree or a stub and continues its vociferations.

Possibly the female may indulge also in the circling and winnowing performance, for I have seen two or more birds at a time executing this, and in one case we thus traced a bird to its nest. Watching where it alighted, after much flying around, a member of our party flushed it from a nest of four handsomely marked, pointed eggs, in the grass near a little bush. I embraced the opportunity to set the camera by the nest, with

Photo by H. K. Job   Courtesy of Outing Pub. Co.
WILSON'S SNIPE ON NEST

thread attached, and thus secured some interesting pictures.

The usual haunts of this Snipe are open meadows or fresh-water marshes, where the ground is wet and soft, and where there is grass enough to conceal it. It migrates down across the United States from mid-September to freezing-up time, and is much hunted. Flushing suddenly from the grass, it darts off with rapid, erratic flight, uttering reiterated squeaky notes, commonly represented as *scaip, scaip,* or *escape,* suiting the action to the word. It winters from the Southern States to as far south as Brazil.

On the Louisiana marshes, in the winter of 1915–16, I found it very abundant. Usually it is found in scattered parties on the meadows, but here I found it in large flocks, sometimes noting several hundred in flight in a compact mass. Smaller parties, or "wisps," say of twenty to

Drawing by R. I. Brasher
WILSON'S SNIPE (⅜ nat. size)
A favorite with sportsmen

Plate 32

Louis Agassiz Fuertes.

WILSON'S SNIPE   *Gallinago delicata* (Ord)

$\frac{7}{8}$ nat. size

forty, were frequently darting about, especially toward evening. Near the camp of Messrs. Ward and McIlhenny, where I stayed, there were a series of muddy flats, interspersed with bunches or patches of grass, which were fairly alive with Snipe. In the morning I could see one or more of them lying beneath many a tussock dozing. Unless flushed, they stayed there until sundown, or till it became overcast, whereupon they could be seen running about over the open mud and shallow water, busily probing for worms. By building a blind at the edge of one of these flats and carefully awaiting sudden intervals of sunshine late in the afternoon, I secured motion pictures and others of them thus engaged.

HERBERT K. JOB.

The food of Wilson's Snipe is known to include crane-flies ("leather-jackets"), locusts, grasshoppers, crawfishes, and the predacious diving beetles which cause trouble in fish hatcheries and destroy much of the natural insect food of fishes. To the extent that it preys upon these insect forms — and that is very considerable — it must be reckoned a useful bird.

DOWITCHER

Macrorhamphus griseus griseus (*Gmelin*)

A. O. U. Number 231   See Color Plate 33

Other Names.— Robin Snipe; Sea Pigeon; Driver; Red-breasted Snipe (summer); Brown Snipe (summer); Brown-back (summer); Gray Snipe (winter); Gray-back (winter).

General Description.— Length, 11 inches. Color

sides, thickly speckled with dusky; a series of dusky specks from gape through and behind eye; bill and feet, dull dusky-greenish; iris, brown. IN WINTER: Forehead, head, neck, back, shoulders, and long inner secondaries, dark gray, the feathers on back with dusky

Photograph by H. K. Job

DOWITCHERS

A flock on Breton Island Reservation

above, in summer, brownish-cinnamon; in winter, slate-gray. Bill long and slender, upper section overlapping under. Found on sand bars and mud flats, and not in bogs.

Color.— IN SUMMER: Ground color of neck, head, breast, and upper parts, brownish-cinnamon; head and neck, narrowly streaked with dusky-brown; feathers of back, with broad blackish-brown centers; *rump, upper coverts, and tail, white, barred with dusky;* wings, grayish-dusky, the coverts edged with lighter; secondaries, broadly edged and tipped with white; *under parts, rufous,* paler or whitish behind; breast and centers and paler edges; lower back, *rump, and tail, pure white,* with roundish spots of dusky; wing-coverts, like back; secondaries, white-edged and -tipped; primaries dusky-brown; *under parts, white;* throat, sides of breast, and sides, strongly shaded with gray; a dusky stripe from gape through and behind eye; the white stripe between this and crown, pronounced; cheeks and side of head, mottled with pale dusky; lower tail-coverts with roundish dusky spots; bill, dusky, greenish at base; legs, dully greenish-gray; iris, brown with white crescent below.

Nest and Eggs.— NEST: A depression in the ground

on borders of marshy lakes and ponds; a loose structure of grasses and leaves. EGGS: 4, greenish-olive to light clay-color, spotted with dark brown.

Distribution.— Eastern North and South America; breeding range unknown, but probably northern Ungava; winters from Florida and the West Indies south to northern Brazil; in migration regularly on the Atlantic coast, and occasionally in Illinois, Indiana, and Ontario; accidental in Greenland, Bermuda, Great Britain, and France.

The Dowitcher's regular food includes several species of destructive grasshoppers, diving beetles which do much damage in fish hatcheries besides destroying insects which are the natural food of fishes, and various marine worms which prey upon oysters. Its usefulness to man, therefore, is very considerable.

It is a bird of the open meadows, feeding along marshy shores and on sand bars bared by the receding tide, in flocks, and often in the company of other waders. This gregarious instinct, combined with its gentleness, is a fatal trait, and enables gunners to slaughter them unmercifully and sometimes to exterminate every individual in a " bunch." To turn a 12-gauge " cannon " loose among these unsuspicious birds, winnowing in over the decoys with friendly notes of greeting, is about as sportsmanlike as shooting into a bunch of chickens. To catch them with a camera requires skill and patience, and herein lies the hope for future existence of our disappearing wild life — substitution of the lens for the gun!

The call of the Dowitcher is a rather low-pitched series of whistles:— *pheu-pheu-pheu-pheu-pheu*, without the diminuendo of the Yellow-leg's notes.

The Long-billed Dowitcher (*Macrorhamphus griseus scolopaceus*) differs from the common Dowitcher in its larger size, richer coloration, and longer bill. But the two can only be unerringly separated by a close comparison with the specimens in the hand. The Long-billed Dowitcher is known locally as the Greater Long-beak, the Greater Gray-back, and the Red-bellied Snipe. It is found in western North America and South America; it is " supposed to be rare or casual on the Atlantic coast and declared to be the only representative of the genus in the west — which would be important if it were a fact. Nesting and habits same as stock form." (Coues.)

STILT SANDPIPER

Micropalama himantopus (*Bonaparte*)

A. O. U. Number 233   See Color Plates 33, 34

Other Names.— Long-legged Sandpiper; Frost Snipe; Mongrel; Bastard Yellow-legs.

General Description.— Length, 9 inches. Upper parts, in summer, mottled with blackish-brown, white, chestnut, and dusky; in winter, ashy-gray. Under parts, whitish barred with dark. Legs long and slender; toes webbed at base; bill long, slender, and *slightly curved*.

Color.— IN SUMMER: *Forehead, crown, a line from gape through eye broadening on side of head, rufous;* center of crown, dusky; a whitish streak from bill over and back of eye; upper parts, blackish-brown, each feather edged and tipped with white or chestnut; upper tail-coverts, barred with white and dusky; tail, mottled white and ash; wing-coverts, grayish, the feathers edged with lighter; primaries and secondaries, grayish-brown, latter edged with white; under parts from throat, whitish, sometimes with a pale rufous wash, spotted on breast, *barred everywhere below with brownish;* bill, dusky-greenish, darkening at tip; *legs, dusky yellowish-green;* iris, brown with a white crescent below. IN WINTER: Above, ashy-gray, crown narrowly streaked and feathers of back more broadly edged with lighter; wing-coverts, brownish-ash, the feathers lighter-edged; primaries and secondaries, dusky, the latter edged with whitish; a dusky streak from bill through and behind eye; under parts from chin, white, narrowly and thinly barred with dusky; bill, dusky; legs, dull brownish-yellow; iris, brown with a white crescent below.

Nest and Eggs.— NEST: A depression in the ground lined with a few leaves and grass. EGGS: 3 or 4, grayish-white or light drab, boldly marked with spots of chestnut, brown, and lavender, more numerous at the large end.

Distribution.— North and South America; breeds near the coast of Mackenzie and probably south to central Keewatin; winters in South America south to Uruguay and Chile; casual in winter in southern Texas and Mexico; in migration occurs in western Mississippi valley, West Indies, and Central America; less common on the Atlantic coast, and casual in British Columbia, Newfoundland, and Bermuda.

Although considered rare, the Stilt Sandpiper is more numerous along the Atlantic coast than is supposed, since it is frequently mistaken for the Yellow-legs by gunners or by those not trained to close observation. The similarity of the two species is acknowledged by the popular name, "Bastard Yellow-legs," which the sportsmen of Long Island have given to the Stilt Sandpiper. The different color of the long legs will always be a distinguishing mark, however, between these cousins.

It flies in flocks, or individuals may join forces with other species. A Stilt Sandpiper among a number of Semipalmated Sandpipers is instantly noted, his long legs raising his body conspicuously above his smaller companions. Its general habits of feeding are similar to those of the smaller Sandpiper.

KNOT

Tringa canutus *Linnæus*

A. O. U. Number 234   See Color Plates 33, 34

Other Names.— Red Sandpiper; Red-breasted Sandpiper; Red-breasted Plover; Freckled Sandpiper; Ash-colored Sandpiper; Canute's Sandpiper; Gray-back; Silver-back; Robin Snipe; White Robin Snipe; Robin-breast; Beach Robin; Red-breast; Buff-breast; Buff-breasted Plover; Horsefoot Snipe; White-bellied Snipe; May-bird; Blue Plover; Silver Plover.

General Description.— Length, 10 inches. In summer, color of upper parts grayish-brown and the breast rufous-brown; in winter, plain gray above and white below. Bill straight, longer than the head, and flattened and enlarged at tip; toes slender and not webbed at base.

Color.— ADULTS IN SUMMER: Upper parts, grayish-brown narrowly streaked on crown and back of neck with dusky; feathers of back and shoulders, tipped and edged with grayish-white, those of shoulders, tinged with yellowish-brown; *rump and upper tail-coverts, white* with traverse bars of dusky-brown; tail, grayish edged with ashy-white; line over and back of eye, *sides of head, chin, throat, and under parts, plain rufous-brown* shading into lighter on flanks, into white on under tail-coverts; latter with arrowhead spots of dusky; wing-coverts and secondaries, grayish edged with lighter; primaries, plain dusky gray; bill and feet, greenish-black; iris, brown. ADULTS IN WINTER: *Above, plain grayish;* crown, streaked with darker gray, feathers of back, wing-coverts, and secondaries, edged, or not, with whiter; rump and upper tail-coverts, white with dusky spots and bars; primaries, dusky, lighter

Drawing by R. I. Brasher

KNOT (⅔ nat. size)

A bird that is known on the shores of every continent

tipped; *below, white;* sides of breast and sides, with dusky markings more distinct and wedge-shaped on sides; an indistinct dusky line from gape through and back of eye; legs and bill, dusky-greenish; iris, brown.

Nest and Eggs.— NEST: A depression in the ground, lined with grass. EGGS: 4, light pea-green, speckled with brown.

Distribution.— Northern and southern hemispheres; breeds from northern Ellesmere Land south to Melville Peninsula and Iceland, and also on Taimyr Peninsula, Siberia; winters south to southern Patagonia, and from the Mediterranean to South Africa, India, Australia, and New Zealand; casual in winter on the Atlantic coast of the United States; in migration occurs on the Atlantic coast of North America and over most of the eastern hemisphere; rare in the interior of North America and on the Pacific coast.

A flock of Knots tripping along the beach in their spring plumage with rufous breasts gives the observer the impression that some Robins have acquired nautical propensities and come down to the ocean for a change of food. While following the retreating surges gleaning minute crustacea left stranded by the recession of the waves they talk in soft low notes to one another and are so preoccupied that they often come within a few feet of a motionless watcher.

After nesting in the extreme North they return to the coast in the autumn with an entirely different dress, no longer with the robin's breast, but with a soft gray above and white below.

Like some other maritime birds, individuals often remain as far south as Long Island, New York, all summer, being apparently not interested in marital duties — wise bachelors or old maids who prefer a good table and comfortable climate to the long journey and inclemency of the Arctic Circle, where those with a proper sense of domestic responsibility settle down for a few weeks and raise a family.

When not harassed by gunners they are remarkably gentle and unsuspicious, and I have laid in a hollow scooped out of the sand while a flock fed all around me, one or two actually peeping over the edge of the pit, within three feet of my face!

The Knot is an industrious eater of grasshoppers which are injurious to crops, and of crawfishes which do much damage in rice and corn fields in the South and to levees by boring into and weakening them. It also feeds upon the marine worms which are destructive parasites of the oyster, and upon the diving beetles which prey upon the natural insect food of fish. For these services it is entitled at least to such protection as will guard against any decrease of the species.　　　　　　　　　　　R. I. BRASHER.

PURPLE SANDPIPER

Arquatella maritima maritima (*Brünnich*)

A. O. U. Number 235　　See Color Plate 34

Other Names.— Rock Sandpiper; Rock Snipe; Rock Plover; Rock-bird; Rockweed Bird; Winter Rock-bird; Winter Snipe.

General Description.— Length, 9 inches. Principal colors, black and white. Legs short and strong. General build, short, thick, and squatty.

Color.— ADULTS IN SUMMER: *Upper parts, black;* crown, streaked with yellowish or grayish-white; back and shoulders varied with chestnut, pale buff, or whitish, the reddish color on sides, the paler colors tipping the feathers; sides of head, with a rufous wash, separated from the crown by a whitish line; under parts, white shaded on throat and breast with tawny and here and there streaked with blackish; rest of lower parts with dusky-gray markings; rump and upper tail-coverts, plain dusky; wings, dusky; lesser wing-coverts, narrowly tipped with white; greater coverts, broadly tipped with the same; secondaries, mostly white increasing in size toward the inner feathers; inner tail-feathers, dusky; outer ones, gray.

ADULTS IN WINTER: Entire upper parts, soft blackish-brown with purple reflections, each feather lighter bordered; greater and lesser wing-coverts, inner secondaries, and shoulders, edged and tipped with white; secondaries, broadly tipped with white; primaries, deep dusky; upper tail-coverts and middle tail-feathers, like color of back; outside tail-feathers, light ashy; throat and *breast, brownish-ash* shading into the white of rest of under parts; feathers of side, with wedge-shaped light dusky centers; lores, dusky; eye-ring, whitish; bill, yellow with dusky tip; feet, dull orange-red.

Nest and Eggs.— NEST: Slight depression in the ground, thinly lined with dry grass. EGGS: 4, grayish olive, boldly and distinctly marked with rich burnt umber over the entire surface.

Distribution.— Northern hemisphere; breeds from

Plate 33

Knut Gaant Fuertes

RUDDY TURNSTONE
Arenaria interpres morinella (Linnaeus)
SANDERLING
Calidris leucophaea (Pallas)

RED-BACKED SANDPIPER
Pelidna alpina sakhalina (Vieillot)
STILT SANDPIPER
Micropalama himantopus (Bonaparte)
BREEDING PLUMAGES
All ½ nat. size

DOWITCHER
Macrorhamphus griseus griseus (Gmelin)
KNOT
Tringa canutus Linnaeus

Melville Island, Ellesmere Land, and northern Greenland south to Melville Peninsula, Cumberland Sound, and southern Greenland, and in Norway, Russia, Siberia, Iceland, and Faroe Islands; winters from southern Greenland and New Brunswick to Long Island; casual in migration to the Great Lakes, Georgia, Florida, and Bermuda, and in the Eastern Hemisphere south to Great Britain and the Mediterranean.

A member of the Snipe family feeding on the wintry beach seems almost as much out of place as a Hummingbird and the observer is likely to think the bird's journey has been interrupted by injury.

I have seen Purple Sandpipers on the rocky Maine coast in December, searching carefully in seaweed for their food and apparently indifferent to the cold. As nearly as I could make out they seemed to be feeding on small mussels and clams, which they swallowed shell and all.

Although nowhere common in America, since its principal line of migration follows through Norway into other parts of Europe, it can be found during the winter months as far south as Long Island, N. Y., where, like the Ipswich Sparrow, it is less rare than is generally supposed because few observers brave the open wind-swept dunes in winter.

Two varieties of the Purple Sandpiper occur in Alaska. These are the Aleutian Sandpiper (*Arquatella maritima couesi*) and the Pribilof or Black-breasted Sandpiper (*Arquatella maritima ptilocnemis*). When first described these two subspecies were supposed to be separate species from each other and from the Purple Sandpiper, although a close relationship between the three was acknowledged. Careful study has established their exact status. In their respective winter plumages the Aleutian and Purple Sandpipers are not distinguishable and in the other seasons there is very little real difference between them, but the Aleutian both breeds and winters within the boundaries of Alaska, occasionally straying over to Plover Bay, Siberia. The Pribilof Sandpiper breeds on the St. Lawrence, St. Matthew, and Pribilof islands and winters on the coast of southeastern Alaska.

R. I. BRASHER.

PECTORAL SANDPIPER

Pisobia maculata (*Vieillot*)

A. O. U. Number 239   See Color Plate 35

Other Names.— Grass Snipe; Jack Snipe; Grass-bird; Meadow Snipe; Cow Snipe; Brownie; Brown-back; Triddler; Hay-bird; Fat-bird; Short-neck; Squat Snipe; Squatter; Krieker; Marsh Plover.

General Description.— Length, 9 inches. Color above, brownish-black; below, white marked with dusky on breast. *Tail double notched, the middle tail-feathers pointed and longer than all the others.*

Color.— Crown, streaked with blackish-brown and chestnut; sides of head, *neck, and breast, pale yellowish-brown, spotted with dusky brown; upper parts, brownish-black, each feather edged with ashy or chestnut,* shoulder feathers with lighter margins; outer upper tail-coverts, white with arrowhead spots of dusky; lesser coverts, brown with broad brownish-ash edges; secondaries and greater coverts, brownish, edged and tipped with white; primaries, dusky black; *central tail-feathers, brownish-black with lighter edges;* rest of tail-feathers, ashy, margined with white; throat, abdomen, and under tail-coverts, white; sides, yellowish-brown spotted with dusky; bill and legs, dusky-greenish; broad, indistinct stripe above, and a ring around, eye, whitish.

Nest and Eggs.— NEST: On the ground; a mere depression, sparsely lined with grass. EGGS: 4, greenish-drab, spotted and blotched with brown.

Distribution.— North and South America; breeds on the Arctic coast from northern Alaska to mouth of Yukon and northeastern Mackenzie; winters in South America from Peru and Bolivia to northern Chile, Argentina, and central Patagonia; in migration very rare on Pacific coast south of British Columbia, except in Lower California; common in fall migration in Mississippi valley and on the Atlantic coast, rare in spring; casual in northeastern Siberia, Unalaska, and Greenland; accidental in Hawaii and England.

" During the mating season the male Pectoral Sandpiper develops a great pouch, formed of the skin of the throat and breast, which he is able to inflate until it is nearly as large as the body. He now becomes a song bird, and flutters upward twenty or thirty yards in the air, as if emulating the famous Skylark, and, inflating his great pouch, glides down again to the ground; or he flies slowly along the ground, his head raised high and his tail hanging straight down, uttering a succession of booming notes. As he struts about the female his low notes swell and die away in musical cadences." (Forbush.)

Although migrating in flocks the "Kriekers" scatter when a good feeding meadow is reached, and are generally flushed from the grass singly. They prefer the bayside meadows, and are seldom seen along the margins of ponds or on the beaches. It is probable that they "fatten up"

on some favorite food further north, for they are extremely fat when they arrive on the Long Island (N. Y.) marshes in September. They "lie" well, flushing within easy gunshot range with a flight similar to that of Wilson's Snipe but less rapid. The zigzags are shorter, the course rapidly straightens out, and if the "sportsman" waits a few seconds after they spring, it is not difficult to add them to the "bag." When the early morning mists of September hang low over the meadows Pectoral Sandpipers, magnified by the fog, appear nearly as large as Wilson's Snipe. R. I. BRASHER.

WHITE-RUMPED SANDPIPER

Pisobia fuscicollis (*Vieillot*)

A. O. U. Number 240   See Color Plate 35

Other Names.— Bonaparte's Sandpiper; Schintz's Sandpiper; Sand-bird; Bull Peep.

General Description.— Length, 7 inches. In summer, the upper parts pale brownish with dusky stripes and the lower parts white with brownish markings; in winter, brownish-ash above and whitish below. Middle tail-feathers pointed and longer than others.

Color.— ADULTS IN SUMMER: Crown and upper parts, pale brownish, each feather with a large dusky center, forming stripes on back; crown, striped with dark brown; shoulders, more chestnut; *rump and upper tail-coverts, white;* central tail-feathers, brownish-black, the rest light grayish, broadly edged and tipped with white; sides of head, neck, and breast, washed with pale yellowish-brown, spotted with darker; an indistinct dark brown streak from bill through and behind eye; wing-coverts and secondaries, grayish-brown edged with lighter; primaries, dusky; chin and throat, white; abdomen and rest of under parts, white; bill and feet, dusky-greenish; iris, brown surrounded by a white ring. ADULTS IN WINTER: *Crown, back of neck, back, and shoulders, brownish-ash,* indistinctly streaked

with darker; *rump and upper tail-coverts, white;* central tail-feathers, dusky; the rest, light ash; some feathers of shoulder and back, deep chestnut edged with white; wing, as in summer; a broad streak over eye, chin, throat, and under parts in general, whitish faintly spotted with pale brown; a streak from bill through and behind eye, dark brownish-ash; bill, dusky horn, lighter at base; feet, dusky-greenish; iris, brown surrounded by a white ring.

Nest and Eggs.— NEST: A depression in the ground, lined with a few leaves. EGGS: 4, light olive or olive-brown, boldly spotted and marked with deep sepia, chiefly at large end.

Distribution.— North and South America; breeds along the Arctic coast from northwestern Mackenzie to Cumberland Island; has occurred in summer west to Point Barrow and east to Greenland; winters from Paraguay to southern Patagonia and the Falkland Islands; in migration most abundant in the Mississippi valley, less so on the Atlantic coast; casual in the Bermudas, Great Britain, the West Indies, and Central America.

The White-rumped Sandpiper is usually found among the Least and Semipalmated Sandpipers tripping over awash seaweed or running along the shore. They seldom associate with flocks of their own kind, but prefer the company of other species. In autumn plumage they can be easily confused with the smaller Sandpipers, but close scrutiny will reveal the white upper tail-coverts — a conspicuous identification mark. Their

habits are similar to those of other members of the family and they are naturally unsuspicious unless repeatedly disturbed.

An important part of the diet of the White-rumped Sandpiper consists of grasshoppers of species known to be injurious to crops. This is a real service to man which should not be overlooked when measures for the adequate protection of the birds are considered.

Plate 34

Louis Agassiz Fuertes

PURPLE SANDPIPER
Arquatella maritima maritima (Brünnich)
SANDERLING
Calidris leucophaea (Pallas)

RED-BACKED SANDPIPER
Pelidna alpina sakhalina (Vieillot)
STILT SANDPIPER
Micropalama himantopus (Bonaparte)
AUTUMN AND WINTER PLUMAGES
All ½ nat. size

DOWITCHER
Macrorhamphus griseus griseus (Gmelin)
KNOT
Tringa canutus Linnaeus

BAIRD'S SANDPIPER

Pisobia bairdi (*Coues*)

A. O. U. Number 241   See Color Plate 35

Other Name.— Grass-bird.

General Description.— Length, 7 inches. Color above, brownish-black; below, white with pale brownish on breast. Resembles the Pectoral Sandpiper but smaller and breast less heavily streaked.

Color.— ADULTS: Entire upper parts, brownish-black, each feather bordered and tipped with light reddish-yellow, these tips broader and nearly pure white on shoulders; coverts and secondaries like back, latter lighter tipped; central tail-feathers, brownish-black; remainder, successively lighter, all narrowly bordered with white; *breast pale brownish with faint spots and streaks of dusky;* throat and under parts, white; bill and legs, dusky; iris, brown. YOUNG IN AUTUMN: Sides of head, throat, breast, and upper parts, including wings, nearly uniform pale yellowish-brown, each feather darker centrally; crown (strongly), sides of head, throat, and breast (more faintly), streaked or spotted with brown; rest of under parts, white; bill, dusky, lighter at base; legs, dull olive.

Nest and Eggs.— NEST: A depression in the ground under shelter of tuft of grass, lined with a few leaves and grasses. EGGS: 4, buffy, spotted with shades of chestnut-brown.

Distribution.— North and South America; breeds along the Arctic coast from Point Barrow to northern Keewatin; winters in Chile, Argentina, and Patagonia; occurs regularly in migration from the Rocky Mountains to the Mississippi River, and in Central America and northern South America, and irregularly in autumn on the Pacific coast from Alaska to Lower California and on the Atlantic coast from Nova Scotia to New Jersey; casual in summer in Guerrero, Mexico; accidental in England and South Africa.

Although it is slightly larger than the Least and Semipalmated Sandpipers it is not easy to distinguish the Baird's Sandpiper from those species. Its general color in the field is more yellowish-brown and it is found almost exclusively along the prairie sloughs and lagoons of the Middle West. Its habits are similar to other small Sandpipers; it runs along the shore in the same confiding way, and unless frightened will sometimes feed almost at the observer's feet.

LEAST SANDPIPER

Pisobia minutilla (*Vieillot*)

A. O. U. Number 242   See Color Plate 35

Other Names.— Peep; Wilson's Stint; Ox-eye; Mud-peep; Sand-peep; Little Sand-peep.

General Description.— Length, 6 inches; the smallest Sandpiper, and not heavier than an English Sparrow. Color above, grayish-brown; below, white with the breast darker. Much like the Semipalmated Sandpiper, but the feet with *no* webs.

Color.— ADULTS IN SUMMER: *Entire upper parts, dusky brown* striped on head and neck with chestnut, each feather on back and shoulders edged with chestnut and tipped with whitish; center tail-feathers, blackish edged with chestnut, others, gray edged with white; wing-coverts and secondaries, brownish edged with bay; secondaries, tipped with white; primaries, dusky; breast, washed with pale rusty and spotted with brown; a diffuse streak from bill through and back of eye, dusky; bill and *legs, dusky greenish;* iris, brown with white eye-ring; throat, abdomen, and rest of under parts, white. ADULTS IN WINTER: Entire upper parts, pale grayish-brown, each feather darker centrally; secondaries and primaries, white-tipped; breast, shaded with very pale brownish-gray, spotting obsolete; bill as in summer; *feet, yellowish-green.*

Nest and Eggs.— NEST: Near water; a mere depression in the ground, lined with leaves and grass. EGGS: 3 or 4, creamy-buff to light drab, heavily spotted with chestnut and lavender.

Distribution.— North and South America; breeds from northwestern Alaska, southern Arctic islands, and northern Ungava to Yakutat Bay, Alaska, valley of the Upper Yukon, northern Mackenzie, central Keewatin, southern Ungava, Nova Scotia, and Sable Island; winters from California, Texas, and North Carolina through the West Indies and Central America to Brazil, Chile, and the Galapagos; in migration occurs throughout the United States and west to northeastern Siberia and the Commander Islands, north to Greenland, and in Bermuda; accidental in Europe.

To the lover of unspoiled Nature our grand open sea beaches would not seem like the real thing were it not possible at times to see flocks of innocent little Sandpipers running gracefully along the margin, chased by the advancing waves. The tiniest atom of its tribe, the Least Sandpiper, accompanied by several other kinds, is still with us, and is perhaps increasing, thanks to the outlawry of shooting them under the Federal

It was my good fortune to be able to study its nesting habits when I found it breeding on the Magdalen Islands, Gulf of St. Lawrence. Picture there, on these islands, broad expanses of meadowy country, carpeted with short grass and moss, interspersed with patches of low spruce and juniper, and dotted with small shallow ponds. Here, in early June, we may listen to a sweet, twittering little song, and spy the author,

Drawing by R. I. Brasher

LEAST SANDPIPER (⅔ nat. size)

The baby among shore birds

Law. It will be a sorry day when we need such tiny things for food, each one affording but a mere taste.

This species and the Semipalmated Sandpiper consort together and resemble each other so closely that it is hard at a distance to tell them apart. There is a slight distinction in habit, in that the Least Sandpiper is more apt to be found on marshes, while the other prefers the beach, though there is no certain distinguishing of them in this way. As things go, they are comparatively common in May and again in August and the first part of September quite generally over the country, wherever there are any considerable bodies of water, particularly on both our sea-coasts, also in the Mississippi valley, and on the shallow prairie sloughs of the Northwest.

Whereas most of the larger shore birds cross to the interior of the continent to breed, the Sandpipers as a class seem not to avoid the northern Atlantic coast in the spring flight and in the nesting season. This is true of the Least Sandpiper. Though it breeds in the far Northwest, it also does so on our eastern coasts, well to the north.

not a Warbler but our little Sandpiper, the male bird, circling about on quivering wings, singing to his little mate who loiters on the edge of a

Photo by H. K. Job   Courtesy of Houghton Mifflin Co.

AN ANXIOUS MOTHER

Least Sandpiper watching the photographer near her babies

One day, a June 13, a tiny bird fluttered almost from beneath the feet of my companion, and there was our first nest of the Least Sandpiper, a little hollow in the northern moss, lined with dry bayberry leaves, and holding four eggs, large for the size of the bird, and wide across, though somewhat pointed. The tiny owners trailed around at our feet in abject despair. Finally we compromised by persuading the female to allow me to photograph her on the nest, after which we parted company.

On another occasion, beside the crude cart-road leading to the fisherman's house where we were staying, a pair of these birds appeared greatly worried over our passing. They ran about, alighted on the wire fence, and scolded plaintively. This set us to searching, but it was some time before I discovered the four tiny young, very recently hatched, huddled together on the ground among the sparse grass of the adjoining pasture, and a tell-tale egg-shell near by. Little buff-colored balls of down, ornamented with black spots, they were as pretty bird-babies as I have ever seen. Somehow, these episodes with breeding shore birds of Arctic proclivities, in this crisp northern clime, appealed to me with very special fascination.

HERBERT K. JOB.

RED-BACKED SANDPIPER

Pelidna alpina sakhalina (*Vieillot*)

A. O. U. Number 243a   See Color Plates 33, 34

Other Names.— American Dunlin; Black-bellied Sandpiper; Brant-bird; Red-back; Red-backed Dunlin; Lead-back; Ox-bird; Fall Snipe; Crooked-billed Snipe; Crooked-bill; Little Blackbreast; Winter Snipe; Simpleton; Stib; Black-heart Plover (Ontario).

General Description.— Length, 9 inches. In summer, upper parts chestnut and the lower parts white with a black patch; in winter, upper parts dark ashy-gray, under parts pale ashy-white. Bill, rather long and terminal third bent slightly downward.

Color.—ADULTS IN SUMMER: *Crown, back, shoulders, rump, and upper tail-coverts, chestnut,* crown, streaked with dusky, rest of feathers of upper parts with dusky centers, many with whitish tips (especially behind); tail, wing-coverts, and secondaries, ashy-gray; *secondaries, broadly white-tipped,* coverts with darker centers; primaries dusky, some inner ones edged with white at base; sides of head, back of neck, chin, throat, and rest of under parts, white; *abdomen, with a broad velvety-black patch;* other whitish parts above, streaked with pale dusky; bill, dusky-yellow; legs, dark horn-color; iris, brown with a dusky spot in front. ADULTS IN WINTER: Entire upper parts, dark ashy-gray, lightening over eye and streaked with whitish on back of neck; feathers of back, faintly outlined with lighter; wing-coverts and secondaries, more brownish; feathers, darker centrally, secondaries narrowly white-tipped; primaries, deep dusky, the inner ones whitish at base forming a conspicuous *white spot;* chin, throat, and rest of under parts, pale ashy-white; black area of summer plumage entirely absent; under parts from throat, obsoletely streaked with dusky; bill and legs, dusky-greenish; iris, brown.

Nest and Eggs.— NEST: A hollow in the ground, in or near salt marshes or fresh-water lakes and ponds. EGGS: 4, pale greenish to brownish-buff, spotted with dull umber, chestnut, and sepia.

Distribution.— North America and eastern Asia; breeds on the northern coast of Siberia west to mouth of the Yenisei, and from Point Barrow to mouth of Yukon, and in Boothia and Melville peninsulas, and northern Ungava; winters on the Pacific coast from Washington to southern Lower California and from New Jersey (rarely Massachusetts) south to Louisiana and southern Texas, and in Asia from China and Japan to the Malay Archipelago; rare in migration in the interior of the United States except about the southern end of Lake Michigan.

Although the Red-backed Sandpiper is found often in the interior of North America, in New England it is confined mainly to the neighborhood of the sea and largely to the salt marshes, but also frequents sand bars and mud flats. It is an active little bird usually keeping in companies, which run about nimbly and fly very rapidly, performing varied evolutions in concert, as if drilled to act together. In the breeding season it has a rather musical flight song, which never is heard except in its northern home, so far as I know. When frightened or flying it has a hoarse, grating note.

There seem to be two well-defined migration routes of this species: one from Alaska and Siberia down the Pacific coast of North America, and one from Hudson Bay, Ungava, and the lands to the north down the Atlantic coast.

The Atlantic birds winter mainly in the United States, and the Pacific birds are common in winter only as far south as southern California. The future of this species, therefore, is in our hands. It can be protected or exterminated by the people of the United States and Canada. In spring the eastern migration passes more to the westward, and the species appears in numbers on the Great Lakes, becoming rare to the northeast of Massachusetts.

The Red-backed Sandpiper feeds largely on worms, crustaceans, and insects.

EDWARD HOWE FORBUSH, in *Game Birds, Wild-Fowl and Shore Birds.*

SEMIPALMATED SANDPIPER

Ereunetes pusillus (*Linnæus*)

A. O. U. Number 246   See Color Plate 35

Other Names.— Peep; Little Peep; Sand-peep; Black-legged Peep; Ox-eye; Sand Ox-eye.

General Description.— Length, 6½ inches. Principal color above, chestnut; below, white with spots on breast. *Toes, webbed at base;* bill, straight and enlarged at tip; tail, double-notched.

Color.— ADULTS IN SUMMER: Above, varied with black, pale chestnut, ashy, and white, each feather dusky centrally with a reddish edge and whitish tip; *rump and upper tail-coverts, dusky,* more whitish on sides; central tail-feathers, brown, others, ashy-gray; wing-coverts and secondaries, brownish and rufous, edged with lighter; primaries, plain dusky; a dusky line from gape through and behind eye and a white line above; lower parts, pure white tinged with pale rufous on breast, where spotted with pale dusky; bill, black; legs, dusky green; iris, brown. ADULTS IN WINTER: Above, plain ashy, the feathers lighter-tipped; light ends of secondaries, less conspicuous as is also the line through eye; under parts, pure white with dusky spotting very faint; bill, legs, and iris, as in summer.

Nest and Eggs.— NEST: A hollow in the ground, lined with dry grass. EGGS: 3 or 4, from grayish to olive, usually boldly spotted and splashed with brown or chestnut, but sometimes finely dotted over entire surface.

Distribution.— North and South America; breeds from the Arctic coast of North America south to mouth of Yukon and to southern Ungava; winters from Texas and South Carolina through West Indies and Central America to Patagonia; migrates mainly east of the Rocky Mountains; casual in British Columbia, Pribilof Islands, and northeastern Siberia; accidental in Europe.

Photograph by H. K. Job

TURNSTONES AND SEMIPALMATED SANDPIPERS

Plate 35

Louis Agassiz Fuertes.

PECTORAL SANDPIPER
Pisobia maculata (Vieillot)
AUTUMN

WHITE-RUMPED SANDPIPER
Pisobia fuscicollis (Vieillot)
SPRING   AUTUMN

LEAST SANDPIPER
Pisobia minutilla (Vieillot)
SPRING   AUTUMN

All ½ nat. size

BAIRD'S SANDPIPER
Pisobia bairdi (Coues)

SEMIPALMATED SANDPIPER
Ereunetes pusillus (Linnaeus)
SPRING   AUTUMN

The Semipalmated Sandpiper is a sociable little bird usually found in company with other small Sandpipers, especially in that of the Least Sandpiper to which it is similar in general habits and appearance. It is partial to the open sand beaches — following the receding waves, seizing its minute crustacean food from the backwash, and cleverly eluding the returning surf. It is more of a sand bird and less of a mud bird than the Least Sandpiper. Positive identification in life is impossible unless a very close view is obtained, enabling the observer to see the semi-webbed feet.

It is constantly on the move, but, notwithstanding its great activity, it becomes very fat when food is abundant. On a windy day I have seen little groups of them settle down under the lee of a marsh tussock, preening their feathers and indulging in a siesta of repletion, keeping up a continuous peeping of contentment. These loafing spells become more frequent as the autumn days wane, and they are loath to leave a sunny nook under a bank sheltered from the strong northwest wind. I have sailed a sharpie within ten feet before they would take wing with querulous *tu-weets tu-weets* of resentment.

In its winter plumage the Western Sandpiper (*Ereunetes mauri*) can only be distinguished from the Semipalmated by its longer bill; in the summer the color of its upper parts is richer and more rusty with stronger markings. The curious and remarkable thing about this bird is that while it breeds in a narrow strip of territory along the northwestern coast of Alaska, it is a common winter resident in the southeastern United States from North Carolina to Florida.

This long journey across the continent is not paralleled by any other shore bird; it is, however, comparable to that of several species of ducks. Just what route this migration follows is unknown as there are no records from the interior to show which way the birds passed. The Western Sandpiper also winters from Lower California to Venezuela. The individuals that pass the winter in eastern South America probably migrate over the seas from Florida.

R. I. Brasher.

SANDERLING

Calidris leucophæa (*Pallas*)

A. O. U. Number 248   See Color Plates 33, 34

Other Names.— Ruddy Plover; Beach-bird; Surf Snipe; White Snipe; Beach Plover; Whitey; Bull Peep.

General Description.— Length, 8 inches. In summer, principal color above, chestnut; in winter, pale bluish-ash. Under parts always white, but the breast finely spotted in summer. *Only three toes* (hind toe missing); front toes with narrow marginal webs.

Color.— Adults in Summer: Entire upper parts, varied with black, ash, and chestnut, on back and shoulders each feather black centrally, broadly margined with reddish and tipped with white; wing-coverts, secondaries, and primaries ashy, the feathers lighter on edges of coverts, *secondaries, white-tipped,* and *a white spot at base of primaries;* rump, upper tail-coverts, and central tail-feathers, dusky, tipped and edged with ashy white; rest of tail-feathers nearly white; under parts, white, finely spotted with dusky and chestnut on sides of throat and breast; bill and legs, dusky; iris, brown. Adults in Winter: Upper parts, pale bluish-ash, the crown narrowly streaked with darker and the feathers on back fading into white on edges; shoulders and inner secondaries, with darker centers; wing-coverts, like back; *secondaries, largely white;* primaries, dusky, whitening at base; an indistinct dusky line from bill through eye; line above eye, cheeks, and entire under parts, pure white; bill and legs, black; iris, brown.

Nest and Eggs.— Nest: A depression in the ground, lined with grass or leaves. Eggs: 4, light olive-brown, speckled and spotted with different shades of brown, chiefly at large end.

Distribution.— Northern and southern hemispheres; breeds from Melville Island, Ellesmere Land, and northern Greenland to Point Barrow, Alaska, northern Mackenzie, Iceland, and in northern Siberia; winters from central California, Texas, Virginia, and Bermuda to Patagonia, and casually to Massachusetts and Washington; also from the Mediterranean, Burma, and Japan to South Africa and various Pacific islands, including Hawaii.

In the sunny days of September, where the white-maned horses of the sea, urged onward by the winds, charge in long rows and thunder down upon the sands of Cape Cod, the Sanderling is in its element. Matching the very sand in color it is almost invisible while squatted on the upper beach at high tide, waiting for the recession of the waters; but as the ebb begins, the little flock scatters along the shore, retreating before each wave, following down the backwash, until sometimes forced to fly by the oncoming surge, intent upon the flotsam and jetsam of the sea washed up for their delectation, spread for a brief moment upon the sloping sands and then carried back into the deep. The Sanderling neglects no opportunity. It follows its prey at times until up to its breast in the wave but always nimbly avoids immersion. Because of this habit, the Sanderling is beter known to many as the Surf Snipe. If disturbed the little flock rises, flies out over the surf and turns, flying up or down the beach, now low in some great sea hollow, now just skimming the crest of a foaming breaker, but they soon swing in again and drop-ping upon the sands resume their absorbing occupation.

The Sanderling's common note is a sharp *chit*. The bird may be distinguished from the little "Sand-peeps," which it much resembles, by its larger size, and from other Sandpipers by its light color and whitish head. When in flight it shows a line of conspicuous white spots on the wing. When in hand it may be readily distinguished from all other Sandpipers by the lack of a hind toe — a characteristic of the Plovers. In the spring and autumn migrations the Sanderling is not uncommon on the Great Lakes and is recorded from various parts of the Mississippi valley, but the sea is its first love. Its flights are largely made over the ocean and it can rest on the water if necessary and swim with the ease of a duck. EDWARD HOWE FORBUSH.

HUDSONIAN GODWIT

Limosa hæmastica (*Linnæus*)

A. O. U. Number 251 See Color Plate 38

Other Names.— Red-breasted Godwit; Ring-tailed Marlin; Spot-rump; Field Marlin; Goose-bird; Black-tailed Godwit; Black-tail; American Black-tailed Godwit; White-rump; Smaller Dough- or Doe-bird.

General Description.— Length, 16 inches. In summer, color of upper parts brownish-black mottled with lighter colors, under parts, chestnut; in winter, upper parts plain dull ashy, under parts lighter ash shaded with buffy; always a white spot just above the tail.

Color.— ADULTS IN SUMMER: Upper parts brownish-black with greenish gloss, variegated with rufous, yellowish, or white, lighter colors scalloping edges of feathers; *rump, blackish; upper tail-coverts, conspicuously white;* tail, black, white at base and white-tipped; head and neck, streaked with dusky; *under parts, rich chestnut crossed with numerous black bars,* these bars tending to spots on breast and neck; rear under parts, crossed also with white bars; bill, pale reddish, terminal third black; legs, bluish-gray; iris, brown. ADULTS IN WINTER: General plumage, plain dull ashy lightening on head, neck, and under parts where shaded with pale buffy; tail, as in summer; *upper tail-coverts, conspicuously white;* bill, flesh-colored with dusky tip; feet, bluish-gray. Plumages intermediate between the two are common.

Nest and Eggs.— NEST: A hollow scooped out of the ground, lined with a few leaves and grasses. EGGS: 4, dark olive-drab marked with still darker brownish shade of the ground color.

Distribution.— North and South America; breeds from the lower Anderson River southeast to central Keewatin; winters in Argentina, Patagonia, and the Falkland Islands; in migration occurs principally east of the Great Plains, most commonly on the Atlantic coast in autumn and in the Mississippi valley in spring; casual in Alaska.

The Godwits constitute a genus (*Limosa*) of the Snipe and Sandpiper family, and include about half a dozen species of which two are American birds. Two others, the Pacific Godwit (*Limosa lapponica baueri*) and the Black-tailed Godwit (*Limosa limosa*), are included in check-lists of North American avifauna — the first because a few individuals have strayed from Siberia to the islands off Alaska and there reproduced their kind, and the second because of its accidental occurrence in Greenland. The Godwits are characterized by a very long and slightly upward-curved bill, which is grooved nearly to the tip; the shanks are partly bare; the middle or outer toes are partly webbed; the wings are long and pointed; the tail in length equals or somewhat exceeds the wing. Their prevailing color is reddish or brownish, but there is considerable variation of color according to age, sex, and season.

Marked peculiarities of the genus are that the females are larger than the males, and that incubation is performed by the males. The birds are found in marshes, salt-water meadows, and along the shores of bays or lakes. They place their nests on the ground, but not invariably near water, and lay three or four eggs, of a generally drab hue, marked with dark brown. Their food, which consists of aquatic insects, shell-fish, worms and the like, they capture by probing the sand or mud with their long bills, or by following retreating waves and snatching up the small creatures thus left stranded.

Of the Hudsonian Godwit Mr. Forbush says: "During my boyhood I frequently heard old gunners about Boston tell their tales of the Goose-bird which was well and favorably known all along our coast. But it is impossible now to tell with certainty whether these tales referred to one or both of the Godwits. The Hudsonian Godwit is now less rare than the larger species, but few are seen or taken regularly on the Massachusetts coast. It is shy, like its larger relative, but a good bird caller finds no difficulty in luring it to his decoys.

" The breeding range and migration of this species are more or less shrouded in mystery. The eggs have been found once by MacFarlane in the Anderson River region, which proves that the birds breed near the coast of the Arctic Sea, and that is about all we know of its breeding range, except that it summers in Keewatin. We must assume that the species goes to South America by sea, like the Eskimo Curlew, and lands on Cape Cod and Long Island in numbers only when driven there by storms. It was considered rare by Wilson and Audubon, as it probably never was seen on the coast of the Middle and Southern States in any numbers unless driven in by a severe storm." (*Game Birds, Wild Fowl and Shore Birds.*)

The Hudsonian Godwit feeds to a considerable extent upon mosquitoes and horse-flies, as examination of its stomach has amply proved. It is therefore to be counted a useful bird, since the insects it destroys are known to be harmful.

MARBLED GODWIT

Limosa fedoa (*Linnæus*)

A. O. U. Number 249   See Color Plate 38

Other Names.— Great Marbled Godwit; Great Godwit; Red Curlew; Brant-bird; Marlin; Red Marlin; Brown Marlin; Spike-billed Curlew; Spike-bill; Badger-bird; Dough- or Doe-bird.

General Description.— Length, 21 inches; largest shore bird, except the Long-billed Curlew. Prevailing color, reddish, darker above; no white spot at base of tail. Bill curved slightly upward.

Color.— A light dull yellowish-rufous, browner and richer above but varying much in intensity with individuals; broad line over eye, sides of head, chin, and upper throat, more whitish; an indistinct dusky line from bill through and behind eye; crown, brownish; neck all around, spotted with dusky; upper parts with brownish-black center on each feather; rump, tail-coverts, and tail, barred with blackish and brown; primaries, rufous, outer webs and ends of a few outer ones dusky; *throat, breast, and sides, traversely barred with brown, the markings narrow;* bill, flesh-colored, dusky on ridge and terminal half; legs, bluish-ash; iris, brown.

Nest and Eggs.— NEST: On the ground in a dry field but not far from water; a depression, lined with grass. EGGS: 4, creamy-buff to light olive-drab, thickly spotted with various shades of umber brown.

Distribution.— North America; breeds from valley of the Saskatchewan south to North Dakota (formerly to Iowa and Wisconsin); winters from southern Lower California, Louisiana, Florida, and Georgia to Guatemala and Belize; casual in California in winter; in migration occurs on Pacific coast north to British Columbia, and on the Atlantic coast to the Maritime Provinces (formerly) and south to the Lesser Antilles; accidental in Alaska.

My first acquaintance with the Marbled Godwit was one beautiful June day in North Dakota, when I was wading in a large slough, deep not only in mud and water, but in the delights of inspecting nests of Canvas-back, Redhead, Ruddy Duck, and various other interesting water birds. All at once I began to hear loud outcries, and a flock of about twenty big brown birds with long straight bills swept past me and alighted in the grass just back from the shore. In great excitement I followed, and with my binoculars had a splendid view of them as they strode about on their stilt-like legs and caught insects.

Not until I visited Saskatchewan did I locate their breeding-grounds. There I found them nesting in scattered pairs, very commonly over the dry prairies. Like the large Curlew, they are partial to an alkaline country. Though they are always in the general vicinity of some slough, their actual nesting is back on the dry prairie.

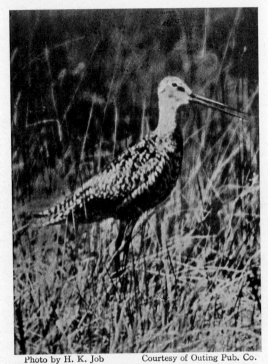

Photo by H. K. Job   Courtesy of Outing Pub. Co.

GREAT MARBLED GODWIT

On Saskatchewan prairie

Amid the rather short dry prairie grass a slight hollow is selected, a frail nest of grass constructed, and four large handsome eggs are deposited the latter part of May or early in June. The nest is not especially concealed, except by the vastness of the surroundings and the blending coloration of the brooding bird, who sits

quite close, so that the nest is found largely by accident. One day while driving our team and outfit over the trackless prairie, we were startled by an almost human scream, as a large brown bird fluttered from under the feet of the horses. Lucky it was that the nest was not trampled, so I was able to take photographs of it. My companion on the trip, A. C. Bent, afterwards found another nest on which the female sat so persistently that actually he lifted her from it by hand without having her make the slightest effort to escape.

When the young are hatched, the birds become almost as violent and noisy in their demonstrations as the Willet. They follow one around on the prairie, flying about, alighting nearby, and trotting off, ever shrieking that incessant din of *god-wit, god-wit,* from which I assume their name may have been derived. On one occasion a Godwit followed me nearly all day and kept up this screaming, until in the afternoon it got so hoarse that its voice would break into a sort of gasp or croak, as though it had a bad cold. Hence I nicknamed this absurd creature my " Catarrh-bird." Under these circumstances they were so tame that I was able to take with a reflecting camera all the photographs of them that I needed.

Formerly this species was quite abundant along the Atlantic coast on its migrations, whereas now it is only an accidental straggler. I have seen a few in winter in Louisiana, but most of them migrate beyond our borders to warmer climes. It is a handsome, interesting species which, like nearly all the larger shore birds, is in danger of extermination unless the radical measures already enacted are rigidly enforced.

HERBERT K. JOB.

The Marbled Godwit is of very real service to farmers by reason of the fact that it feeds freely upon various species of grasshoppers which are very injurious to crops. It should, therefore, receive adequate protection, especially during its breeding season.

GREATER YELLOW-LEGS

Totanus melanoleucus (*Gmelin*)

A. O. U. Number 254   See Color Plate 36

Other Names.— Big Tell-tale; Greater Tell-tale; Tell-tale Godwit; Yellow-shins; Winter Yellow-legs; Big Yellow-legs; Big Yellow-legged Plover; Greater Yellow-shanks; Cucu; Big Cucu; Long-legged Tattler; Stone-bird; Stone Snipe; Yelper.

General Description.— Length, 15 inches. Color above, blackish-brown; below, white with brown spots on breast and neck. Bill longer than head, slender, and either straight or with end half very slightly curved upward; *legs and toes long and slender.*

Color.—ADULTS: Head, neck, breast, and lower parts, white streaked with dusky brown on forehead, crown, and back of neck, spotted with arrowhead marks on front of neck, breast, and sides; chin, throat, and sides of head, with small dusky markings; a conspicuous white eye-ring with a dusky spot in front; lores, whitish; *upper parts from neck, wing-coverts, and secondaries, blackish-brown,* each feather broadly edged and tipped with lighter, greater coverts and secondaries, barred; quills, plain dusky brown; *rump and tail, white,* the latter narrowly streaked with light brown; bill, greenish-dusky, lighter basally; *legs, light chrome yellow.* YOUNG: Similar to adults, but lighter above, the streaks below limited to the neck and upper breast, and the legs yellow.

Nest and Eggs.—NEST: A mere depression, usually unlined, in the ground. EGGS: 4, grayish or deep buff, spotted with rich dark brown and lavender over the entire surface but more thickly at large end.

Distribution.— North and South America; breeds from Lake Iliamna, Alaska, and southern Mackenzie to southern British Columbia, Ungava, Labrador, and Anticosti Island; winters from southern California, Texas, Louisiana, and Georgia (casually North Carolina) south to Patagonia; occurs in Bermuda in migration.

On Hatteras Island, North Carolina, about five miles north of its famous lighthouse, there is, in ordinary seasons, an extended series of shallow, grassy beach-ponds. During the month lookout at all times. They watch and listen and are first to give the alarm. With shrill cries they leap upon the wing and go flying away, generally collecting into a company as they proceed.

Drawing by R. I. Brasher

GREATER YELLOW-LEGS (¼ nat. size)

Easily attracted to decoys, hence a favorite with gunners

of May, these are inhabited by large numbers of shore birds of many kinds. I have seen here at least ten thousand on the wing at a time when disturbed from their feeding by the discharge of a gun.

Among the feathered squadrons there are always many Yellow-legs. When Hudsonian Curlews are absent the Greater Yellow-legs is the largest bird among them. This gathering place at Cape Hatteras is similar to many others all up and down the coast. Yellow-legs are the sentinels of such assemblies, and keep a sharp

Sometimes they do not go far, but circle back and fly about in the offing, rarely ceasing to call. In motion their wing-beats are deliberate, and, when approaching others among which they are preparing to settle, they have a way of slowly sailing on extended wings that renders them an easy shot for the gunner.

Yellow-legs are extensively hunted, although as food their flesh does not rank so high as some others of the Sandpiper family, as for example Woodcock and Upland Plovers. They are shot chiefly over wooden models cut out and painted to represent the bird and stuck up in the mud near a shooting blind. To these decoys they often come with little hesitation, especially if to this deception the hunter adds an additional lure by imitating their call with a fair degree of accuracy.

There is a widespread idea that these birds appear later in the autumn than the Lesser Yellow-legs, so they are much called " Winter Yellow-legs." " Tattler " and " Tell-tale " are also popular names for this species. The breeding grounds are mainly north of the United States, to which territory they retire in May, but by July many individuals are back. In fact, the tide of the migration of the Yellow-legs that ebbs and flows along our coast and interior waterways, seems never to cease, for every

month in the year they are found in many Southern States. One reason for this is the fact that not all are mated any one season and numbers of the unpaired birds do not go north at all. In the Gulf States many Greater Yellow-legs pass the winter, but the great bulk go farther afield and scatter throughout the lands to the south as far as Patagonia.

Their food consists of minnows and such insects and other small forms of life as are obtainable in and about the water. Where bars and mud flats are exposed at low tide, there the Yellow-legs are wont to come. Along the shores of ponds, lakes, and rivers of the interior they are found, and in fact, few, if any, shore birds have so extended a range.

T. GILBERT PEARSON.

YELLOW-LEGS

Totanus flavipes (*Gmelin*)

A. O. U. Number 255　　See Color Plate 36

Other Names.— Common Yellow-legs; Lesser Yellow-legs; Little Tell-tale; Lesser Tell-tale; Lesser Yellow-shanks; Yellow-legged Plover; Summer Yellow-legs; Little Yelper; Small Cucu; Little Stone-bird; Little Stone Snipe; Lesser Long-legged Tattler.

General Description.— Length, 11 inches. An exact miniature of the Greater Yellow-legs, from which it differs only in size.

Nest and Eggs.— NEST: A depression in the ground under shelter of tuft of grass or bushes, or in the open. EGGS: 4, creamy, buffy or clay-color, usually boldly marked, splashed, or blotched with burnt

umber, blackish, and lavender, but sometimes with small spots over entire surface.

Distribution.— North and South America; breeds from Kotzebue Sound, Alaska, northern Mackenzie, central Keewatin, and southern Ungava to the valley of the upper Yukon, southern Saskatchewan, and northern Quebec; winters in Argentina, Chile, and Patagonia, and casually in Mexico, Florida, and the Bahamas; in migration occurs mainly east of the Rocky Mountains (rare in spring on the Atlantic coast) and in the Pribilof Islands, Greenland, and Bermuda; accidental in Great Britain.

Photograph by H. K. Job

YELLOW-LEGS IN MANITOBA SLOUGH

Plate 36

SOLITARY SANDPIPER (Wilson)
Helodromas solitarius solitarius

GREATER YELLOW-LEGS (Gmelin)
Totanus melanoleucus

SPOTTED SANDPIPER (Linnaeus)
Actitis macularia

IMMATURE   ADULT

SUMMER PLUMAGES
All ¼ nat. size

YELLOW-LEGS (Gmelin)
Totanus flavipes

The Lesser Yellow-legs formerly was one of the most numerous of all the shore birds of North America, and still holds its numbers better than many other species.

No longer ago than 1870 the flocks were quite numerous about some of the inland ponds and lakes in Massachusetts in August, particularly in dry seasons, when the ponds were low. I remember that they were always watchful, but they were readily attracted by a whistled imitation of their call, and if even one was shot out of the flock the others hovered about until many had paid the penalty of their sympathetic concern. Of late years at those same ponds, a single bird or a pair is seen occasionally, but the flocks are gone, perhaps never to return. Its habits are similar to those of the Greater Yellow-legs, and it feeds largely on insects, including ants.

EDWARD HOWE FORBUSH, in *Game Birds, Wild-Fowl and Shore Birds.*

SOLITARY SANDPIPER

Helodromas solitarius solitarius (*Wilson*)

A. O. U. Number 256   See Color Plate 36

Other Names.— Green Sandpiper; American Green Sandpiper; Wood Sandpiper; American Wood Sandpiper; Solitary Tattler.

General Description.— Length, 9 inches. Color above, dark olive-brown, speckled with white; below, white with dark spots on breast and neck; the barred tail-feathers are very conspicuous in flight. *Bill, slender, straight, and longer than head.* Seldom found elsewhere than near inland lakes and woodland streams.

Color.—*Above, dark glossy olive-brown* streaked with whitish on head and neck, elsewhere finely speckled with white; upper tail-coverts, whitish, heavily spotted with color of back; middle tail-feathers, brownish-olive, *remainder, white, barred with 3 or 4 bands of olive-dusky; below, white;* breast and sides of neck, shaded with brownish, streaked and spotted with dusky; sides, with some bars of dusky; bill, dusky-greenish; legs, dull greenish; iris, brown, rarely white.

Distribution.— North and South America; summers from central Keewatin, northern Ungava, and Newfoundland south to Nebraska, Illinois, Indiana, Ohio, and Pennsylvania; probably breeds regularly in the northern part of its range, locally and casually in the southern part; winters from the West Indies to Argentina; recorded from Greenland, Bermuda, and Great Britain.

That dark and dainty sprite, the Solitary Sandpiper, is almost the only Sandpiper of the wooded wilderness. It is a bird of mountain, forest, hill, and plain, but is rarely, if ever, seen on the sandy beaches of the sea, where other Sandpipers play. It is not so solitary as its name would imply but it frequents solitary places where other Sandpipers seldom or never appear. It is seen singly or in small scattered companies of a few individuals about mountain lakes or streams, near little ponds, ditches, or muddy, stagnant pools, almost anywhere throughout its range, and even occasionally on tidal streams and in salt marshes. At times it frequents the same feeding ground with Yellow-legs or Spotted Sandpipers, but may be distinguished from the former by its much smaller size and dark legs and from the latter by the great quantity of white on its spread tail and its darker upper parts. Its notes, *peet-weet, peet-weet,* are very similar to those of the Spotted Sandpiper and it has the same habit of nodding or bowing its head but its hinder parts are not quite as active and expressive as are those of its spotted congener.

There is some uncertainty about our knowledge of the breeding habits of this bird. It has been reported as nesting on high mountains, on the ground, in the nests of other birds, and in hollow trees, all of which may be true, but at the present time we have little reliable data regarding its home life. In the breeding season it is seen singly or more rarely in pairs and then it is known to alight upon the tree-tops and to emit a rather weak and ineffective flight song. It is graceful and elegant, moves lightly and easily and flies swiftly and often wildly, erratically, and high in the air like a Snipe. When the ponds and lakes are low during a long drought in August or September, the Solitary Sandpiper may be seen along the exposed mud flats and sandbars, often going into the water up to its belly. In the autumn it has a habit of wading in stagnant ditches and stirring up the bottom by advancing one foot and shaking it rapidly. This is done so delicately that it does not roil the water, but it starts from their hiding places the minute organisms that lie concealed there, and the bird, plunging in its bill and head, often clear to the eyes, catches them deftly as they flee from the disturbance. This bird seems to feed very largely on aquatic insects, small mollusks, etc., but it destroys grasshoppers, moths, and other destructive land insects, some of which it pursues and catches easily on the wing.

EDWARD HOWE FORBUSH.

The Western, or Cinnamon, Solitary Sandpiper (*Helodromas solitarius cinnamomeus*) is not always distinguishable from the eastern Solitary Sandpiper. It averages larger and the spots on the upper parts are or approach a cinnamon brown. It occurs in western North and South America, breeding north of the United States.

WILLET
Catoptrophorus semipalmatus semipalmatus (*Gmelin*)
A. O. U. Number 258   See Color Plate 37

Other Names.— Semipalmated Snipe; Spanish Plover; Stone Curlew; Duck Snipe; Will-willet; Pillwill-willet; Bill-willy; Humility; Pied-wing Curlew.

General Description.— Length, 16 inches. Color, gray, light below and dark above, with dark markings; a good deal of white on wings, and the rump and upper tail-coverts white. Bill, slender, straight, and longer than head; *toes, webbed at base.*

Color.— ADULTS IN SUMMER: General color, ashy, lighter below; crown and back of neck streaked with dusky; shoulders and back with spots and specks of the same color; *rump, upper tail-coverts, and tail, white,* the tail barred with narrow traverse streaks of brown; primaries, dusky-brown with a *large white space at base,* this color invading secondaries; primaries beneath, blackish, the white showing two conspicuous areas in flight; lores, whitish; a dusky streak from bill to eye; throat, narrowly streaked; breast and sides, thickly marked, with narrow traverse arrowhead bars; bill, bluish-horn, blackening toward tip; legs, pale lavender; iris, brown. ADULTS IN WINTER: Above, light ashy with a tinge of brown, with little or no darker marking; upper tail-coverts, white; wing, similar to summer plumage; below, pale ashy or white shaded with gray on breast and sides; sides of head, pale brown; bill, paler than in summer; a white eye-ring.

Nest and Eggs.— NEST: In a tussock of grass or weeds, close to the water, in fresh- or salt-water marshes; a carelessly built structure of small reeds and grass. EGGS: 4, greenish-white or dark brownish-olive, boldly marked with spots in various shades of brown and lavender.

Distribution.— North and South America; breeds from Virginia (formerly Nova Scotia) south to Florida and the Bahamas; winters from the Bahamas to Brazil and Peru; accidental in Bermuda and Europe.

Drawing by R. I. Brasher

WILLET (⅓ nat. size)

A noisy, self-assertive bird

Here is a noisy, self-assertive bird, if there ever was one. Willet life, literally, is a perfect "scream." And yet this forward creature has been nicknamed "Humility," because it probes for worms in the humble mud in the intervals between the periods when it lifts up the voice on high. Constitutionally, the bird seems unable to keep its mouth shut, as though it had blown off the safety valve and was compelled to keep going, from sheer inability to stop, with a compelling motor power behind. Its relatives, the two species of Yellow-legs, have somewhat the same inquisitive and assertive dispositions, though apparently in lesser degree. Gunners have frequently lodged complaint that the noisy Willet warns away their game.

The acme of its fantastic performance comes during the nesting season, particularly when the young are abroad. Then as long as one is minded to remain on the marsh, the birds, fairly beside themselves, fly about yelping and screaming. On Smith's Island, Va., I watched one, perched on the dead fork of a bush out on a broad marsh. With absolute mechanical precision, for a quarter of an hour at a stretch, with hardly an apparent pause to get breath, the bill would open and shut, like clock work, to the tune of *yip, yip, yip,* and so on, rapidly reiterated. When it took to wing it would start up its *pill-willet* cries.

Usually the nest is hard to find. I have watched the birds on the marshes of the southern coast and by the sloughs on western prairies, but never had the luck to locate a nest till about May 10, 1904, when I was on a cruise along the coast of South Carolina. We landed on an uninhabited island, mostly marsh, but with a beach in front, backed by a narrow ridge of sand between beach and marsh. Clumps of coarse beach grass grew all along this ridge, and from nearly every other clump, as we advanced, a Willet sprang from her four large dark mottled eggs, until on that one island we had examined over fifty nests. These were frail structures of dry grass, lining hollows scratched in the sand under the grass clumps.

It need not be assumed from this that the Willet is an abundant bird, for it is another of our rapidly "vanishing shore birds." Formerly it was common along our Atlantic coast, but now the sight of one is a rarity.

During the fall migration, it is seen casually in muddy sloughs or on the flats and marshes of the sea-coast more reserved than is its wont, as

Photo by H. K. Job   Courtesy of Houghton Mifflin Co.

WILLET ON NEST

though sobered by the thought of exile from the fields of its vocal exploits. During winter it is absent on its annual junket to varied southern scenes as far remote as Brazil and Peru.

HERBERT K. JOB.

The Western Willet (*Catoptrophorus semipalmatus inornatus*) differs from the eastern Willet in larger size and in shades of color, but its general appearance and habits are the same. This geographical variety breeds from central Oregon, southern Alberta, and southern Manitoba, south to northern California, central Colorado, southern South Dakota, and northern Iowa, and on the coasts of Texas and Louisiana; in winter it occurs from central California, Texas, Louisiana, and the Gulf coast of Florida to Mexico and Lower California. It is sometimes found in the Atlantic State during migration.

UPLAND PLOVER

Bartramia longicauda (*Bechstein*)

A. O. U. Number 261   See Color Plate 37

Other Names.— Bartramian Sandpiper; Bartram's Sandpiper; Bartram's Plover; Upland Sandpiper; Uplander; Hill-bird; Field Plover; Highland Plover; Pasture Plover; Grass Plover; Prairie Plover; Prairie Pigeon; Prairie Snipe; Papabotte; Quaily.

General Description.— Length, 12 inches. Color

above, blackish-brown; below, grayish-white. *Bill, shorter than head; gape, wide; neck, long; tail, long and graduated;* outer and middle toes webbed at base; inner toe free. Found mainly in pastures and old fields away from water, even at the sea-shore.

Color.—Above, blackish-brown, all feathers edged with tawny or whitish, the brown prevailing on crown and back, the lighter edgings of latter producing a streaked effect; on long inner secondaries, the dark color mere small bars; wing-coverts marked with whitish; primaries, dusky, *outer one barred with white;* rump and upper tail-coverts, plain brownish-black; middle tail-feathers, dark brown with rufous edges and irregularly barred; rest of tail-feathers, orange-brown with numerous broken bars or spots of black and a subterminal black bar; line over eye and under parts, grayish-white, tinged with yellowish-brown on breast and sides of head; breast and sides, with each feather marked by a brownish arrowhead-shaped spot; bill, yellowish-green, dusky at tip; legs, yellowish-olive; iris, brown.

Nest and Eggs.— NEST: A slight depression in open dry prairies, lined or not with grass. EGGS: 4, pale buffy or cream, spotted with dark brown and lavender.

Distribution.— North and South America; breeds from northwestern Alaska, southern Mackenzie, central Keewatin, central Wisconsin, southern Michigan, southern Ontario, and southern Maine to southern Oregon, northern Utah, central Oklahoma, southern Missouri, southern Indiana, and northern Virginia; winters on the pampas of South America to Argentina; in migration occurs north to Newfoundland and in Europe; accidental in Australia.

My early recollections of the Upland Plover, once a familiar game bird, are of open rolling grassy tracts on Cape Cod, Mass., interspersed with patches of bayberry bushes, in late July and August, and some very shy brown birds that, despite most of my attempts to stalk them, would rise wildly well out of gunshot and with shrill cries fly on to the next hillside, alighting and watching in an erect attitude, their heads projecting from the short sparse grass.

Upland Plover shooting is now becoming a thing of the past, under the protection of Federal Law. This is as it should be, for here we have another species which is in great danger of extermination. Little by little, both through excessive shooting and by the destruction of nests in cultivated areas, it has been growing more and more scarce. Once it was a common bird in the Eastern States, but now only an occasional lone pair is found there. The grassy prairies of the Northwest are now its principal breeding ground, but owing to their increased reclamation for agricultural purposes, it is being further pushed out. This is a lamentable declension from the days when in New England it was comparable in abundance to the Meadowlark, and pairs were nesting in nearly every field.

Classing it as a "shore bird," is only on the basis of structure and relationship, for otherwise there is no bird which is less fond of the vicinity of water. Its haunts are dry grassy fields, where it lives chiefly on insects injurious to the fields, such as cutworms and grasshoppers. Here is where it nests, the last of May and early June. The female sits closely, and on the prairies of North Dakota, Manitoba, and Saskatchewan I have found nests only by flushing the brooding bird, which allows one almost to step upon her before she will leave. The nest is in rather thick bunches of prairie grass, a simple affair of dry grass leaves. Four is the invariable number of eggs which I have found. The bird is almost exactly the color of dead grass, and even when the nest has been found and revisited, it is astonishing how hard it is to discern the brooding bird. In one case she allowed me to open by hand the grass which covered her, set up the camera and photograph her within two feet of the lens. Shy as the birds become under persecution, they are gentle in nesting time. On the western prairies they are much less shy than in the East.

As soon as the young are able to fly, in July, they all begin to migrate south, and most of them are gone before August is far advanced. This was the reason why the older laws allowed Upland Plover shooting in July. In the summer of 1912 I was in Manitoba. At the opening of this early hunting season, a gunner came out near our camp and shot nearly forty Upland Plovers, while his boy picked up little downy chicks and carried them in his pocket. I reported this to the head authorities, who are excellent conservationists, and the law was changed. It will need the best of care, by every State and Province, and the coöperation of public sentiment, to save from extinction this beautiful and valuable species. HERBERT K. JOB.

The investigations of the Government biologist show that the Upland Plover is naturally an industrious destroyer of many different species of noxious insects. There can be no doubt that the bird feeds upon the highly destructive locust, and also upon grasshoppers, the clover-root curculio, bill-bugs (which destroy much corn), crawfish, which are a pest in corn and rice fields and also weaken levees by their burrowing, and various grubs which damage garden truck, corn, and cotton crops.

Plate 37

Louis Agassiz Fuertes.

WILLET
Catoptrophorus semipalmatus semipalmatus (Gmelin)
SPRING   AUTUMN

UPLAND PLOVER
Bartramia longicauda (Bechstein)
BUFF-BREASTED SANDPIPER
Tryngites subruficollis (Vieillot)

All ⅔ nat. size

BUFF-BREASTED SANDPIPER

Tryngites subruficollis (*Vieillot*)

A. O. U. Number 262   See Color Plate 37

Other Name.— Hill Grass-bird.

General Description.— Length, 8 inches. Color below, buff; above, dusky brown. Bill shorter than head, slender, hard at tip; gape wide; tail rounded, central feathers projecting; *toes not webbed.* Prefers dry upland fields and is rarely seen on the shore.

Color.—ADULTS IN SUMMER: Above, dusky-brown, finely streaked on head with pale yellowish-buff, this streaking running down back of neck to feathers of back and shoulders which are edged and tipped with tawny; primaries, secondaries, and coverts, grayish-brown, the last two with lighter edges; *inner webs of primaries and both webs of secondaries, pearly white marbled with black;* lores, sides of head to above eye, throat, breast, and all under parts, plain buff unmarked except by a few brownish spots on side and chest; central tail-feathers, brown; others, rufous with a subterminal dusky bar; bill, dusky; legs, dusky-greenish; iris, brown. ADULTS IN WINTER: The broad edgings of feathers above, narrowed to whitish semi-circles; under parts, whiter; wing and tail, as in summer.

Nest and Eggs.— NEST: A depression in the ground, sparsely lined with grass and withered leaves. EGGS: 4, grayish or pale olive-buff, sharply spotted with rich burnt umber.

Distribution.— North and South America; breeds along the Arctic coast from northern Alaska to northern Keewatin; winters in Argentina and Uruguay; most abundant in migration in the Mississippi valley; occasional on the Atlantic coast in fall; casual on the Pacific coast north to St. Michael, Alaska, and to northeastern Siberia; straggles to Bermuda and Europe.

The Buff-breasted Sandpiper is rather a rare bird upon the Atlantic coast, and possibly always has been, as it breeds in northern Alaska and its main migration route does not touch the Atlantic coast.

Formerly it was very abundant in Texas, and still is common there, but decreasing. The reports of its decrease in the West are very impressive. Apparently it is on the way to extinction. It is usually a very gentle and confiding bird and pays little attention to the hunter. It is valuable as an insect eater, particularly in the West, but in its pursuit this fact is overlooked and its food value only is considered. Doctor Hatch found it living upon crickets, grasshoppers, ants and their "eggs," and other insects, and on minute mollusks taken from the shores of shallow ponds in the warmest part of the day.

EDWARD HOWE FORBUSH, in *Game Birds, Wild-Fowl and Shore Birds.*

SPOTTED SANDPIPER

Actitis macularia (*Linnæus*)

A. O. U. Number 263   See Color Plate 36

Other Names.— Peep; Peetweet; Teeter-peep; Teeter-tail; Teeterer; Tip-up; Tilt-up; Sand Lark; See-saw; Sand-peep; Sand Snipe; River Snipe.

General Description.— Length, 7 inches. Color above, ashy-olive; under parts pure white, unspotted in winter, but in summer with round black spots. Bill straight, slender, and about as long as head; outer and middle toes, webbed at base; inner toes, free; tail, rounded and half as long as wing. This is the only Sandpiper which has *large* and distinct spots on its under parts; it nearly always teeters when alarmed; and in flight shows a white line on the wings. Found most often near streams and ponds.

Color.—ADULTS IN SUMMER: Crown and upper parts, including wings, soft ashy-olive, finely varied with dusky, in streaks on head and neck, elsewhere in wavy irregular crossbars; line from bill to eye and back of it, olive-dusky; a line over eye and entire under parts, pure white; *under parts, as far as under tail-coverts, with numerous sharp, circular black spots,* more crowded on the female; primaries and secondaries, brownish-black, largely *white* at base, not showing in folded wing; feet, grayish flesh color; bill, flesh color with black tip; iris, brown surrounded with a white ring. ADULTS IN WINTER, AND YOUNG: As in summer, but without marking above or below; breast, slightly grayish and wing-coverts more strongly outlined with lighter.

Nest and Eggs.— NEST: A depression in the ground in the vicinity of water; rather well constructed of grass, leaves, and weed stems. EGGS: 4, creamy, buffy, or grayish, blotched with blackish and purplish-gray.

Distribution.— North and South America; breeds from tree limit in northwestern Alaska, northern Mackenzie, central Keewatin, northern Ungava, and Newfoundland south to southern California, Arizona, southern Texas, southern Louisiana, and northern South Carolina; winters from California, Louisiana, and South Carolina to southern Brazil and central Peru; straggles to Great Britain and Helgoland.

Probably there is no shore bird more widely and intimately known all over the country than the Spotted Sandpiper, which is popularly nick-

Photo by S. A. Lottridge

NEST AND EGGS OF SPOTTED SANDPIPER

named "Teeter" or "Tip-up," from its nervous habit of constantly tilting its body, and "Peet-weet" from its notes. As typically seen, it runs along the shore of a pond or stream, stops and wags its head and body up and down several times, then runs again, and, if further approached, flies out over the water with a peculiar quivering flight, the wings being held straight out, with alternations of quivering downward beats and brief intervals of soaring. Usually it circles back and alights not far from the same place. It is not by any means, however, confined to the vicinity of open water, but is often seen in meadows, and even on dry uplands, particularly in cultivated fields where crops are growing.

Most shore birds breed far to the north, but here is one species which is remarkably impartial in its topography. Though it breeds in northern Alaska, it also does so nearly all over the United States, even down on the Gulf of Mexico, alike on seaboard and interior. In this praiseworthy originality it is entirely unique, surpassing even the Robin, which does not breed so far south.

In the northern States I have usually found fresh eggs during the last week of May, generally four in number. The nest may be found in many sorts of situations. Probably that most preferred is just up from the shore of a pond or stream, under a bunch of grass or a clump of weeds. Usually nests are quite well hidden, but I have seen them easily visible, under sparse weeds on open gravelly shore. However, they are often placed quite a distance from water, in pastures or among crops, quite often in fields of corn or potatoes.

Some shore birds "act up" to draw away intruders from their nests, when these are being approached. The Spotted Sandpiper makes no such attempt until after being flushed, when both birds appear and run about anxiously.

The female is a close sitter, and discloses her secret by fluttering out when closely approached. Owing to this habit, I have inspected dozens of nests, whereas, if the bird would discreetly withdraw, the well-hidden nest would seldom be found, except when placed in cultivated fields.

Photo by H. K. Job

SPOTTED SANDPIPER ON NEST

Some of these birds winter on our southern coasts, but the majority pass on further, penetrating into Brazil and Peru. HERBERT K. JOB.

LONG-BILLED CURLEW

Numenius americanus *Bechstein*

A. O. U. Number 264   See Color Plate 38

Other Names.— Big Curlew; Hen Curlew; Old Hen Curlew; Sickle-bill; Sickle-billed Curlew; Sabre-bill; Smoker.

General Description.— Length, 26 inches. Prevailing color red, darker above than below. Its appearance is similar to that of the Marbled Godwit, but it is easily distinguishable from the latter by its longer and *curved* bill, the upper section of which is longer than the lower and slightly knobbed at the tip. Toes, webbed at base.

Color.— Crown, rufous-brown with blackish streaks; back and shoulders, brownish-black varied with cinnamon-brown, each feather having several indentations of this color; wing-coverts, with more rufous and whitish; secondaries and tail-feathers, pale brownish barred with dusky; inner primaries, rufous-brown, changing to dusky on outer ones; entire under parts, varying from yellowish-brown to rufous, usually deep-ening to chestnut under wings and fading to whitish on throat and sides of head; breast, with dusky streaks tending to arrowheads; bill, dusky above, pale flesh-color below; legs, bluish-gray. Very constant in plumage irrespective of age, sex, or season.

Nest and Eggs.— NEST: A grass-lined depression in the ground on open prairies. EGGS: 3 or 4, pale buffy to grayish-buff, spotted with darker brown and lavender.

Distribution.— North America; breeds from central British Columbia, southern Saskatchewan, and Manitoba to northeastern California, northern New Mexico, and northwestern Texas; winters from central California and southern Arizona south to Guatemala, and on the Atlantic coast from South Carolina to Florida, Louisiana, and Texas; formerly a regular migrant north to Massachusetts and rarely to Newfoundland, now a straggler east of the Mississippi, north of Florida; casual in the West Indies.

From being an abundant species on the south Atlantic coast a century ago, this interesting, spectacular species, the Long-billed Curlew, is now almost unknown in the eastern United States. The only time I ever saw it in the East was about 1886, in August, over the marshes of Marshfield, Mass., when I saw a single wedge-shaped flock of these great birds with absurdly long down-curved bills. Audubon found them coming to roost at night by thousands, on November 10, 1831, on an island off the coast of South Carolina. Seeing that, in May, 1904, probably on the same island, I saw some ten thousand Hudsonian Curlews come to roost at dusk, I could not but wonder if he could have been mistaken in the species. At any rate, where it was once well known it is now unknown. The species is in real danger of extinction, and it is well that the Federal Law now places them under absolute protection.

My personal experience with this great Curlew has been chiefly in summer, in the nesting season, on the prairies of Saskatchewan. Evidently it is gradually disappearing, for during extended explorations in North Dakota, from May to October, I failed to see a single one. Various settlers told me that it had been common in " the eighties " and previously, but that it had since become rare. It seems to prefer those prairie regions where the soil has an alkaline tinge and the sloughs are surrounded by the typical bare alkaline flats. In such regions in Saskatchewan

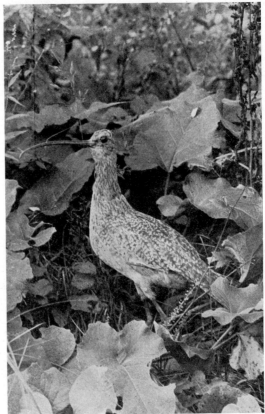

Courtesy of S. A. Lottridge

LONG-BILLED CURLEW

This interesting species is now almost unknown in the eastern
United States

I found them in scattered pairs. Conspicuous in size, they also make themselves so by their reiterated loud, high-pitched, trilling cries, especially when they have young or eggs in the vicinity. They are shyer than the Marbled Godwits which share with them these alkaline plains.

Photo by H. K. Job   Courtesy of Outing Pub. Co.

YOUNG LONG-BILLED CURLEWS

The nest is a simple hollow in the prairie, amid rather sparse grass, lined with dry stems. Three or four very large eggs make the usual complement. It is hard to find, as the male bird gives the alarm when an intruder approaches, and the female joins him. Perhaps they become some-

what accustomed to the cowboys who ride around after the cattle, since all of the nests which I knew about were discovered by cowboys on horseback through flushing the bird from the nest. Though the anxious parents are in evidence, flying or trotting about at a distance and whistling, they give no definite clue as to the direction in which the chosen spot is located.

One evening at sundown after a forty mile drive over the plains, we were approaching a ranch, in rolling prairie country, when we noticed two birds squatting together in the short grass. They proved to be young of this species, quite large, yet still in the downy stage, very pretty and interesting. There was just enough light to take photographs of them by time-exposures. Meanwhile the parents were flying about, swooping angrily past us at close range, screaming most vociferously. Altogether it was a spectacle which I would not have missed for a good deal.

HERBERT K. JOB.

The Long-billed Curlew is evidently a persistent eater of the highly injurious locust, as is shown by the fact that ten stomachs of the bird were found by Government experts to contain forty-eight locusts each. This would be sufficient reason for giving it a place among the birds of great economic value to man. But the bird's usefulness does not stop here, for it is known to feed freely also upon various injurious grasshoppers, and it is more than likely that its diet includes other noxious insects, so that its usefulness is beyond question of a doubt.

HUDSONIAN CURLEW

Numenius hudsonicus *Latham*

A. O. U. Number 265   See Color Plate 38

Other Names.— Jack Curlew; Jack; Striped-head; Crooked-billed Marlin; American Whimbrel; Short-billed Curlew.

General Description.— Length, 18 inches. Can be distinguished from young Long-billed Curlews only at close range.

Color.— *Top of head, uniform blackish-brown with well-defined whitish central and side stripes;* a distinct streak of dusky from bill through and behind eye and a pronounced broad whitish streak above it; upper parts, blackish-brown variegated with white, ocher, or pale brown in the same pattern as the Long-billed Curlew but tone less rufous; primaries and their coverts, dusky, the former *broken-barred with paler;* tail, ashy-brown with a number of narrow blackish bars; beneath, very pale brownish-white; breast, with

dusky streaks changing to arrowheads or broken bars on sides; bill, dusky, yellowish below for about one-third its length, darkest at tip; feet, grayish-blue; iris, dark brown.

Nest and Eggs.— NEST: Like that of Long-billed Curlew. EGGS: 4, creamy to pale olive-gray, boldly marked with shades of umber-brown.

Distribution.— North and South America; breeds on the coast of Alaska from mouth of Yukon to Kotzebue Sound, and on the coast of northern Mackenzie; winters from Lower California to southern Honduras, from Ecuador to southern Chile, and from British Guiana to mouth of the Amazon; migrates mainly along the Pacific and Atlantic coasts; rare in the interior; casual on the Pribilof Islands and in Greenland and Bermuda; accidental in Spain.

Plate 38

LONG-BILLED CURLEW
Numenius americanus Bechstein
HUDSONIAN CURLEW
Numenius hudsonicus Latham

ESKIMO CURLEW
Numenius borealis (J. R. Forster)

All ⅞ nat. size

MARBLED GODWIT
Limosa fedoa (Linnaeus)
HUDSONIAN GODWIT   SPRING
Limosa haemastica (Linnaeus)

Why should the long, slender bills of the Curlew and the Ibis be bent downward? One might as well ask why the similar bills of the Godwit and the Avocet should be bent upward and those of the Woodcock and the Snipe remain almost straight. These questions never have been satisfactorily answered. They remain among the fascinating problems of ornithology yet to be solved.

The Hudsonian Curlew, or Jack Curlew, as it August and reach their maximum numbers there late in the month.

When feeding they usually scatter about over the ground, moving slowly and sedately, except when in pursuit of some particularly lively prey. Berries they pick from the bushes with their bills. They feed in fields where grasshoppers abound and in blueberry patches. Along the coasts, where the species is most common, the flocks frequent flats, beaches and low grassy

Drawing by R. I. Brasher

HUDSONIAN CURLEW (¼ nat. size)

It is extremely shy and difficult to stalk

is commonly called by gunners, is an illustration of the Darwinian theory. It has survived, while other species have disappeared, because it was fitter — better able to avoid the hunter. No bird is more exposed to persecution, as it migrates the entire length of North and South America, from the Arctic Ocean to the Straits of Magellan, but it frequents places rather remote from the centers of civilization, breeds in the Far North, is extremely shy and difficult to stalk, and so perpetuates its race.

The main lines of its migration are down the east and west shores of both continents but there is also a scattering flight through the interior. Little is known about the bird's breeding habits but as soon as the young are grown the slow migration begins. The main flight moves from the west coast of Hudson Bay to the shores of New England and southward. The birds appear on the islands of the St. Lawrence River early in hills not far from the sea. When flying to or from their feeding grounds they usually pass about thirty yards high, except on windy days, when they fly close to the ground or water. In New England they feed at the edge of the water or wade in shallow pools picking up their food with the head apparently held sidewise. Fiddler crabs and the large gray sand spiders form an important part of their diet. These Curlews also consume June bugs and other beetles and some worms. They are sometimes seen singly, flying and circling high in air, and occasionally a small flock is noted migrating like a flock of Geese or Ducks. Formery they were numerous on Cape Cod and Nantucket, but now-a-days most of them pass out to sea, though many still visit the marshes of the Carolinas. In spring they have a soft, rather mournful call, *cur-lew,* and the alarm note is *pip-pip-pip-pip*.

EDWARD HOWE FORBUSH.

HUDSONIAN CURLEW

Courtesy of *Recreation*

ESKIMO CURLEW

Numenius borealis (*J. R. Forster*)

A. O. U. Number 266   See Color Plate 38

Other Names.— Fute; Dough- or Doe-bird; Little Curlew; Prairie Pigeon.

General Description.— Length, 15 inches. Color like that of the Hudsonian Curlew, but more reddish. Bill slender, curved, and about twice the length of head; toes, webbed at base.

Color.— Upper parts, brownish-black variegated with pale cinnamon-brown; *crown, without central light line;* streak over eye of whitish; under parts, tawny ocher to whitish, marked everywhere with dusky streaks, bars, or arrowhead spots, these markings very

numerous except on chin; bill, black, paler at base below; feet, lead-gray; iris, brown.

Nest and Eggs.— NEST: Usually on the open plains; a mere depression in the ground, lined with a few dry leaves or grass. EGGS: 4, ground color variable, from pale green, gray, or brown to olive-drab, with numerous bold markings of sepia and umber-brown, more crowded around large end.

Distribution.— North and South America; breeds on the Barren Grounds of northern Mackenzie; winters in Argentina and Patagonia; now nearly extinct.

It is a great pity that we must speak of the Eskimo Curlew in the past tense. Its disappearance is but another tribute to the effectiveness of modern fire-arms and the short-sighted selfishness of the average American hunter. In the seventies and early eighties Eskimo Curlews in countless numbers came annually to the coast of Massachusetts and earlier writers mention them as being very plentiful in the Carolinas. Their summer home was in the Barren Grounds and other

regions in the northern part of North America. In autumn they collected in Newfoundland in enormous flocks. One observer declares that they came in millions that darkened the sky. After following down the coast to Nova Scotia they launched out over the ocean for South America, and many of them never sighted land until they reached the West India Islands. Whether during this long journey they ever rested on the water, or whether they continued their voyage without pause, is not known. Autumn gales, however, diverted many of them from their course and they landed on the Bermuda Islands as well as along the coast of the northern States. Tens of thousands thus came to the islands and beaches of New England where, according to Forbush, they were mercilessly shot for food. Because at this season they were always extremely fat they were known generally as " Dough-birds."

After reaching South America the Curlews proceeded southward, spreading out over the continent as far as Patagonia. Here they passed the winter. In March and April the g⁻ ⁻ flights would appear on the shores of those ⸤ ates bordering on the Gulf of Mexico. Passing a gantlet of gun-fire the survivors journeyed up the Mississippi valley to northern Canada, and so on to their breeding grounds. It will thus be seen that their migrations were among the most extensive of any undertaken by our North American birds.

Since 1900 perhaps a dozen specimens have come to the attention of ornithologists — all dead birds — and it is of course possible that a few may still exist. But the great flocks are gone and the species is doomed.

Like all the Curlews this bird was an inhabitant of regions where water abounds. Along the coast they fed in the beach-pools and marshes but not generally on the sandy beaches so commonly frequented by Sandpipers and some of the Plovers.

In the spring and summer their great joy was to wade in the ponds, sloughs, and shallow, grassy lakes of the interior. They were of no special economic value to the farming interests of the country, for they did not feed on insects injurious to crops, but they were of much value as a food product, and with proper laws enforced for their conservation the great flocks might have been spared indefinitely for the pleasure and benefit of mankind.

T. GILBERT PEARSON.

PLOVERS

Order *Limicolæ;* family *Charadriidæ*

THE Plovers comprise the family *Charadriidæ* of the order of Shore Birds and include about seventy-five species of comparatively small birds, which, during the breeding season, have a cosmopolitan distribution. The birds generally are migratory and they are likely to cover great distances in their journeys between their summer and winter homes, this being particularly true of the Golden Plover. Eight species occur in North America. Externally the Plovers differ markedly from the Snipes in having a comparatively short and pigeon-like bill, which is hardened and somewhat swollen at the end, and is ill-adapted for probing in mud or soft sand, and they must, of necessity, feed from the surface. For this reason, also, Plovers are often found feeding in the dry uplands not frequented by the Snipe. Furthermore, in the Plovers the body is relatively shorter and plumper than in the Snipes, and the neck is much shorter and thicker. Plovers' wings are long and pointed, and, except in a few species, when folded extend to or beyond the end of the tail, which is comparatively short, generally rounded, and consists of twelve feathers. Their plumage varies greatly, and in some species shows considerable seasonal changes.

They nest on the ground and lay usually four eggs, which are marked or spotted with dark colors in a manner that makes them hard to detect among the pebbles by which they are likely to be surrounded. But one brood is raised in a season. The young when hatched are covered with soft buff or grayish down, spotted with blackish. Whether or not the chicks know that these colors are protective, it is certain that they lie very still among the pebbles and grass when an intruder approaches, and therefore may easily be overlooked.

Plovers' voices usually are mellow, piping whistles which have singular carrying power.

BLACK-BELLIED PLOVER

Squatarola squatarola (*Linnæus*)

A. O. U. Number 270   See Color Plate 39

Other Names.— Black-breast; Black-breasted Plover; Bull-head; Bull-head Plover; Beetle-head; Bottle-head; Chuckle-head; Hollow-head; Owl-head; Whistling Plover; Whistling Field Plover; Pilot; May Cock; Swiss Plover; Ox-eye; Four-toed Plover; Gump; Gray Plover (autumn); Mud Plover; Pale-belly (young).

General Description.— Length, 12 inches. In summer, upper parts black and white, lower parts black; in winter, whitish all over but tinged with brown above. *Four toes,* but hind toe very small; outer and middle toes webbed at base; bill rather short.

Color.—ADULTS IN SUMMER: *Forehead, crown, sides of head to upper level of eye, back of neck, and sides of same, pure white* with a few dusky spots on nape and center of neck; rest of upper parts, including coverts, shoulders, and inner secondaries, white, each feather with a small exposed dusky area, these forming bars on the inner secondaries; tail and upper coverts, barred with dusky; *below, including lores, chin, throat, part of side of head, breast, and abdomen, pure blackish-brown;* under tail-coverts, white; primaries, dark brown blackening at ends *with large white areas* at base; bill and feet, dusky-gray; eye, remarkably large and lustrous, deep brown. ADULTS IN WINTER: Ground color all over, whitish; upper parts, tinged with pale brown; crown, yellowish streaked with dusky; sides of head, back of neck, throat, and breast, finely streaked with brownish; feathers of back, of wing-coverts, and of inner secondaries, with wedge-shaped dusky centers; rest of under parts, unmarked, thus showing none of the black area so conspicuous in summer; bill, feet, and eye as in summer; intermediates between these two plumages, showing an admixture of black and white below, are very common. YOUNG: Upper parts, lighter with a golden shade on each feather; under parts, whitish; breast, streaked with grayish.

Nest and Eggs.— NEST: A mere depression in the ground, lined with grass and leaves. EGGS: 4, light buffy-olive to deep olive-buff, heavily spotted with sepia or black.

Distribution.— Nearly cosmopolitan; breeds on the Arctic coast from Point Barrow to Boothia and Melville peninsulas, and also on the Arctic coast of Russia and Siberia; winters from the Mediterranean to South Africa, in India and Australia, and from California, Louisiana, and North Carolina to Brazil and Peru; in migration occurs throughout the United States and in Greenland and the Bermudas; accidental in the Hawaiian Islands.

The largest of our Plovers, the Black-bellied or Black-breast, is also the shyest. I recall that once, in boyhood, I was trying to creep up on a flat to get a shot at a small flock — of course in vain. A fisherman said to me, as I returned: " Sonny, you might as well try to walk up to an old Black Duck in broad daylight as to them 'ere Plovers."

Drawing by R. I. Brasher

BLACK-BELLIED PLOVER (¼ nat. size)

The largest and shyest of the Plovers

Thanks to their wariness, it is quite possible, even at the present, to see small parties or flocks of these stout birds standing well out on the flat, at the water's edge. At the first approach of danger, off they go, with their mellow call of *tee-u-ree-e*. Plump bodies and large heads, as well as the white rump, white on the extended wings, and the conspicuous black patch under the wings against light feathers, make them easy of distinction from the darker Golden Plovers. Unlike the latter, which resort to dry fields to secure grasshoppers and other insects, these "Beetle-heads," as they are sometimes called by fishermen and gunners, mostly confine themselves to flats and beaches and to pools in the marsh.

Solid though they are, comparatively, I made the discovery one day that they could go where I could not. A small flock were feeding well out at the water's edge, at low tide, on a muddy shore, in winter, on the coast of Louisiana. I managed to wade out with my heavy motion-picture camera near enough to show them up with the telephoto lens. When I started to return, I thought I should have to stay there. When I pulled the tripod legs out of that tenacious mud, I sank down so that I could not extricate myself without putting down the tripod again and leaning on it till it was as deep in mud as before. Theoretically this might have continued forever, but finally I managed to stagger to dry land without disaster.

As with the Golden Plover, there is decided difference between the plumages of adult and young, notably so in the case of this species. These "pale-bellies" are readily distinguished. They arrive on the New England coast early in September, whereas the adults begin to appear about July 25. The young linger late in the fall, sometimes being noted well through November.

Even back in the palmy days when the Golden Plover was sometimes abundant, it seemed to me that the Black-breast did not habitually fly about in such large flocks as its relative, nor did these smaller flocks fly as high or perform such sightly evolutions in the air. They were, however, accustomed, in some localities, to congregate in a very large mass on some favorite dry sand-bar or flat, to scatter again when they left the rendezvous.

Photo by H. K. Job   Courtesy of Houghton Mifflin Co.

BLACK-BELLIED PLOVER ASLEEP

Also like the Golden Plover, they breed on the Arctic coast and penetrate on the southward migration as far as Peru. But their routes are quite different, and some of them winter on our Gulf and south Atlantic coasts.

HERBERT K. JOB.

GOLDEN PLOVER

Charadrius dominicus dominicus (*Müller*)

A. O. U. Number 272   See Color Plate 39

Other Names.—American Golden Plover; Green Plover; Three-toed Plover; Whistling Plover; Three-toes; Common Plover; Spotted Plover; Field Plover; Green-back; Golden-back; Brass-back; Greenhead; Pale-breast; Muddy-breast; Muddy-belly; Bull-head; Toad-head; Hawk's eye; Squealer; Field-bird; Pasture-bird; Frost-bird; Trout-bird; Prairie-bird; Prairie Pigeon; Pale-belly (young).

General Description.—Length, 11 inches. Upper parts conspicuously spotted with yellow, lower parts black. Bill small and slender; *no hind toe;* wings long. Bobs its head very frequently.

Plumage.—ADULTS IN SUMMER: Forehead, broad stripe over and behind eye and continuing down side of neck and breast, pure white; *crown, back of neck, back, and shoulders, blackish-brown,* streaked on crown and back of neck, and each feather of rest of upper parts sharply indented all around with golden yellow; wing-coverts and secondaries, more brownish, but showing some golden-yellow spotting; primaries, plain dusky-gray darkening at tips and whitening at base, but no pronounced white areas as in the Black-breasted Plover; tail, white with brownish bars; lores, throat, side of head in front of white stripe, breast, and under parts, pure brownish-black; bill, dusky; feet, lead color; eye, large and lustrous brown. ADULTS IN WINTER: Above, somewhat as in summer but colors less intense; more greenish-yellow and paler brown; sides of head, neck, breast, and under parts in general, brownish or grayish-white, narrowly streaked on sides of head and throat, mottled on neck, breast, and abdomen, with dark grayish-brown; an obscure dusky stripe behind eye; bill, legs, and eye as in summer. YOUNG: Above, dusky mottled with dull whitish spots, becoming yellow on the rump; below, ashy, deeper on lower neck and breast.

Nest and Eggs.—NEST: A slight depression in the moss or ground. EGGS: 4, creamy-white to buffy-brown, spotted boldly with blotches of brown and black.

Distribution.—North and South America; breeds from Kotzebue Sound along the Arctic coast to mouth of the Mackenzie, and from Melville Island, Wellington Channel, and Melville Peninsula south to northwestern Hudson Bay; winters on the pampas of Brazil and Argentina; migrates south across the Atlantic from Nova Scotia and New Brunswick; a few pass south through the Mississippi valley, and all migrate north by this route; in migration to California, Greenland, and Bermuda; formerly abundant, now becoming rare.

In the Golden Plover we have a noble and beautiful species which has woefully decreased in numbers and may even be in danger of extermination. Its wonderful migrations have been much written about. Breeding along the Arctic coasts of northwestern North America, the Golden Plovers in August proceed eastward to Labrador, and down the coast to the peninsula of Nova Scotia. Thence they launch forth over the open Atlantic, straight south, passing several hundred miles off the New England coast, unless driven ashore by easterly gales. Continuing, they

Courtesy of American Museum of Natural History

GOLDEN PLOVER

(Winter plumage)

A noble and beautiful species which has woefully decreased in numbers pass the West Indies, cross the Gulf of Mexico and appear on the coast of Brazil. Being able to alight on the water and feed among masses of drift-weed makes such a long journey possible. Reaching land, they keep on down to the pampas of Argentina. Returning north to breed, they pass, in April and May, up through the interior United States, especially the Mississippi valley, neglecting the Atlantic coast, and thus again reach the breeding grounds.

The autumnal flight on the New England coast used to be a great event, watched for with eagerness by the local gunners. If a tropical hurricane came up the coast between about August 20 and the middle of September, with its violent onshore gales from the northeast, there would be a wonderful influx of Golden Plovers, driven off their course, accompanied by equally great flocks of the Eskimo Curlew, now, alas, probably extinct.

The last really great flight of both these species which I witnessed was in late August, 1883, at Chatham, Mass., at the southern end of the projection of Cape Cod. The wind was shrieking, and I hardly could stand against it on the exposed headlands, where I watched great compact masses of these wonderful birds, high in air, blowing in from the sea. They alighted, as was their wont, on the upland grassy pastures as well as on the marshes, where they eagerly levied toll on their favorite grasshopper diet, while the gunners also took toll of them. Thus early in the season all were in the changing adult plumage, the pale-bellied young not arriving till about mid-September.

In Nova Scotia, before they launched forth on their great voyage, I have watched large flocks of them perform wonderful aërial evolutions over the marshes, swinging high and low many times before alighting. They came quite readily to tin or wooden decoys before a well-placed blind. During the spring flight, in May, I have watched them on the North Dakota prairie, when they were in their exquisite breeding plumage. As they faced me, their coal-black breasts so blended with the black loam soil that it was hard at first to make them out. Apparently realizing their concealing coloration, they would stand perfectly still till I came within fifteen or twenty paces, whereupon they would dart off together in their swift flight, piping their melodious calls.

HERBERT K. JOB.

KILLDEER

Oxyechus vociferus (*Linnæus*)

A. O. U. Number 273   See Color Plate 39

Other Names.— Killdeer Plover; Noisy Plover; Chattering Plover; Killdee.

General Description.— Length, 10 inches. Color above, olive-brown; below, pure white. A front view of the bird shows *four black* bands, two on head and two on breast. Wings, long and, in flight, showing a white V; tail long and rounded; bill slender.

Color.— ADULTS: Forehead, white from eye to eye, prolonged below; above this, a black band; a brownish-black patch from gape along lower side of head; a white collar around neck continuous with white throat; a broad diffuse stripe of the brownish-black back of eye; crown, back, shoulders, wing-coverts, and secondaries, plain olive-brown; *rump and upper tail-coverts, orange-brown* deepening to chestnut behind; several inner pairs of tail-feathers, olive-brown shading into black, then lightening again and changing into rusty tips, others with the orange-brown at rump, black subterminal bars, and pure white tips, the outer pair, mostly white, with several broken black bars on inner webs; primaries, dusky with a white space on outer webs and a longer one on inner webs; secondaries, mostly white, but with black areas increasing from within outward; *a black breast-band encircling neck; below this a white space, and below this again another black breast-band not extending around neck;* rest of under parts, pure white; bill, dusky; legs, leaden gray; iris, brown; eyelids, orange or red. YOUNG: Black of adults replaced by gray; feathers of upper parts marked with rusty-brown.

Nest and Eggs.— EGGS: Deposited on the bare ground in fields, usually near water; 4, dull buffy, thickly spotted and blotched with brown and sepia.

Distribution.— North and South America; breeds from central British Columbia, southern Mackenzie, central Keewatin, and central Quebec south to the Gulf coast and central Mexico; winters from California, Arizona, Texas, Indiana, New Jersey, and Bermuda south to Venezuela and Peru; casual in Newfoundland, Paraguay, and Chile; accidental in Great Britain.

The Killdeer gets its name from its loud, strident, and frequently reiterated cry, which somewhat resembles the words "Kill deer" or the syllables "Kill-dee." It is a true Plover, and a member of the important shore-bird family which are usually to be found near the water or in moist places. But the Killdeer also occurs frequently on perfectly dry land, many miles from

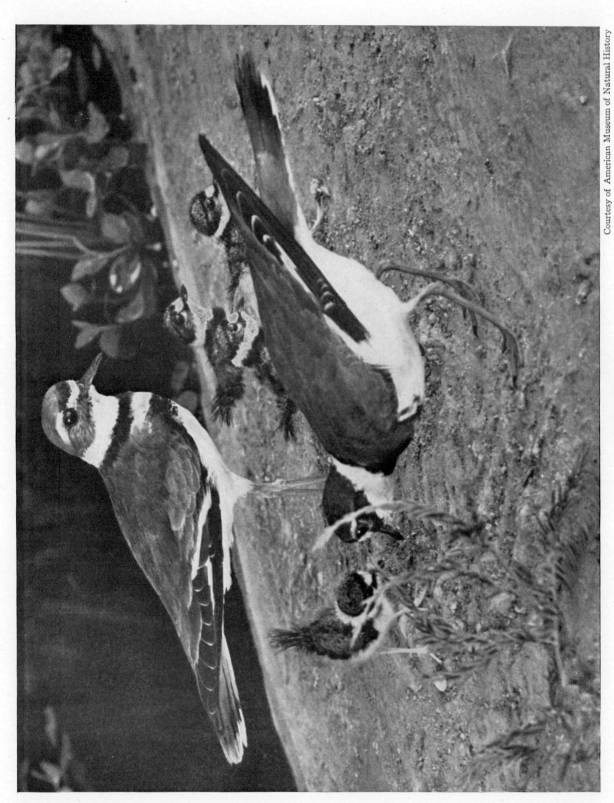

KILLDEERS

Adults and young in first plumage

ponds, streams, or the ocean. It seems to be especially fond of freshly plowed fields, where it feeds voraciously upon worms, grubs, and bugs of various kinds. On the ground it runs about rapidly and in a somewhat nervous manner, frequently uttering its somewhat petulant cry, which, under these conditions, is sometimes abbreviated to the last syllable, *dee*.

The Killdeer is especially solicitous about its eggs or young. When the incubating bird is flushed from her nest, she resorts to all of the tactics of the ground-building birds, fluttering away with one or both wings dragging as if broken, sometimes almost rolling over, often stopping to gasp and pant as if totally exhausted, and keeping up meanwhile an incessant screaming. In the meantime the male bird circles around at a safe distance, adding his protests and denunciation, and the two continue the uproar until the intruder has withdrawn.

On the wing the bird is swift, graceful and somewhat erratic, for which reason it has been much pursued as "game" by amateur gunners and others who should have known better. This "sport" is forbidden by the Federal Migratory Bird Law, which prohibits the hunting of these birds until 1918. The bird should, indeed, be protected at all times, not only because the shooting of it is killing for the mere sake of killing, since its flesh is not edible, but because it makes itself exceedingly useful by destroying great quantities of noxious insects.

There can be no doubt as to the economic value of the Killdeer's feeding habits, for its regular diet is known to include mosquitoes, the fever tick, which spreads the dreaded Texas fever among cattle; crane flies ("leather-jackets"), which are destructive to wheat and grass; grasshoppers, the clover-root curculio, various weevils which attack cotton, grapes and sugar beets; bill-

Photo by H. T. Middleton

EGGS OF KILLDEER

Laid in a depression of the ground

bugs which often do much damage to corn; wireworms and their adult forms, the click beetles; the southern cornleaf beetle; horse flies; crawfishes; the diving beetles which are injurious in fish hatcheries; and the marine worms which prey upon oysters.

GEORGE GLADDEN.

SEMIPALMATED PLOVER

Ægialitis semipalmata (*Bonaparte*)

A. O. U. Number 274   See Color Plate 39

Other Names.— Semipalmated Ring Plover; Ring-necked Plover; Ring-neck; Ring Plover; Red-eye; Beach-bird.

General Description.— Length, 7 inches. Upper parts color of wet sand; lower parts white; *one* black ring around neck. Bill short; outer and middle toes webbed to the second joint; hind toe missing.

Color.—ADULTS: A narrow black bar extending from eye over top of bill to other eye with the white space above it, and this in turn bordered by another black stripe reaching from eye to eye across front of crown; below eye (narrowly) and behind it a dusky stripe; a white bar around back of neck continuous with white of chin and lower sides of head; below this, *a broader bar of dusky encircling neck and upper breast; crown and upper parts, dark brownish-gray;* tail, like back darkening toward end, white-tipped; primaries, dusky; narrow, white spaces at base; secondaries, largely white except long inner ones which are like the back; greater coverts, white tipped; entire under parts, white; bill, yellow, with black tip; feet, pale flesh color; eye-ring, bright orange; iris, hazel. YOUNG: Black of adults replaced by brownish-gray; feathers of upper parts with buffy edgings.

Nest and Eggs.— NEST: A mere depression in the ground, lined with leaves or grass. EGGS: 4, buffy to olive-buff, spotted and blotched with dark brown and black.

Distribution.— North and South America; breeds from Melville Island, Wellington Channel, and Cumberland Sound to the valley of the upper Yukon, southern Mackenzie, southern Keewatin, and Gulf of St. Lawrence; winters from southern Lower California, Louisiana, and South Carolina to Patagonia, Chile, and the Galapagos; casual in Siberia, Greenland, and the Bermudas.

The Semipalmated Plover is the common Plover of the Atlantic seaboard, for during the migrations there are probably more of them to be seen than of all the other Plovers combined, but even at that they are far from being numerous as they once were. In my boyhood I have seen flocks of hundreds, while now it is a matter of dozens. Yet we are fortunate in having them still with us to illustrate the Plover type on our beaches and flats — birds with heads proportionately large, with robin-like actions in racing off for a few yards, then standing still to gaze and meditate, though with the body more horizontal than the Robin, then stooping to conquer the small marine life at their feet.

They frequent both beaches and flats, preferably the latter, and sometimes pools on the marsh. Here they scatter out in feeding but bunch together in flight. From the flats, before we discover them, comes that singularly attractive characteristic call which always makes my pulses bound in response. When they take to wing these notes are speeded up and reiterated as the flock circles out over the water and dashes past. They are with us in May, and again in August and September, being more numerous in the latter period, reinforced by the new generation. Through August we see the adults, with their distinct black breast-bands, but it is not till September, usually, that the grayer young begin to appear, illustrating one of the strange phases of bird habits, that in many cases the young make the long untried journey southward after most of the parents have gone on before. They are found in the interior, as well as on the coast, but mostly along the larger bodies of water, or on marshes where there are shallow sloughs and mud-flats.

The breeding-grounds are mostly in the Far North, even beyond the Arctic Circle. The southernmost point where they are known to breed is the Gulf of St. Lawrence. There I have studied them, on the Magdalen Islands, finding a scattered

Drawing by R. I. Brasher

SEMIPALMATED PLOVER (⅔ nat. size)

A graceful little Plover and skillful in the art of concealment

Plate 39

Louis Agassiz Fuertes.

AMERICAN GOLDEN PLOVER
Charadrius dominicus dominicus (Müller)
SPRING   AUTUMN
BLACK-BELLIED PLOVER
Squatarola squatarola (Linnaeus)
SPRING   AUTUMN

KILLDEER
Oxyechus vociferus (Linnaeus)

SEMIPALMATED PLOVER
Aegialitis semipalmata (Bonaparte)

All ⅔ nat. size

colony on a long sandflat, bordering a lagoon, that stretched for miles between two of the larger islands. The little creatures would run ahead of me, piping plaintively. Careful looking finally revealed a number of their nests, back from the lagoon, in the sand and broken shells above high-water mark, or further back in the tracts where sparse tufts of beach-grass grew from the sand. The nests were more ·than the mere scratched-out hollows of the Piping Plover, in having at least a few grass-stems or scraps of dried sea-weed surrounding the hollow, or even partly filling it. The eggs were usually four, sometimes only three, handsome, boldly marked, resembling, save for their pyriform shape, Terns' eggs more than those of Piping and Wilson's Plovers.

Breeding seemed to be at its height the tenth of June. By that time a very few young were just hatched. They are darker than the Piping Plover chicks, but have similar ways. I had quite an experience in catching and tethering one of them to a blade of grass. Sitting quietly on the sand near by, I watched the mother run about anxiously, and finally venture up to snuggle the baby, while I took snapshots of them with the reflecting camera.   HERBERT K. JOB.

The Semipalmated Plover's diet includes several species of injurious grasshoppers, as well as mosquitoes which seriously molest cattle and certain species of which it is now well known

Photo by H. K. Job   Courtesy of Houghton Mifflin Co.
SEMIPALMATED PLOVER
Brooding tethered chick

may be carriers of dangerous diseases. It is known also that the bird feeds upon locusts. The usefulness of this Plover is, therefore, beyond question.

RINGED PLOVER

Ægialitis hiaticula (*Linnæus*)

A. O. U. Number 275

Other Names.— Ringed Dotterel; Ring Plover.
General Description.— Length, 7½ inches. Coloration very similar to that of the Semipalmated Plover, but usually the white spots on the lower eyelids and a white patch behind the eye are better marked. No web between middle and inner toes; hind toe missing.
Nest and Eggs.— NEST: A slight depression in the sand amid broken shells. EGGS: 4, pale buff or cream color, spotted with dark reddish-brown approaching black.

Distribution.— Eastern Arctic America and Old World; breeds from central Europe and Turkestan to Siberia, Spitzbergen, Iceland, Greenland, and Cumberland Sound; winters on shores of the Mediterranean and throughout Africa; accidental in Barbados, Chile, India, and Australia.

The well-known Ring Plover of Europe was long supposed to be confined to that continent, but it is now known that the bird breeds freely in Greenland and there are definite records of its appearance in America, one specimen having been taken at Great Slave Lake. It resembles the Semipalmated Plover, though it is somewhat larger, the black band on the breast is wider and the white stripe on the forehead extends backward and downward over the eye, while it lacks the web between the middle and inner toes of the Semipalmated. Its general habits are plover-like.

This Plover must be considered a very useful bird because it persistently destroys several species of grasshoppers which are known to be injurious to crops. It should, therefore, be protected against molestation which is at all likely to lessen materially its numbers, or to change its normal habits.

PIPING PLOVER

Ægialitis meloda (Ord)

A. O. U. Number 277

Other Names.— Ringneck; Pale Ringneck; White Ringneck; Belted Piping Plover; Western Piping Plover; Clam Bird; Mourning Bird; Beach Plover; Sand Plover.

General Description.— Length, 7 inches. Upper parts, color of dry sand; under parts, snowy white. *Toes, not webbed;* hind toe missing; bill short.

Color.— Forehead, white; a black band on front of crown from eye to eye; lores, streak behind eye, chin, throat, sides of head, a half collar around back of neck, and entire under parts, pure snowy white; crown and *upper parts, very pale ashy-brown;* a black band on upper breast tending to encircle neck but not meeting; an indistinct dusky streak behind eye; primaries, dusky with white spaces at base; secondaries and greater coverts, mostly white; long inner secondaries, similar to back; upper tail-coverts and base of tail, white, latter blackening toward end, and outer pair of feathers, entirely white; an orange-red ring around eye;

basal half of bill, orange yellow, front half, black; feet, yellowish; iris, brown. ADULT FEMALE: The crown bar is usually dark brown and the breastband much reduced and brownish. YOUNG: No trace of dark color on head, and little, if any, on sides of neck; feathers of upper parts with pale or rusty edgings; bill, mainly black.

Nest and Eggs.— EGGS: Generally laid among stones on the beach; 4, clay color or creamy-white, thinly and uniformly marked with sepia specks, sometimes mere points.

Distribution.— Eastern North America; breeds locally from southern Saskatchewan, southern Ontario, Magdalen Islands, and Nova Scotia south to central Nebraska, northwestern Indiana, Lake Erie, New Jersey (formerly), and Virginia; winters on the coast of the United States from Texas to Georgia, and in northern Mexico; casual in migration to Newfoundland, the Bahamas, Greater Antilles, and Bermuda.

Truly a bird of the beach-sand is the Piping Plover. With propriety it might have been named the " Sand Plover." It looks the part, for it lives on the sand and so closely resembles the sand in color that it is rendered almost invisible till it moves. Then whoever it is that approaches may notice a whitish streak projecting itself ahead over the intensely bright dry sand so rapidly that it might more readily seem to be something flying than running. Its piping calls are plaintive and pretty, harmonizing finely with the general spirit of the extended beach, the dazzling sand, and the flowing sea with its monotonous undertone.

Somehow the sea-beach hardly seems fully genuine without it. None the less many of our beaches have lost this little gem of a resident. With the advent of increasing throngs of summer visitors, the eggs are stepped on or picked up, and the birds are shot by vandals or are forced to move on. At some times it has seemed that these birds would be exterminated, but law and public sentiment have come to the rescue, and in some quarters they still cling tenaciously to their old haunts. They are found not only on the sea-coast, but on the sandy or pebbly shores of the larger inland lakes.

The eggs of this Plover generally number four and are laid in a rather deep, well-rounded cavity, in almost clear sand, when there is such, but otherwise on shingle or pebbly areas, at the top of beaches. They are laid in the latitude of southern New England during the latter part of

May or in early June. I have even found fresh eggs in July, but such cases are more likely second layings, after the first set is destroyed, as shore birds as a class seem to rear but one brood each season. The eggs are distinct from those of other allied species in being finely speckled instead of coarsely marked.

Photo by H. K. Job   Courtesy of Doubleday, Page & Co.

NEST OF PIPING PLOVER

The young look like little bunches of cotton-batting blowing over the sand. Though born out in the open glare of the sun on the hot sand, they cannot at first endure much heat, but are carefully brooded by their parents, or else hide under drift-weed or in the clumps of beach-grass.

The food of these little Plovers is the tiny

marine life cast up by the waves on the broad white beaches where they spend their innocent lives and beautify the impressive surroundings. The sight of a big man with a gun chasing the little things has always seemed to me an atrocity, happily now made a crime, both by State enactments and by the laws of the nation.

HERBERT K. JOB.

SNOWY PLOVER

Ægialitis nivosa *Cassin*

A. O. U. Number 278

Other Name.— Snowy Ring Plover.

General Description.— Length, 7 inches. Color above, ashy-gray; below, snowy-white; *no complete white ring around neck. Bill slender,* shorter than head; hind toe missing.

Color.—ADULT MALE IN SUMMER: Forehead, line over eye, sides of head and whole under parts, snowy white; broad black bar from eye to eye; crown, pale orange-brown; narrow black streak from back of eye tending to meet its fellow on nape; rest of upper parts, pale ashy-gray; several pairs of tail-feathers, like back, darkening toward ends; two or three outside pairs, entirely white; primaries, dusky with a brownish central space; greater coverts, ashy-gray, white-tipped; primary coverts, darker, also white-tipped; outer secondaries, dark brown, long inner ones, color of back; a broad black patch on each side of breast, not meeting on back of neck or front of breast; bill and feet, black; iris, brown. ADULT FEMALE IN SUMMER: Band over eye and stripe back of it, with breast patch, dusky-gray; otherwise similar to male. ADULTS IN WINTER: Black parts replaced by grayish brown; otherwise similar to summer plumage.

Nest and Eggs.—NEST: A depression in the sandy beach. EGGS: 3, pale buff or clay color with numerous scratchy markings of dark brown and black.

Distribution. — Western United States, to South America; breeds from central California, northern Utah, and southern Kansas south to northern Lower California and southern Texas; winters from southern California and Texas south along both coasts of Central America, and on the west coast to Chile; casual in Oregon, Wyoming, Ontario, Louisiana, Florida, Bahamas, Cuba, Venezuela, and Brazil.

Something like poetic license must be invoked as an excuse for calling this Plover " snowy," since in point of fact only about half, and that the lower half, of the bird is white, while the upper parts generally are buffy-gray. It is essentially a bird of the western United States. Its note is similar to that of the Piping Plover and so are its habits, especially that of searching for marine crustacea and worms along the seashore, following the receding waves and retreating before them as they come sliding in.

The male and female take turns at incubating the eggs and the bird who is on the nest is fed by the other. But for the tracks made by the birds in these visits, the eggs usually would be exceedingly hard to find, as their color often makes them blend perfectly with the sand and drift about them.

The breeding habits of the birds were closely observed at Santa Barbara, California, by Henry W. Henshaw, and the following graphic description of their conduct when their nest was discovered is included by Dr. Baird in *North American Birds:* " Great was the alarm of the colony as soon as his [Mr. Henshaw's] presence was known. They gathered into little knots, following him at a distance with sorrowful cries. When her nest was seen to be really discovered, the female would fly close by him and make use of all the arts which birds of this kind know so well how to employ on like occasions. With wings drooping and trailing on the sand, she would move in front till his attention was secured, and would then fall helplessly down, and, burying her breast in the sand, present the very picture of despair and woe, while the male bird and the other pairs expressed their sympathy by loud cries."

WILSON'S PLOVER

Ochthodromus wilsonius (*Ord*)

A. O. U. Number 280

General Description.— Length, 8 inches. Color above, ashy-gray; below, pure white. Head large; bill long and large; outer toes webbed halfway.

Color.—ADULT MALE IN SUMMER: Forehead, white, extending backward above eye; narrow black band across fore crown, *not* reaching eyes; lores, dusky; a white collar continuous with throat, around neck; upper parts, pale ashy-gray tinged with brown or ocher on back of head and neck, feathers of back and wing-coverts, with lighter edges; primaries and central tail-feathers, dusky; the outer pair whitish; others, color of back, growing darker toward end, and white-tipped; a black half ring on fore-breast not completed around neck; rest of under parts, pure white; secondaries, except inner ones, mostly white on inner web, darker on outer; bill, black; legs, flesh color; iris, dark brown; *no colored ring around eye.* ADULT MALE IN WINTER: Black replaced by dusky-gray. ADULT FEMALE: Black on breast of male replaced by dark gray, with a rusty tinge; otherwise similar to summer male. YOUNG: Differ only from the adult female in having no black on crown or lores.

Nest and Eggs.— EGGS: Laid among the loose pebbles of the open beaches; 3, pale olive or greenish-gray, spotted and splashed all over with blackish-brown.

Distribution.— Southern North America; breeds from Texas eastward along the Gulf coast, and from southeastern Virginia (formerly New Jersey), south to the northern Bahamas; winters from southern Lower California, Texas, and Florida south to southern Guatemala and probably to the West Indies; casual in Nova Scotia and New England, and at San Diego, California.

Wilson's Plover looks like a bleached and faded copy of the Semipalmated, or else a more robust and darker type of the Piping Plover. Its much larger and stouter bill, however, proclaims its identity, as does the fact that it is seen in summer on the southern coast, southward of the breeding range even of the Piping Plover, though these ranges may overlap occasionally on the coast of Virginia. Its favorite haunts are the more retired sand beaches and bars from that State southward and on the Gulf coast, preferably on the ocean front, though it feeds to some extent back on the flats or along inlets. Following the water-line, we meet it singly or in pairs, though there may be several pairs along a good stretch of beach. Later in the summer, from about July, when the young are on wing, there may be a semblance of flocking.

By keeping our eyes well "peeled," carefully watching the sand as we walk along, we may spy the spotted eggs lying in a slight cavity of the sand, usually among scattered shells or bunches of weeds or grass, in the dry flat area of white sand above high-water mark. The only nest-building, aside from the scratching out of the hollow, is to line it with a few chips of broken shell. It is hard to see what particular purpose this may serve, unless possibly to make the eggs a little less conspicuous. At the best they are not readily found, and the birds themselves give little clue to the whereabouts of their treasures. They are not very shy, and patter along the sand ahead, uttering flute-like notes. For a while they keep flying on ahead, and presently will circle out over the water to the rear.

Photo by H. K. Job   Courtesy of Houghton Mifflin Co.

WILSON'S PLOVER

Its favorite haunts are the more retired sand beaches

I have found their eggs in southern Florida in late April, and on the shores of South Carolina toward the middle of May.

HERBERT K. JOB.

MOUNTAIN PLOVER

Podasocys montanus (*J. K. Townsend*)

A. O. U. Number 281

Other Name.— Prairie Plover.

General Description.— Length, 9 inches. Color above, grayish-brown; below, white; bill slender; tail short, less than half the length of wing; hind toe missing; no web between middle and inner toes.

Color.—ADULTS IN SUMMER: Above, uniform grayish-brown, usually pure but in some cases the feathers edged with tawny or ocher; a sharp black line from bill to eye; a black bar across fore-crown varying in width from a mere line to a band nearly half the length of the crown in width; central tail-feathers, color of back, blackening toward end, outer ones, pale, all white-tipped; *below, pure white without belt or patches* but breast sometimes shaded with rusty or gray; primaries, blackish, some of the inner ones white toward base; bill, black; legs, lead color; iris, brown. ADULTS IN WINTER: Black crown bar and loral stripe, absent; plumage, more rusty; otherwise, as in summer. YOUNG: No pure white or black markings, and even more buffy than winter adults.

Nest and Eggs.— NEST: On the open prairies; a depression in the ground, lined with leaves and grass. EGGS: 3 or 4, cream to light olive, finely and thickly dotted with sepia, black, and lavender.

Distribution.—Western North America; breeds from northern Montana and western Nebraska south to northern New Mexico and northwestern Texas; winters from northern California and southern Texas to southern Lower California and central Mexico; accidental in Florida.

On the central table-land of the Rocky Mountains, near Sweetwater, Wyoming, was captured the first specimen of the Mountain Plover to be described. From the altitude of this point, the bird received its name. In reality, however, its unofficial name of Prairie Plover is more appropriate. It frequents the barren prairies as well as the well-watered regions of the western United States but not the marshes and beaches.

It is a quiet bird, attending consistently and constantly to its business of chasing and capturing insects. It feeds freely upon locusts, as is shown by the fact that sixteen stomachs of the bird which were examined, contained an average of forty-five locusts each. Also included in its diet are various species of harmful grasshoppers and it deserves, therefore, to be considered a useful bird.

SURF-BIRDS AND TURNSTONES

Order *Limicolæ;* family *Aphrizidæ*

THE Surf-birds and Turnstones constitute the family *Aphrizidæ* of the order of Shore Birds. There are but three species, all of which occur in North America. The subfamily of Surf-birds seem to be more closely related to the Sandpipers than to the Plovers, and the only known species is the one which is found on the coasts and islands of the Pacific. The Turnstone subfamily includes two species. Structurally they are related to the Plovers and the Surf-birds. The bill is shorter than the head, and is curved slightly upward, a peculiarity which assists the bird in turning over stones in search of its food, and from which it derives its name. The legs are short and stout, the wings long and pointed, the tail short and slightly rounded, and the plumage parti-colored in summer and neutral in winter. The birds lay four eggs, usually on almost barren rocky coasts, and conceal them very cleverly by selecting a nesting site with which their varied colors harmonize very closely.

SURF-BIRD

Aphriza virgata (*Gmelin*)

A. O. U. Number 282

Other Name.— Plover-billed Turnstone.

General Description.— Length, 10 inches. Color above, dark ashy-brown streaked and varied; below, dull white with dark markings; bill stout with rounded tip; tail, slightly notched.

Color.— ADULTS IN SUMMER: Above, dark ashy-brown streaked with whitish on head and neck and varied with chestnut and black on back and wing-coverts; *upper tail-coverts and basal half of tail, pure white; rest of tail, black tipped with white;* primaries, dusky, tipped with white; greater coverts, white-tipped; large space on secondaries, also white; under parts, dull white or ashy variegated with brownish-black marks; throat and fore-breast, narrowly streaked, these streaks changing on breast proper to crescentic bars; rest of under parts, sparsely spotted; bill, black; legs, greenish-yellow; iris, brown. ADULTS IN WINTER: Head, neck, breast, and upper parts generally, uniform dusky-brown with darker shaft lines; no white or reddish; wings and tail, as in summer; beneath, dull white faintly spotted. YOUNG: Above, brownish-gray with white edgings to feathers; below, white streaked with dusky.

Nest and Eggs.— Unknown.

Distribution.— Pacific coast of North and South America; breeding range unknown, but probably in the interior of northwestern Alaska; winters in Chile to Straits of Magellan; occurs in migration from Kobuk River, Alaska, to southern South America.

Ornithologists have been divided as to whether the Surf-bird should be considered a Plover or a Turnstone, and after much argument have compromised by giving it distinct generic rank. Evidently the bird occurs frequently on the Hawaiian and other islands in the Pacific Ocean, and it is known also to visit the Pacific coast of the United States, but nowhere is it abundant. Its breeding grounds are unknown. The bird frequents the outer beaches of the sea-coasts, where it permits the spray from the heavy surf to dash over it; hence the name given to it.

RUDDY TURNSTONE

Arenaria interpres morinella (*Linnæus*)

A. O. U. Number 283a   See Color Plate 33

Other Names.—Turnstone; Sea Dotterel; Sea Quail; Sand-runner; Stone-pecker; Horsefoot Snipe; Brant-bird; Bead-bird; Checkered Snipe; Red-legs; Red-legged Plover; Chicken; Chicken Plover; Chicken-bird; Calico-back; Calico-bird; Calico-jacket; Sparked-back; Streaked-back; Chuckatuck; Creddock; Jinny; Bishop Plover.

General Description.— Length, 9 inches. Upper parts chestnut, black, and white; lower parts black and white; bill with sharp tip inclined upward; tail slightly rounded.

Color.—ADULT MALE IN SPRING AND SUMMER: Forehead, cheeks, sides of head, and back of neck, white with a bar of black from side of neck to below eye, continuing forward and meeting its mate over base of bill and enclosing a white loral patch; another black streak on side of neck; top of head, streaked with black and white; *lower hind neck, back and shoulders, variegated with black and chestnut; rump and upper tail-coverts, snowy-white,* the latter black in center; tail, white with a broad subterminal black band; center tail-feathers, white-tipped; wing-coverts and inner secondaries, mixed black and chestnut; greater coverts, mostly white; *middle secondaries, entirely white* becoming gradually more dusky outwardly, producing an oblique white wing bar; primaries, dusky, largely white at base; *under parts, snowy-white; breast and throat, jet-black, encircling a white patch;* bill, black; *feet, orange-red;* iris, deep brown. ADULT FEMALE IN SPRING AND SUMMER: Less strongly colored; chestnut replaced by plain brown, especially on wing-coverts; darker parts restricted; black not glossy. ADULTS IN WINTER: Chestnut absent, the blacks mostly replaced by browns or grays, the patch on chest smaller and much broken.

Nest and Eggs.— NEST: A hollow scratched in the ground and lined with bits of grass or seaweed. EGGS: 4, greenish-gray spotted and blotched heavily with yellowish and umber-brown.

Distribution.— North and South America; breeds on Arctic shores from Mackenzie River east, probably to Melville Peninsula, and north to Melville Island; winters from central California, Texas, Louisiana, and South Carolina to southern Brazil and central Chile.

Shore birds as a class are foremost among the earth's greatest travelers. The typical species of this class breed on the Arctic tundra, and, when winter approaches, migrate nearly to the further end of the South American continent. Such a wanderer is the Turnstone, a beautiful species, richly colored, and possessed of great powers of flight. The month of May finds it rapidly passing across the United States, following both the Atlantic and Pacific coasts and also through the interior. In the latter it is found along the larger bodies of water, but also on the sloughs of the prairies, especially where alkaline conditions produce open muddy shores. Some flocks are seen as late as the first week of June. Returning

one exceptional chance to watch. It was in late afternoon toward the middle of September, on a sandy shore, slightly muddy, where shells and débris had been washed up. The select company was "one little Turnstone and I," the latter armed with binoculars, the former too busy to notice intruders. He was a fine gentleman, dressed in the gaudiest "calico" possible for the fall fashions, yet not too proud to work for his supper. His method was not unlike that of the proverbial bull in the china shop, for he trotted about, "tossing" nearly everything that came in his way. Inserting the "wedge" under a pebble, a shell, or what not, he would give a real toss of his imperious head, and flop over it

Courtesy of Am. Mus. Nat. Hist.

TURNSTONE (⅔ nat. size)

His method was not unlike that of the proverbial bull in the china-shop

bands begin to appear as soon as the last of July, and during August the main southbound tide is on.

Their prevailing habit is to keep in compact flocks, more often about a dozen, when often they fly in lines, as well as bunched up. None the less they are also found scattering, two or three, or even a lone one. They fly very fast, usually with a sort of trilling, rapidly reiterated series of notes. They are well known to hunters, frequently by the names of Chicken Plover, Calicobird, and others.

Their favorite haunts are stony beaches on the open coast and also inlets with gravelly or partly muddy shores. For feeding purposes they carry no knife, like the Oyster-catcher, but have an arrangement no less effective for their purpose — a wedge-shaped bill. How they use this I had

would go. Presently he tackled a shingle, and had a hard time to budge it. He tried it on all sides, and then again, until at last he lifted and threw it over. His efforts seemed to be well rewarded, for he fed there some little time, as though many slugs and worms had taken refuge beneath it. It is in search of such prey that the turner of stones operates, a cog in the wheel of the system of nature, which decrees that every possible corner and crevice of the great system shall have its guardian, even the tiny spot of ground beneath the pebble on the beach.

HERBERT K. JOB.

The Turnstone's diet is not confined to the animal food mentioned, but includes grasshoppers of species which often menace seriously various crops. Its service in keeping down these pests is undoubtedly very valuable, and for this reason alone the bird deserves careful protection at all times.

The Black, or Black-headed, Turnstone (*Arenaria melanocephala*) averages a trifle smaller than the Ruddy Turnstone. In its summer plumage the crown and upper back are black with a greenish-bronzy gloss; the rest of the head, neck, throat, and chest are black, the forehead and sides of the head spotted with white, and a white spot in front of the eye; the rest of the under part of the body is white. In the winter, the head, neck, and chest are sooty-black without spots. The nesting and other habits of this Turnstone duplicate those of the Ruddy Turnstone. It occurs on the Pacific coast of North America, breeding from Kotzebue Sound south to the valley of the lower Yukon, and wintering from British Columbia south to Lower California. Sometimes it wanders north to Point Barrow, Alaska, and over to northeastern Siberia.

OYSTER-CATCHERS

Order *Limicolæ*; family *Hæmatopodidæ*

THE Oyster-catchers (*Hæmatopodidæ*) include ten species, and are virtually cosmopolitan in their distribution. Three species occur in North America, and all are essentially maritime birds. They are found (excepting by accident) only along the ocean fronts, where they get the principal parts of their diet, oysters, clams, mussels, and various shell-fish, whose shells they force apart with their strong, wedge-shaped bills. They also feed on marine worms and insects.

These birds have very stout legs and strong feet from which the hind toe is lacking. The plumage is chiefly black on the upper parts and white underneath. The bill of the living bird is bright red. On the ground Oyster-catchers walk with a deliberate and dignified stride, or run with ease and considerable speed. Their flight also is swift and graceful, though when flushed when they are feeding they are not likely to fly far. They build no nest but lay in a slight depression in the sand usually three eggs, which are buffy white, blotched and speckled with dark brown. Various observers have declared that incubation is performed entirely by the female, but that she covers the eggs only at night or on cloudy days and at other times leaves her work to the sun and the hot sands.

OYSTER-CATCHER

Hæmatopus palliatus *Temminck*

A. O. U. Number 286

Other Names.— American Oyster-catcher; Mantled Oyster-catcher; Brown-backed Oyster-catcher; Sea Crow.

General Description.— Length, 21 inches. Head black, back brown, and under parts white.

Color.— *Entire head and neck all around, glossy bluish-black,* frequently with a glaucous shade; *back,* shoulders, rump, and upper tail-coverts, *dusky-brown,* the side and central coverts white; *tail, white at base,* then brownish shading to blackish at ends; inner secondaries, dusky-brown, outer ones, pure white; greater coverts, broadly tipped with white forming a conspicuous area in combination with the white of secondaries; primaries, dusky-blackish at ends; *entire under parts from the breast, pure white;* bill, vermilion or coral-red, yellowish at end; legs, pale purplish flesh color; iris and eye-ring, red or orange.

Nest and Eggs.— NEST: A slight depression on sandy beaches. EGGS: 2 or 3, white or cream, spotted and blotched with dark brown, black, or lavender.

Distribution.— Coasts of North and South America from Texas, Louisiana, and Virginia (formerly New Jersey), south on both coasts of Mexico to the West Indies, southern Brazil, and central Chile; casual north to New Brunswick; breeds probably throughout its range.

Should we seek out the loneliest of the barren beaches or bars of glistering sand which are so characteristic of the coasts of the southern States, here and there at considerable intervals we are likely to meet scattered pairs of a rather large shore bird, very conspicuous from its black and white plumage. With high-power binoculars we can see their large bright-red bills, though they are so very shy that we could hardly distinguish this last feature without such aid. They are Oyster-catchers, birds which literally carry about with them each its oyster-knife, in order to be able to feed upon the oysters, mussels, clams, or other shell-fish which they encounter. Locally they are sometimes called " Sea-Crows " by the fishermen, which is not an inapt descriptive title, though their notes, which are clarion flute-like calls, are certainly more melodious than crow-talk.

Though they are often seen upon the more retired beaches of the mainland, the real type location is the little " sea island," of very small and low degree, which at high tide is a mere little strip of white sand, with areas of shell cast up by the sea. This is where, the year around, we may find the curious birds and from April to June their nests. Really it seems almost like pleasantry to imply that they ever have a real nest. To provide such homes for its eggs, all the bird needs to do is to squat on the sand, turn around a few times, and there will be found as

good a habitation as it ever cares to occupy. In more ways than one is this home insecure, for it requires but a sudden heavy squall or storm to raise the water level and drive the waves over the low bar. The water may be over it but a short time, yet the mischief is done. This and other birds of the sea never appear to claim their eggs

Drawing by R. B. Horsfall   Courtesy of Nat. Asso. Aud. Soc.

OYSTER-CATCHERS AT HOME

or to make any effort to save them after they have once been floated off even for a short distance.

Possibly the prodigal parents may not think the eggs worth saving, so small is their number. Two eggs is the clutch I have always found, though sometimes they are said to have three. Where

Drawing by R. I. Brasher

OYSTER-CATCHER (½ nat. size)

Each carries with him his own oyster-knife

the Oyster-catchers are seen flying on ahead as one advances, and then returning in a circuit, it is likely that there are eggs or young not far off. The eggs are hard to find, though they lie right out in the open, on the highest and driest part of

Photo by H. K. Job   Courtesy of Houghton Mifflin Co.

OYSTER-CATCHER

On nest, South Carolina

the bar, often among shells and bunches of drifted sea-weed, with which they aptly blend. The young are even harder to discover, unless they are seen to run. I have searched a bar, as it were, with a fine-tooth comb before detecting

the little creatures — exactly the color of the sand — lying outstretched by some weed or bit of débris.

One very absorbing experience which I have had was in photographing an Oyster-catcher at her nest. The open sand-flat afforded no possible concealment. At night I placed a bunch of sea-weed near the two eggs. In the morning I set the camera under this, and, attaching a spool of strong thread to the shutter, had my friends bury me in the sand, at the thread's end, all but head and arm. When the rest of the party left the island, the birds walked right past me, gazing without fear at the apparently disconnected head cast up by the waves. Soon the female was shielding her eggs from the blazing Carolina sun. Then excitedly I pulled the thread and the picture was mine!   HERBERT K. JOB.

The Black, or Bachman's, Oyster-catcher (*Hæmatopus bachmani*) is peculiar to the Pacific coast of North America, breeding from Prince William Sound, Alaska, west through the Aleutian Islands and south to central Lower California, and wintering from southern British Columbia to Lower California. It averages about two inches shorter than its eastern congener. Its head and neck are dull bluish-black, and the rest of its plumage brownish-black. In habits it, also, is strictly a shore-bird.

Photo by Clyde Fisher   Courtesy of Nat. Asso. Aud. Soc.

ON ORANGE LAKE

The Island, here shown, was purchased by the National Association of Audubon Societies for a bird reservation